D1580175

A BEAST BOOK
FOR THE POCKET

INVESTIGATORIBVS NATVRAE
DILIGENTISSIMIS QVORVM
SCRIPTIS NITITVR HIC
OPVSCVLVM VNIVERSIS
BREVITER GRATIAS AGO

A
BEAST BOOK
FOR THE POCKET

The Vertebrates of Britain
Wild and Domestic
other than Birds and Fishes

BY

EDMUND SANDARS

OXFORD UNIVERSITY PRESS
LONDON : HUMPHREY MILFORD

OXFORD UNIVERSITY PRESS
AMEN HOUSE, E.C. 4
London Edinburgh Glasgow New York Toronto
Melbourne Capetown Bombay Calcutta Madras
HUMPHREY MILFORD
PUBLISHER TO THE UNIVERSITY

COMPANION VOLUMES
each 10s. 6d. net.

A BIRD BOOK FOR THE POCKET. By
EDMUND SANDARS.

A BUTTERFLY BOOK FOR THE POCKET.
By EDMUND SANDARS.

A FLOWER BOOK FOR THE POCKET.
By MACGREGOR SKENE.

FIRST PRINTED 1937
SECOND IMPRESSION 1943
THIRD IMPRESSION 1944

SET IN GREAT BRITAIN AT THE UNIVERSITY PRESS, OXFORD
AND REPRINTED FROM PLATES BY
THOS. FORMAN AND SONS LTD., NOTTINGHAM

PREFACE

THIS book is intended to give, in the shortest space, some account of the Vertebrates, other than Fish and Birds, to be found in the British Isles, or off their coasts. These include Mammals, Reptiles, and Amphibians, whether wild or domesticated. I have included domestic animals because I see no good reason for separating them from their wild cousins. They are more usually seen and better known, and the care which has been devoted to their breeding throws much light on all animal heredity. Among the wild creatures I have excluded all foreign animals to be found only in zoological collections, public or private, and such as are to be found only in fur farms (e.g. Silver Foxes), but have included three species (the Grey Squirrel, the Sika Deer, and the Muskrat) which, though originally so imported, have escaped and naturalized themselves.

In the case of the domestic animals the treatment of 'breeds' is not exhaustive, and no attempt has been made to describe those of the Dog. An entire volume of this size would be needed for the types of Dog which the fancier and the show-bench have evolved. I have tried to gather and set out such facts as are common to all breeds of each domestic animal, with a brief review of the breeds found here. Those now common here (e.g. Friesian Cattle) have been included in spite of a known foreign origin.

After preliminary articles on each Class, Order, or other group the plan of the book is to treat each species separately, giving: (1) the English name; (2) the scientific name; (3) the habitat; (4) a general description of the visible form, indicating the characters which distinguish it from other species; (5) a general idea of the teeth, (6) of the limbs, and (7) of any notable peculiarity of internal structure; (8) its life history, the young, their number and development; (9) its yearly life as affected by the seasons; (10) its daily life, including manners and behaviour; (11) food; (12) gait, on land, in air or water, and (13) its voice. A heading 'Varieties' is added for the record of albinisms or similar oddities and for such local races as have been distinguished as sub-species.

The small maps showing the distribution of each species are of course mere approximations. The data for accurate planning is rarely available except in the case of Man and some domestic animals. The shading from sparse dots to blackened areas is meant to show numerical density. These maps must be read separately: comparative density as between species cannot be indicated. There are thirty times as many Sheep in the United Kingdom as there are Horses, and countless myriads of Field Mice cannot be compared with a few dozen Polecats. I have, however, tried to make the general depth of shading vary and to avoid blackening the maps of the rarer species.

In the case of a Domestic Animal, the heading 'habitat' is replaced by a reference to its 'origin', so far as anything is known, and to its 'uses' to Man, while the heading 'varieties' covers the 'breeds'.

For the scientific names I have followed the B.M. List, 1935.

Under the system of scientific names devised by Linnaeus each species bears two names, the first that of the genus to which it belongs and the second that of the species itself. Thus the Red Squirrel is called *Sciurus vulgaris*. Recently the so-called Trinomial System has been widely adopted, whereby local races or nationalities, instead of being regarded as mere varieties of the species, are called 'Sub-species' and bear three names, those of the genus, species, and sub-species. Where a species is so divided, the original race, first known and described, is called the 'typical' sub-species and takes as its own the specific name repeated. Thus the Red Squirrel of Sweden, first described by Linnaeus, becomes *Sciurus vulgaris vulgaris*. The more recently separated sub-species get a newly invented third name (as for the British Red Squirrel, *Sciurus vulgaris leucourus*). As in my small Bird Book, I have adopted the device of squaring or cubing a word when twice or thrice repeated. Thus, I have used *Sciurus vulgaris*[2] instead of *Sciurus vulgaris vulgaris* and, for the Badger, *Meles*[3] for *Meles meles meles*.

In this book where there are sub-species, but only one of

them has been found in these Islands, the three names of the sub-species will be given under the two of the species and anything specially relating to the sub-species will be found in the text. If more than one sub-species is found here, the species is treated first and each sub-species separately under the heading 'varieties'.

In three cases, all belonging to the Mouse family (in which the process of sub-dividing into species and sub-species has been carried to great lengths), I have chosen to treat the genus as my unit and to relegate both species and sub-species to the heading 'varieties'. These three cases are the Long-Tailed Field Mice (genus *Apodemus*), the Bank Voles (genus *Clethrionomys*), and the Short-Tailed Voles (genus *Microtus*).

I have enlarged the Index so that it may also serve as a Glossary. The scientific names, with such translations as seem useful, are given under the English names of the various animals. Contrary to usage, I have not added a letter to show whether the words are Latin or Greek. If the reader does not know, he will not care. Technical terms are inserted alphabetically with a brief explanation.

Man himself I have included, with extreme brevity, partly to give an idea of the method adopted in describing our fellow inhabitants of these islands and also because our own structure helps us to understand that of the others and the likeness strengthens the idea of our common kinship. For the same reason I have chosen to take the various groups from Man to the Newts, rather than in the reverse order.

Many of the facts contained in the introductory notes on the various Classes, Orders, or other groups have been repeated when dealing with the individual animals because I am aware that readers, particularly when using a book of this kind for reference, find it tedious to refer to such articles and do not read them.

The small amount of anatomy given is to help to recall the likeness, and some of the main differences, between the Vertebrates. The special stress upon the teeth is due to their importance in classification and as a guide to the habits of the various creatures.

I have relied upon my plates to cover as much description as possible and, to that end, have drawn them to one of three scales. These serve respectively for the large beasts, $\frac{1}{16}$th (the Hoofed Beasts and the Seals), for the middle-sized beasts, $\frac{1}{8}$th (Flesh Eaters and the Hares and Rabbits), and for the small beasts, $\frac{1}{2}$ (all the rest). The Whales alone refuse to fall within this simple scheme and have had to be treated in a manner apart. The above remarks apply to the coloured plates alone. Diagrams and the series of skeletons, &c., have their scale recorded.

I have fought hard against the use of all technical terms in the text, anatomical or other. Some wriggle in (such as 'vertebra'), but most have been put within brackets, or in notes, so that the book can be read without them, and they are explained in the Glossary-Index.

One great fact of nature must be borne constantly in mind, its variability. No two individuals are exactly alike in dimensions, colour, character, and features. This we recognize, easily, in Man, and, with a difficulty which increases with our ignorance, in the case of other creatures. The shepherd knows his Sheep apart. All general descriptions are, therefore, only more or less true, and every statement must be read with this knowledge. About 10 per cent. margin must be allowed on all measurements to cover these variations. All measures exceeding 6 inches (about 150 mm.) are given in inches or feet, and all smaller measures in millimetres. An inch is roughly equal to 25 mm.—accurately to 25·3995 mm. Weights, when given, are stated in English pounds, avoirdupois. Where certain special measures are in customary use, as the 'hand' for the height of Horses, I have added them in brackets.

My work has been to collect, compress, and as the French say, to 'vulgarize', and I am grateful to the many writers who have given me the materials and to those who have helped me by revising special parts of the manuscript. I have added few facts of my own, and I can only hope that this book may give others some of the pleasure that I have myself derived from its composition.

October, 1936   EDMUND SANDARS

CONTENTS

MAMMALS

Class *MAMMALIA*

MAMMALS are back-boned creatures which have hair and suckle their young. There are more primitive Mammals elsewhere in the world which differ greatly from those found in this country, but what follows applies merely to the group of fully developed Mammals (*Eutheria*) to which alone all our species belong.

All Mammals have a Skeleton, and all except some of the Whales have Teeth. They are hot-blooded, maintaining a constant blood temperature, and the blood circulates by means of a four-chambered heart. Their bodies are divided into two parts by a complete membrane called the Diaphragm. They have hair and a number of glands secreting such liquids as milk and sweat.

The *Skeleton* consists of the skull, a back bone, the ribs, breast bone, and four limbs.

The *Skull* is a complicated bony case made up of many separate bones more or less joined together and holding the brain, the eyes, nose, ears, and mouth. Here one need only say that it ends at the back in two rounded knobs (*condyles*) side by side, which rest upon the first vertebra[1] of the back bone, and that the lower jaw consists of two bones[2] only, one on each side, joined together in front at the point of the chin.

The *Brain* is the organ in which the Mammals most clearly show their superiority over the other Classes of creatures. This centre of nervous activity, which at its first appearance in the lower types of life is a mere thickening of the nerves, has in the Mammals become a single organ from which all conscious, and much unconscious, nerve and muscular control is derived. The brain differs greatly in different groups of Mammals in two main respects, size and surface area. It may be smaller or larger in proportion to the body which it directs, and it may be smooth-surfaced or, on the contrary,

[1] Atlas. [2] Mandibles.

7

may be covered with a network of inward folds which make it resemble the kernel of a walnut. These folds are called 'convolutions' and add greatly to the area of the brain surface. It is found that the larger the brain (particularly the forward part[1]) and the more deeply and extensively it is folded, the higher is the level of the animal's intelligence. Man, justly, ascribes his own superiority over his fellow Mammals to the great size and complicated surface of his brain.

The *Back bone* runs from the Skull to the end of the Tail and is composed of a number of individual bones, called Vertebrae, placed like a row of barrels end to end. These ends are usually flat, though in some Hoofed Beasts they are rounded in front and hollowed at the back. The vertebrae are sometimes, as in the tails of most animals, little or nothing more than this—a mere string of beads. Usually, however, all along the body they have a number of projections extending upward, forward, backward, and sometimes downward. Two such projections usually rise from the upper sides of the barrels and join together above. The general effect is as if small Epstein imps were riding the barrels, kneeling in their saddles so as to leave an arch under their seats.[2] These arches, one behind the other, form a sort of tunnel which carries the main nerves from the brain to the body and protects them.

The column is made flexible by elastic cushions of cartilage between the vertebrae which are specially important in Man to save the brain from the jar of walking.

---

[1] Cerebral hemispheres.

Left side view.   Front view.
TYPICAL VERTEBRAE

[2] Thus:—

The barrels are called the 'Centra.'
The Imps' thighs form the 'Neural Arch' which protects the Spinal Column of nerves.
Their bodies and heads, the 'Spinal processes' or 'Neurapophyses'.
Their shins, the 'Transverse processes' or 'Diapophyses'.
Their forearms, the 'Articulating processes' or 'Zygapophyses', which bind the vertebrae together, and consist of the hands (or 'Prezygapophyses') and elbows ('Postzygapophyses').

For convenience the vertebrae are divided into five groups: those of the neck, ribs, loins, hips, and tail. Those of the neck (*cervical*) are always seven in number, neither more nor less, whether the mammal be a Horse or a Mole. Even the Whales have their seven neck vertebrae, though in some of them they are flattened out like a pile of plates and more or less fused together. Those of the ribs (*dorsal*) have each a pair of ribs attached to projections from their sides. Those of the loins (*lumbar*) extend backward from behind the last rib to the next group. This is a small group of vertebrae (*sacral*) which are consolidated together into one bone (the *sacrum*) to give greater strength to the back bone at this point, where the hip bones are attached. The last group consists of those of the tail (*caudal*). All these groups, except that of the neck, vary in number in different Mammals, and sometimes in members of the same species.

In the Whales there is no sacrum, the whole back bone behind the neck being flexible. In this book the number of vertebrae will be found stated as follows (e.g. for Man): Vertebrae 7-12-6-5-3, the figures representing the various groups in succession, beginning with those of the neck.

The *ribs* circle the body like the hoops of a barrel, those of each side being attached to the vertebrae at the back and to a breast bone.[1] This, like the back bone, is made up of separate bones more or less fused together. Behind the ribs which join the breast bone are others, shorter, which do not reach it, but are joined to it or each other by gristle. These are called 'false ribs'.

The *limbs* of all Mammals are four. The only apparent exception to this is the family of Whales, in which the hind legs consist of mere bones loose in the abdomen. Those of the typical Mammal are depicted in the diagram on p. 10.

Each limb, fore and hind, will be seen to consist of four sections pointing in opposite directions, except the last, which points forward in both limbs. The first sections are the shoulder blade,[2] pointing forward, and hip bone,[3] pointing

---

[1] Sternum.   [2] Scapula.   [3] Os innominatum.

backward. The two shoulder blades are often (as in Man) joined at their lower ends (the point of the shoulder) to two collar bones,[1] which meet the front end of the breast bone and give rigidity. The hip bones, which are complicated in form and composite, attain rigidity by being bent backward and inward until they meet and are joined together. The second

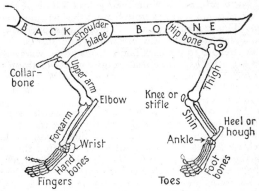

MAMMAL. Diagram of limbs.

sections consist of the upper arm,[2] pointing backward, and thigh,[3] pointing forward. The third sections consist of forearm, pointing forward, and shin, pointing backward. These each consist of two separate bones here called the large and small bones. Of the forearm bones, the large (*radius*) goes from outside the elbow to the thumb side of the wrist, the small (*ulna*) from the elbow-point to the little finger side. Of the shin bones, the large (*tibia*) lies in front of the small (*fibula*). In many animals they are fused into one instead of being separate.

Before reaching the fourth and last section of the limbs,

[1] Clavicles.   [2] Humerus.   [3] Femur.

we come to a number of small bones which together make the wrist[1] and ankle[2] joints. It is not necessary to say more here than that in Man there are 8 bones in the wrist and 7 in the ankle, one of which is the heel.

The fourth sections of the limbs are the Hands and Feet, both pointing forward. In the ideal Mammal these are each made up of 20 bones, that is, of 5 fingers or toes, each with 4 bones: 1 hand (or foot) bone (*metacarpal* or *metatarsal*) and 3 finger or toe bones (*phalanges*). In fact, none of our Mammals have as many as 20 bones. Man, who has most, has only 19, lacking 1 bone of thumb and big toe. The Horse, which has fewest, has only 4 and 2 small survivals.

To these main bones of the limbs must be added a varying number of small[3] bones developed to protect some of the joints, one of which, the Kneecap, will serve as an example.

The following sketch gives some of the different forms of Hand or Forefoot.

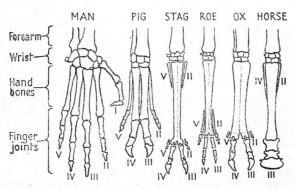

The development of the limbs as described seems to have been by the following stages. In these sketches the near side only is drawn and the two bones of the forearm (large = *radius*

---

[1] Carpals.   [2] Tarsals.   [3] Sesamoid.

and small = *ulna*) and of the shin (large = *tibia* and small = *fibula*) are alone shown separately, the large in white and the small in black.

 (I) The limbs stick straight out, unbending, the two bones parallel. Thus in many extinct fossil animals and (as to forelegs) still thus in the Whales.

 (II) Two joints of each limb bend so as to lift the body off the ground. Thus the Amphibia and Tortoises.

 (III) The two limbs turn (at the point of the shoulder-blade and top of the thigh) backwards and forwards towards each other. The Walrus shows this stage.

 (IV) Lastly, the forefoot turns outwards in a half-circle until it points forwards. In so doing the two forearm bones become crossed, the small behind the large. This is the Mammal type above described.

This rotation of the forearm bones can in some few Mammals (e.g. Man and Cat) be reversed at will—the hand can be turned palm up.

The later stages of limb development differ with the needs of each kind of animal and will be dealt with later. The needs of the Mole and the Bat differ as widely as their limbs. Two main lines of such development may be here mentioned, those seeking (1) dexterity, and (2) speed. In the quest of dexterity the first step is to relieve the hands of some of the work of locomotion and support. The beast learns to sit up, hop, and finally (Man) to walk erect, thus freeing the hands for use as such. The Rat, Cat, Squirrel, and Man show some stages in this process. The fingers are needed and the last stage is attained by the gripping opposition of our thumbs. For great speed, length of leg is the chief need, and this is gained first by lengthening each section of the limb, and then by rising, in movement, to the toes (as do the Cat and Dog, and Man when running) and lastly to the tip of the toes, as do all the Hoofed Beasts. For this many toes are a hindrance, and they have been gradually reduced until we find only one in the Horse.

This way of attaining speed may be illustrated by continuing the set of sketches as follows:

(IV) As above, gives the action of the Flat-foot Walkers (*plantigrades*), which include the Insect Eaters, many of the Rodents, and the Badger.

(V) The rise to the Toes (*digitigrades*), that of our other Flesh Eaters, and

(VI) The further rise to Tip-toe—that of the Hoofed Beasts (*Ungulates*).

Apart from the four leg walkers and Man, we have those groups of Mammals whose realm is the water or the air, in which everything has been sacrificed to swimming or flight. The Whales have lost the hind limbs and the Seals have reduced them to a mere fish's tail doubled, while in both these groups the arms are flippers. The Bats have developed a hand-wing at the expense of any locomotion on land except a laboured crawl.

The *Collar bone* (*clavicle*) stretches from the outer point of the shoulder-blade (*acromium*) to the breast bone and is best developed in those Mammals which need the use of the fore-limbs for free, wide-spreading, movements. It holds out the shoulders and supports muscles which pull the arm sideways (outwards and inwards) as distinct from merely backwards and forwards along the line of the body. It has become obsolete, or nearly so, in such Mammals as use the fore-limbs for support or locomotion only. It is fully developed in the (primitive) Insectivora, in Man (and Monkeys), in the Bats, and (among the Rodents) in the Squirrels and all the Mice, Rats, and Voles. It is modified so as to allow a greater forward stretch of the arm, and reduced to a small detached bone or cartilage, in the Hares and Rabbits and in most of the Carnivora, and it is quite obsolete in the Badger, the Seals, the Whales, and in all the Hoofed Beasts.

The *Tail*. Surviving from the time when its chief use was in swimming or reptilian progress, the tail still serves many uses.

(1) In swimming, it still drives the giant mass of the Whales through the water, and helps to steer the Otter, the Muskrat, and the Water Shrew. In the Seals, superseded by the hind legs, it is small.

(2) In climbing, we see it, prehensile and acting as a fifth hand, behind the Harvest Mouse and, though not prehensile, it acts as a balance and rudder in jumping, climbing, and creeping in the Squirrels, Marten, Dormouse, and the Rats and Mice.

(3) To the Bats the tail and its attached membrane are a part of the flying mechanism, and also a convenient pocket.

(4) It is a signal flag to some Deer and to the Hound, an aid to conversation, and perhaps a way of distracting an enemy's attention, to other Dogs, to Cats and Foxes.

(5) It is a protection against the weather (sunshade or muffler) for the Squirrels, the Fox, and the Cat.

(6) It is a fly-whisk for most of the Hoofed Beasts, and, above all, a local protection against flies for all animals.

Circulation. The Mammals are all hot-blooded, keeping their bodies at a fixed temperature, regardless of external heat or cold. The blood consists of white and red corpuscles, the latter shaped like round disks concave on both sides. These corpuscles together form a liquid stream. It is pumped out of the left side of the heart (*the left ventricle*) into a single great artery (*aorta*) which subsequently divides into smaller channels and these split later into the minute blood-vessels which carry the blood to the skin and to all parts of the body. The blood-stream feeds and cleans the whole system, losing its oxygen and becoming dirty in the process. Then (a bluish-purple in colour) it returns to the right side of the heart (the *right auricle* and *ventricle*) whence it is pumped through the lungs to the left side (*left auricle*) and so back to where we started.

MAMMAL. Diagram of heart and circulation.

Thus all the blood is oxidized by passing through the lungs before being again driven through the arteries by the heart. This is due to the fact that between the right and left sides of the heart is a complete partition, so that the only way from the right side (into which the dirty blood comes) to the left side (from which it is pumped out), is through the lungs which clean it.

Mammals are also distinguished from all other creatures by the fact that a membrane, or sheet of muscle, called the Diaphragm, separates the body into two parts. In the upper, or forward, part are the head, heart, and lungs, while below, or behind it, are the stomach, intestines, and all other organs. The diaphragm acts an important part in the distension of the lungs in breathing.

The *Skin* of Mammals is divided into layers. The outside layer (*epidermis*) is made up of flattened cells which are renewed when rubbed off, so that the skin never wears out. In this layer are formed all the horny growths, nails, claws, hoofs, the enamel of teeth, and the surface covering of hairs. Below this layer comes an under-skin (*dermis*) in which is formed the pulp of the hairs and the ivory of the teeth.

Below these layers of skin lie the blood-vessels which feed and renew it, the nerves which give it sensitiveness, and various glands provided with passages (ducts) which lead up through the skin to the surface. The nerves in different parts of the skin vary greatly in number, so that some places are far more sensitive than others. Thus a man can detect the two points of a pair of compasses on his tongue when only $\frac{1}{25}$ of an inch apart, whereas in the middle of his back they have to be $2\frac{1}{2}$ inches apart before he recognizes that he is being touched by two points and not one. Some glands oil each hair, others give sweat to cool and clean the skin, and others, again, provide milk to suckle the young. The young of all Mammals are born unable to feed themselves and require to be suckled, guided, and educated for a long time. The slowest of all to attain full development is Man.

Milk glands are connected with teats (*mammae*) either at the breast or in the belly or both, which in number correspond very roughly with the number of young born at one time.

The milk of different Mammals varies as between individuals as well as between species. Thus the fat in Cow's milk may be anything between 2 and over 6 per cent. The following table of percentages gives the average composition of the milk of some species.

	Human.	Cow.	Goat.	Sheep.	Mare.	Ass.	Whale.
Water .	88·0	87·5	86·5	83·6	90·1	89·6	70·1
Fat . .	3·5	3·5	4·3	6·2	1·1	1·6	19·4
Protein .	1·5	3·5	4·6	5·1	1·9	2·2	9·5
Sugar .	6·8	4·8	4·0	4·2	6·6	6·1	0·0
Ash . .	0·2	0·7	0·6	0·9	0·3	0·5	1·0

Other glands create digestive juices, exude odours, and collect and exude poisons. The presence of this large number of skin glands is a marked character of the Mammals.

Mammals alone have *Hair*, as distinct from feathers or

16

scales. The Whales have only a very few hairs, and some of them shed these before birth, but they justify the statement that all Mammals have hair. No other creature has. Man, and some over-delicate Pigs, have but a sparse coat of very minute hairs, but most Mammals have a warm covering over nearly the whole body.

The nature of Hair varies greatly. It may be Wool, which is curly and has a rough, scaly surface which makes it 'felt', or mass together, when damped and pressed, or it may have a smooth surface which will not felt, in which case it is called Hair as distinct from Wool. Again, it may be so bristly and stiff as to become a defensive weapon like the spines of the Hedgehog. In this case the skin muscles are so arranged as to erect the hairs at will. These muscles, to a lesser degree, are common to all Mammals. The Dog raises the hair along his back when afraid or angry, the Cat that of the tail, the Hedgehog crosses its bristles, and a Man's hair 'stands on end'. Generally speaking, most Mammals have an undercoat of wool and a longer coat of hair, growing through it. Most animals have moustache and eyebrow hairs,[1] which differ in character from the rest of the coat, being longer, stiffer, and each connected at the root with a nerve. These serve various purposes, but probably the most important is to protect the animal, and especially the delicate eyes and mouth (usually the most forward parts) from contact with objects in the dark.

One of the marked characters of the Mammals is the absence of any brilliant colour markings. Whereas Birds have red, blue, yellow, purple, orange, and green feathers, and patterns made up of several of these colours, the Mammals are restricted to varieties of brown extending from black to white. Among the domestic animals the human taste for oddities, and the protection afforded to varieties so conspicuous that they would be exterminated under natural conditions, have produced more marked patterns and a much greater variety within the species. But none the less, when we speak of a 'red' Cow, she is of a reddish brown; a 'blue' roan Horse's

[1] Vibrissae.

17

coat is made up of black and white hairs; a 'yellow' Dog is only of a pale yellowish brown. In every case the colouring material is the same: the quantity alone differs.[1]

In addition to Hair, there are other horny growths produced by the outer skin, Scales (e.g. on the tails of the Rats and other Rodents), Callosities (e.g. on the Horse's legs), Horns (of some of the Ruminants), and the Nails, Claws, and Hoofs which protect the extremities of all Mammals except the Whales.

Other important products of the skin are the Teeth.

TEETH

The Mammals have teeth in a single row round both upper and lower jaws. They are developed in the skin covering of the jaws—the gums. Although the teeth grow towards and into sockets which form in the jaw bones to receive them, they never become united to,[2] or fused with, the bone. Except in the Whales[3] the teeth differ in shape in different parts of the mouth.[4] There are two successive sets[5] and never more, namely, the 'milk teeth' and the adult teeth, save in the case of the Whales and some Rodents, which have only one set.[6] The milk teeth are shed at varying ages (sometimes at or before birth) as the jaws grow larger, and are replaced from below by the adult teeth, which are both larger and more numerous.

Teeth are of great interest for the following reasons: firstly they differ according to the habits and diet of the animal, secondly they are, in fossils, often the sole surviving part of the whole body, and, thirdly, being part of the skulls which are usually kept in museums, they are at hand for measurement and study and so are much relied upon in classification. Teeth and toes form the grammar of mammal zoology.

All animals' teeth are made up of four distinct materials, pulp, ivory, enamel, and cement. The pulp is the basis of the tooth, formed in the lower layer of the skin, and it gradually

---

[1] Excess gives melanism; deficiency albinism.
[2] Anchylosed.
[3] Said to be homodont.
[4] Such animals are called heterodont.
[5] Diphyodont.
[6] And are called monophyodont.

hardens, on its outer side, into ivory or dentine. The enamel is deposited from the cells of the outer layer of the skin on to the outside of the ivory. The cement is, later, built up outside the enamel, or upon the parts of the tooth nearest the jaw where there is no enamel.

In the case of most teeth, after the tooth is full grown the wide open pulp cavity at the base, which has existed during the growth of the tooth, closes so as to leave only a small channel for the nerve. After this, growth stops and wear is no longer made good. These closed ends of teeth are known as roots. The back or cheek teeth of most Mammals usually have two or more roots apiece. In some teeth, however, the pulp cavity never closes, but continues to feed the tooth, which goes on growing longer throughout its owner's life. Such teeth are known as Rootless teeth or Permanent teeth and rely on wear to keep their shape. There are also cases of teeth (e.g. the molars of the Horse and Bank Vole) continuing to grow until a late stage in the beast's life, and then forming roots.

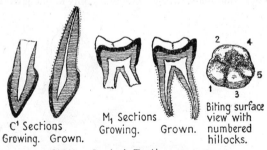

C¹ Sections
Growing. Grown.

M₁ Sections
Growing. Grown.

Biting surface
view with
numbered
hillocks.

MAN. Rooted Teeth.

The above gives an idea of the structure and composition of teeth. In the sections the enamel is shown in black, the ivory shaded, the cement dotted, and the pulp cavities left white.

Incisors fully grown. Pulp cavity remains open.
HARE. Rootless Teeth.

The complete set of Mammal's teeth may be seen in those of the Pig.

The names given to the various groups of teeth are as follows:

The front teeth, three on each side in both jaws, are called INCISORS, or cutting teeth, because their main duty is to cut off the mouthful to be eaten. They are found in varying numbers in all our Mammals, though sometimes only in one jaw. For

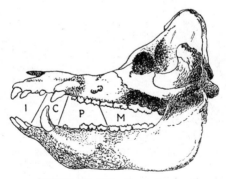

TEETH OF PIG. Scale ⅙

brevity they are represented by the letter i. In the upper jaw they grow upon the forward jaw bone.

The first tooth on the side upper jaw bone and the corresponding lower tooth are in most beasts longer and rounder and are known as the CANINES, because of their prominence in the Dogs. They are fighting teeth, serving above all to kill and hold. The Pig, above, has them well developed, and the Wild Boar, from whom he descends, grows them as long and deadly tusks. There is never more than one such tooth in each jaw, briefly denoted as c.

The rest of the teeth are known as 'cheek teeth', divided into PREMOLARS, or cheek teeth preceded by milk teeth[1] and represented by the letter p, and MOLARS, or cheek teeth which appear for the first time in the adult set and are represented by the letter m. The Pig has 4 premolars and 3 molars. There are never more.

The above jaws of the Pig are described by a formula, written as follows: $\dfrac{3\text{-}1\text{-}4\text{-}3}{3\text{-}1\text{-}4\text{-}3} = 44$. This means that, on each side, there are three upper and three lower incisors; one upper and one lower canine; four upper and four lower premolars and three upper and three lower molars. These formulae save the verbiage required to describe the mouth in detail, and rely upon the fact that the two sides of the mouth are always symmetrical. The fraction form is needed because the upper and lower jaws (though the same in the Pig) often vary. To describe a particular tooth the initial for incisor, canine, premolar, or molar is given with a number following it, either above or below the line according as the tooth meant is in the upper or lower jaw. The numbers are counted from the front of the mouth. Thus, speaking of the Pig's mouth, it may be said that there is a long gap between i^3 and c^1 into which c_1 closes; m^3 has the largest biting surface; c^1 and c_1 are both

---

[1] For accuracy it should be said that in many beasts not all the premolars have precursors in the milk set, but the last tooth in the milk set precedes the last premolar—for example, in the milk set of the Dog there are only 3 milk premolars preceding the 2nd, 3rd, and 4th adult premolars.

rootless teeth and are much larger in the Boar than in the Sow.

The similar formula for the adult human mouth is
$$\frac{2\text{-}1\text{-}2\text{-}3}{2\text{-}1\text{-}2\text{-}3} = 32.$$

In tooth diagrams in this book an arrow shows the direction of the front of the mouth.

All teeth are to some extent capped with enamel, and sometimes, as in Man and all the Carnivora, the surface of the enamel remains intact in use, but some are so formed that, when worn by the opposing teeth, the enamel on their surfaces which are in contact gets worn away, leaving the underlying ivory exposed and forming a more or less flat surface. This surface is made up of the exposed ivory and the vertical edges of the surviving enamel which is often folded and twisted so as to make a complicated pattern. Sometimes a third material is added to the exposed surface by the presence of cement lying on the enamel in the deeper valleys of the original surface. Such teeth, when worn flat by the opposing grinders, show the three differing substances, enamel, ivory, and cement. The result is that the surface becomes a file, always rough until the whole tooth is worn down to the bottom of the deepest hollow in it.

The variety of teeth makes them serve different ends, of which the following are some:

(1) The biting off of the mouthful. This is done in different ways according to the nature of the food. The incisors of Man and Horse serve as examples.

Human Incisors. The opposing teeth are blunt chisels closing one behind the other. Bite a slice of bread and butter and see how it is done.

Horse's Incisors. The opposing teeth are, when unworn, shaped like a sock 'flyped' (to use a Scotch idiom which means turned ready to be put on), and cement fills the in-turned toe. These, as above described, soon wear to a flat grinding, or rather gripping, surface. The gripped grass is torn off by a jerk of the head. This grip and tug method is also that of the Ruminants which have no upper incisors.

the lower projecting almost horizontally and gripping against a hard, bare pad of gum.

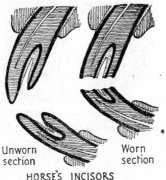

Unworn section   Worn section

HORSE'S INCISORS

(2) The seizing of fish. This needs a sharp and recurved hook and is well seen in the teeth of the Seals, nearly all of which are of that shape.

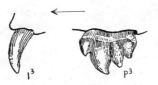

I^3 P^3

COMMON SEAL
Phoca vitulina.

(3) Fighting. For this a long, spear-like tush, interlocking with the corresponding tooth, has been formed. The best examples of this are the canines of the Carnivora, the Cat, Fox, and Dog.

The sketch gives two views of the front teeth of the Fox.

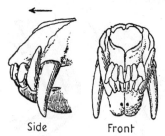

Side   Front

(4) Gnawing. removing the shells of nuts and the like. The incisors of all the Rodents, which are rootless teeth (see sketch on p. 20), are of this type. These teeth have little or no enamel on their backs, so that, in wear, they keep their shapes and chisel-like sharpness.

(5) Flesh slicing. That is to say, cutting up flesh or bones into pieces small enough for swallowing and digestion. The best instances are the so-called Flesh teeth[1] of the Carnivora,

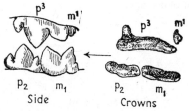

BACK TEETH OF CAT

of which one example will be enough, the flesh teeth of the Cat. They are sharp, knife-like cutting edges, not meeting edge to edge, but slicing, scissor-wise, one inside the other, the points opposing the gaps in the opposite teeth.

[1] Carnassials.

(6) Crushing and grinding, to reduce the food to a pulp and get out its juices. For this, teeth are of many kinds. A few examples are:

The Human Molars. Unbroken enamel-covered teeth, having hillocks on the biting surface joined by ridges (see sketch, p. 19). The opposing points sink into the valleys between these hills in the opposite teeth and, as our jaws move both sideways and fore and aft, the food is bruised and crushed.

The Hedgehog's Molars. Also unbroken enamel-covered

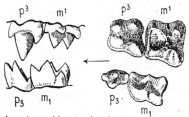

Insect crushing teeth of Hedgehog.

teeth, but far more pointed and steep in their hillocks and with the corresponding hollows deeper. Such teeth serve primarily to crush up the hard shells of insects. They are found in all the Insectivora and the Bats.

The Pig's Molars. These are not unlike ours in general plan,

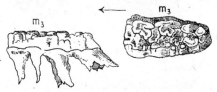

Omnivorous molar of Pig.

the surface consisting of rounded hillocks. In this case, however, they wear through the enamel so as to get a mixed enamel and ivory surface which is better for grinding, as distinct from merely crushing.

The Mouse's Molars. These have a hill and valley system

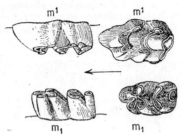

Molars of House Mouse.

more complicated than that of Man, the hills being arranged in three crosswise rows. They wear through to the ivory, to get a grinding surface, and the movement of the jaw is fore and aft only. These, and the Pig's molars, may be regarded as the completely omnivorous teeth.

The Vole's Molars. This family of Mice, whose food is

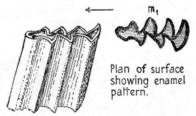

Plan of surface showing enamel pattern.

Rootless molar of Vole. Arvicola amphibius.

mainly found in grass and roots and the hardest of vegetable materials, have very remarkable teeth, the tops of which are flat (or soon wear so), but the sides are marked with deep

26

vertical corrugations or folds showing a pattern of enamel and ivory which varies in each species.

The Horse's Molars. These are the last stage in the development of purely grass-grinding teeth. All the Ruminants have a similar type of teeth, but the Horse's are the best examples. They are complex teeth with deep crescent-shaped[1] hollows

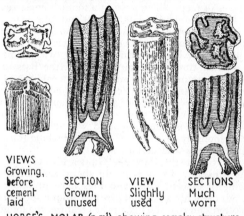

VIEWS
Growing,
before
cement
laid

SECTION
Grown,
unused

VIEW
Slightly
used

SECTIONS
Much
worn

HORSE'S MOLAR (r. m¹) showing complex structure.

in the biting surfaces, as well as corrugations on the outsides. The hollows are filled with cement so that, when the teeth are worn, they have a triple grinding surface as above described. They grow to a great length,[2] but then become rooted and stop growing. They retain their value as grinders until they are worn right down past the enamel of the hollows. This occurs only in very aged horses.

The Order of Whales differs from all our other Mammals in the matter of teeth. In the first place, no Whale has two successive sets of teeth: the single set grown lasts the animal

---

[1] Hence called selenodont.   i.e. hypsodont.

its life.[1] Secondly, the teeth are not generally of differing shapes according to their place in the mouth: each tooth is like its fellows,[2] single-rooted and simple in form, and they are sometimes (e.g. in the Porpoises) very numerous and variable in number. Thirdly, many Whales are without teeth, at any rate after birth, though their embryos almost always have traces of teeth which suggest a toothed ancestor.

Of Mammals only, the lips are soft and muscular.

Having given some of the facts of Mammal structure, there are a few things to be said here about their lives and habits. They are mostly land creatures, though two groups spend much of their time in the air or waters (the Bats in flight, the Seals swimming) and a third (the Whales) lives wholly in the sea. The land animals here treated fall into two main divisions, the survivors of our primeval fauna which walked here while these islands were still united with the mainland of Europe, and those since imported, willingly or unwillingly, wisely or foolishly, by Man. The latter include most of the domestic animals and certain others, the Fallow and Sika Deer, the Rabbit, the Rats, the Guinea Pig, Grey Squirrel, and the Muskrat. There is doubt about some others, thus our domestic Sheep, Cats, and Pigs have probably native blood, but certainly are mainly sprung from imported stock.

It is often said that the bigger the creature, the longer is its time of gestation, the smaller its litters, the longer the time it takes to reach full growth, the fewer its dangers, and the longer its normal life. On some of these points the facts are still largely unknown to us, but to show that these rules are not always true it is enough to take two examples. Roe Deer carry their young longer than the much larger Red Deer, and the Bats produce but one a year, while the Pig may have 40. There is, however, much truth in the above general statement. The largest of all creatures, the Blue Whale, is the slowest of all breeders, with one calf in three years, while those of a fertility which attains almost incredible figures are the small Rodents and the Shrews. There is also undoubtedly

---

[1] They are monophyodont.   [2] And homodont.

28

a general relation between the time taken to develop and the span of life. Man, the slowest creature to mature, is probably also the longest lived of our species. However this may be, one fact must always be remembered: the mortality of any species corresponds to a nicety with its birth-rate. If this were not so, that species would soon either become extinct or overrun the earth. On an average, starvation, disease, accident, enemies, and age, put an end in every year to as many individuals as are born. We have merely to find the latter number to get an estimate of the risks of their lives.

No young Mammal is born capable of getting its own food. All depend on the mother's milk for a time, but they differ greatly in the degree to which the young are developed when born. For example, young Mice are born blind and naked, capable only of sucking. At the other end of the scale, the Lamb is open-eyed, alert, able to stand and to follow its mother within a few hours of birth. The main groups into which our Mammals are divided may be roughly set out in the following order. The most helpless at birth are Man, the Insectivora, the Carnivora, the Rodents, and the Bats. The most active are the Hoofed Beasts and the Whales. The Seals are difficult to place as our two species are unlike in this respect. Other groups also show marked differences and sometimes even between very closely related species. The young Rabbit is blind, deaf, bald, and helpless, while the Leveret is open-eyed, hairy, and active.

The state of the young at birth governs the nesting habit. Those whose young are most mature need no nest and merely lay them in the open. The others must have a safe place in which to keep them warm and sheltered. This they get in various ways. The simplest is to find a suitable spot. Thus the Grey Seal bears its young in a cave, the Rat in a hole, the Bat in a hollow tree, the Weasel in a wheat stack, and the Marten in an old bird's nest. Then comes the burrowing habit, enabling the beasts to make suitable holes for themselves. This habit begins with merely improving an existing hole. Thus the Fox rarely starts a hole of his own. This habit leads to independent excavation such as that of the Field Mouse, Voles, Rabbit, Otter, and Badger. Almost all dwellings are made warmer and more comfortable by adding nesting materials or fur from the creature's own body. In some cases, like that of the Shrew, this nesting material gives the chosen place its only merits.

Lastly we have a small number of Mammals which build independent homes—nests or houses built by themselves of well-selected materials. These few builders are, so far as we are concerned, the Harvest Mouse, the Dormouse, the Squirrels, and Man.

This main division between those with young born mature and no nest, and those with nests and immature young, is also found among Birds. The Peewit bears the same relation to the Thrush as the Sheep to the Squirrel.

The burrowing habit serves not only for the needs of the young, but also to provide a home for all, or a part of, the year, but, except in the single case of the Mole, is used only for the making of dwellings. The Mole alone burrows not only for shelter, but, in the course of his unique subterranean life, in search of food: earthworms, and larvae.

The daily life and manners of our Mammals are almost wholly governed by their food.

Food. No animal can take its food direct from the carbon in the air or the minerals of the soil. This is the monopoly of Plant life. All Animal life is therefore dependent upon vegetation and, directly or indirectly, lives upon plants. Some creatures get their food by eating plants, some by eating other creatures which have eaten plants. Thus we have a division of the Mammals into herbivorous, insectivorous, and carnivorous. Some confine themselves strictly to one or other of these types of food. The Horse, the Ass, and all the Ruminants are vegetarians; the Bats eat nothing but insects; the Seals and Whales, marine life. Most animals, however, do not keep within the limits of any one of these types. Thus the Voles, though primarily plant eaters, also take insects or other creatures, living or dead; the Mice, though living mainly on the softer vegetable substances, will do the same. The Badger, naturally a flesh eater, seeks eagerly for honey. The distinction between insects and flesh is often misleading. Almost all the smaller Carnivora eat insects, while the so-called 'insect eaters' often live mainly upon other forms of life. Thus the Mole, though no insect comes amiss, lives mainly upon earthworms and will eat carrion or anything it can catch.

The process of extending their bill of fare has, with some Mammals, gone so far as to earn them the name of omnivorous. This applies particularly to the Rats, Pig, and Man.

Despite the confusion due to mixed diets, there still remains a division of the land Mammals[1] into those which are hunted and those which hunt. We have then on the one side such creatures as the Voles, the Rabbit, the Hares, and the Deer and, on the other, the Weasels, the Fox, the Cat, and Man. The former live a life of fear and evasion, escaping their enemies either by speed or by hiding. Most of the slayers are themselves in danger of slaughter, if only by Man, so that they also, for that reason as well as to be able to approach their prey unseen, cultivate stealth. These opposite motives of terror and ferocity have, oddly, led almost all our wild creatures to the same result—they are nocturnal, the timid to escape notice, and the fierce partly for the same reason and partly to be on the watch when the timid are about.

All creatures living outside the tropics have one problem to solve—how to keep alive through the winter. The plant life solves it (1) by dying down to the roots to be reborn in the spring, and (2) by limiting its life to a bare existence as hard wood or twig. Both these defences make the plant useless as food to most of the animal world in winter.

To the animal, therefore, the winter presents two problems —how to keep warm and how to get food. The various solutions adopted may be briefly set out as follows:

Extra clothing. Birds 'fluff up' their feathers, making a thick winter coat of air-bearing feathers. Almost all animals grow new and thicker coats of hair in the autumn which are

[1] Those of the sea and air, though all strictly hunters, are, except some of the Toothed Whales, not hunters of other Mammals.

shed in the spring. Man alone adds to his naked body extraneous clothing, variable with the weather. This remedy avails only against cold.

Fire. This remedy against cold is used only by Man, its master. It may be noted that a somewhat similar use is made of the heat of decaying vegetation by some Birds (e.g. the Grebes) and Reptiles (e.g. the Grass Snake) to assist in hatching their eggs.

Transport and storage. This serves to supply food and is the resource of but a few species. Man is almost entirely dependent upon it. He must harvest, gather from afar, and store, to live. The same is true of many insects (e.g. Bees) and the habit of storing food is instinctive to several of the smaller animals (e.g. Rats, Mice, and Squirrels). Dogs show signs of the instinct. There are a few instances of the use of this device by Birds (e.g. the Shrikes).

Migration. This is the main resort of the Birds whose power of flight enables them to follow their food. Almost all Birds move in winter, even if only from hill top to lower ground. The same defence against starvation is used by some animals. Whales follow the shoals of minute creatures on which they live, wandering about the oceans. Seals follow the Fish, and Man migrates to lands where new sources of livelihood are to be found. To a small extent there are migratory movements of other animals. Thus Hares, Otters, Wild Cats, Foxes, and Deer move from the high hill tops to the low lands in hard weather.

Egg-survival. The death of the individual while the next generation alone survives in egg form, which endures cold and is self-supporting, is a frequent method adopted by insects to retain the life of the species. Something similar is believed to occur among the Shrews. The older generation dies off every autumn, leaving only the young of the year to face the winter, thus freeing them from the competition for food which they would suffer if their elders survived.

Hibernation. This is the main resource of many of the creatures which live on insects. It seems to be connected with a low type of brain. All efforts to keep up the blood temperature above that of the surroundings are given up; all exertion is minimized; breathing is greatly reduced (to mere skin aeration of the blood in the Amphibians); the pulse becomes insensible, and a heavy sleep endures till the warmth of spring wakes them and restores their suspended faculties.

Hibernation is the winter life of many insects (Queen Wasp) and of some of the insectivorous creatures—the Hedgehogs and Bats—and of all our Reptiles and Amphibians. Also, to a greater or less extent, of several of our Rodents—Dormice, Harvest Mice, and, partially, of the Squirrels.

Before describing the *Gait* of the land Mammals a few words need explanation.

A 'step' is the forward movement of a leg to take the weight of the body when it is pushed forward. The same word is also used as a measure of distance, meaning the space between the two footprints of the same pair of legs.

A 'stride' is the full series of movements of all legs until they regain the position from which they started, or, as a measure of distance, the length from any footprint to the next footprint of the same leg.

If we begin by considering the movements of only one pair of legs we find that there are four types—the walk, the run, the skip, and the jump. In the 'walk', each leg takes regular and equal steps, one foot coming down before the other has left the ground. The track made is thus: L R L R L, &c.

In the 'run', regular and equal steps are also taken, but, more effort being exerted, the body is lifted so that each foot is off the ground before the other falls. The track is similar to that of the walk, with longer steps. In the 'skip', the steps are no longer equal, one leg (called the 'leading leg') exerting more power than the other, so that the track consists of alternate short and long steps: when the right leg is leading, thus: L R L R L R, &c., or, with the left leading, thus: R L R L R L, &c. In the 'jump' (or 'hop'), both feet leave the ground and come down again almost at the same time and side by side.

33

The track is: $\begin{smallmatrix} L & L & L \\ R & R & R \end{smallmatrix}$, &c. Although the tracks of 'walk', 'run', and 'skip' are represented above as being in a straight line, this is the case only at high speeds. The slower the movement the greater is the width between the right and left footprints. The track in 'jumping' keeps the same width at all speeds, but any difference between the timing of the footfalls (which are rarely exactly simultaneous) shows at high speeds by one footprint being more ahead of the other. In the case of quadrupeds we find that, in travelling slowly, most of them 'walk' with both pairs of legs, the feet being so timed as to fall 1, 2, 3, 4, 1, 2, 3, 4, &c. The hind legs fall on 1 and 3, the forelegs on 2 and 4. In other words, the hind legs precede the forelegs by half the time taken to make a step. The following is the order of the footfalls: LH, LF, RH, RF, LH, LF, &c., and although the walk may begin with any foot, this order never varies. In a very slow walk, like that of a grazing Horse, there is sometimes no foot off the ground, and never more than one at a time. When the walk quickens, one foot is always up and, for half the time, two feet. In the track, the hind feet usually fall almost in the footprints of the fore feet, though this varies with the speed of the walk, the hind legs falling in front in a swift walk and behind in a slow one. The 'walk' is the slow pace of all land quadrupeds except those which progress by jumps, noted later. It is also the gait of the creeping child.

When the animal wishes to increase its speed, it usually does so by 'running' with both pairs of legs. This may be done in three different ways, according to the timing of the two pairs of legs.

The first way retains the same timing as the 'walk', the only difference being that, as both pairs are 'running' and each leg lifts before its fellow (of the same pair) falls, the body is supported by one and two legs alternately instead of by two and three as in a quick walk. This gait of a Horse is easy and comfortable for the rider. To avoid confusion, I call this pace a 'running walk.' In current English use we have no name for this pace,[1] though it has been credibly argued that it was the 'amble' of the palfrey; but it must not be confused with the 'racking' pace, which is totally different and generally known under the name of 'amble.'

The second running pace is the 'amble' or 'rack'. In this the two pairs of legs are in step, the body resting alternately on both right and both left legs. RH falls with RF, and LH with LF. The timing is 1, 2, 1, 2, 1, 2, &c., the order of the footfalls (1) LH and LF, (2) RH and RF, &c., and the track is as follows:

LH LF   LH LF   LH LF
  RH RF   RH RF , &c. The length of each step

may vary, according to the speed. There are no double footprints. This pace (habitual with the Camel) is used by Horses when specially trained to it and sometimes by Dogs. When fast, it is very hard on a rider.

The third and commonest of the running paces is the 'trot'. In this the opposite legs of each of the two pairs are in step with each other, R falling with L. The result is a timing of 1, 2, 1, 2, &c., and the body rests alternately upon the two legs at opposite angles, RH falling with LF and LH with RF. Most animals, particularly the Carnivora, put the hind feet into the vacated footprints of the fore feet, so that the track made is:

LF and LH   LF and LH   LF and LH
  RF and RH   RF and RH , &c.

At full speed, the quadruped usually 'skips' with both pairs of legs, in the long gap after the rise of each leading leg taking the short step of the other pair of legs. This may be done in two ways, either leading with the same leg in both pairs of legs (e.g. Horse) or with the right leg of one pair and the left of the other.

In the 'Canter' of the Horse, both pairs of legs are 'skipping' and the non-leading foreleg falls at the same time as the leading hind leg, the result being a gait in which the timing is 1, 2, 3, 1, 2, 3, &c. If the right legs are leading, the legs fall in the following order: (1) LH, (2) RH and LF, (3) RF, while the

track made is: LH   LF
    RH   RF , &c.

[1] In America a Horse at this pace is said to be 'single-footing'.

The place where the next LH comes down varies with the speed of the canter. It may be behind, level with, or in front of the print of the RF. The full racing gallop of the Horse is the same except that the longer leap of each leading leg defers the fall of the first foreleg until after that of the second hind leg, so that the timing becomes 1, 2, 3, 4, 1, 2, 3, 4, &c. With the right legs leading, the legs fall in the following order: (1) LH, (2) RH, (3) LF, (4) RF, &c., while the track becomes: LH RH LF RF, &c., the footprints being almost in a line. The body is off the ground (with all legs bunched under it) after the leading foreleg has left the ground and before the first hind leg comes down to renew the stride. This gallop (with the skips led by the legs of the same side) has been called a 'Transverse Gallop' because of the fact that the legs fall successively in the form of a $\overset{3\;\;4}{\underset{1\;\;2}{\times}}$ if the animal be looked at from above.

Some other animals (e.g. the racing Greyhound) when at full speed lead with a fore and a hind leg on opposite sides. Thus, if the right foreleg is leading and the forelegs are skipping L R L R L R, &c., the hind legs will be skipping R L R L, &c. Here, as will be seen, if the fall of the first foreleg be deferred until after the second hind leg has left the ground, the legs will fall in the following order: RH, LH, LF, RF, &c. There are two periods of suspension, after LH and after RF, in the first of which the legs are outstretched, fore and aft, and in the second bunched under the body. This gallop is called a 'rotatory' gallop because, if viewed from above, the successive falling legs follow one another round the animal clockwise, thus: $\overset{3\;\;4}{\underset{2\;\;1}{\bigcirc}}$

In any gallop, transverse or rotatory, either foreleg may lead—either the RF, as above, or the LF, as follows:—Transverse $\overset{4\;\;3}{\underset{2\;\;1}{\times}}$, Rotatory $\overset{4\;\;3}{\underset{1\;\;2}{\bigcirc}}$.

GAIT

Some Mammals find their greatest speed in a series of leaps —'jumping' with the hind legs, while skipping with the fore. In this gait the skip of the forelegs is a result of the long jump of the hind, the forelegs being used merely to land after the jump and throw up the fore part of the body so as to be ready for the renewed jump. The forelegs come down one ahead of the other, leaving the usual skipping track of LF,RF, LF,RF, or RF,LF, RF,LF, &c. Meanwhile the hind legs leave a jumping

track: $\frac{\text{LH LH LH}}{\text{RH RH RH}}$, &c., which overlaps that of the second (leading) foreleg, so that the entire track (when the RF leads)

is: LF RF $\frac{\text{LH}}{\text{RH}}$ LF RF $\frac{\text{LH}}{\text{RH}}$, &c.

This pace, that of the jumping land animals, is seen in the Hares and Rabbits, the Cat, and the Roe Deer. The Horse and the Ruminants generally adopt it only for jumping over an obstacle. The Hares and Rabbits, owing to the relative length of their hind legs, use this gait at all speeds, even the slowest. The main difference between their slow and quick speeds is in the length of the gaps between the successive imprints of the four feet.

Many tree-living species in the world (here only the Squirrels) jump not only with the hind feet but with the fore

also, their track on the ground being: $\frac{\text{LF} \quad\;\; \overset{\text{LH}}{}}{\text{RF} \quad \text{RH}}$ $\frac{\text{LF} \quad\;\; \overset{\text{LH}}{}}{\text{RF} \quad \text{RH}}$, &c.

No beast jumps with the forelegs while stepping or skipping with the hind. Of the creatures here described Man alone uses only the hind limbs for progress.

The flight of a Bat is bird-like, the wings pulling the air downwards and backwards and being brought first upwards, partly closed so as to give less resistance to the air, and then forwards horizontally to begin the next stroke.

The true water animals (Seals and Whales) proceed by a waving of the whole body, the fore flippers being used only to steer. The Seals move (as do fish) from side to side, the Whales usually up and down. When a land animal swims, it usually makes the same motions in the water as when ashore. Man alone (unable instinctively to swim) uses a different method, which has to be consciously learned.

All Mammals, except the Whales, have a throat capable of voice production, and although we know little of their methods of speech, there is no doubt that they do convey their ideas by that medium, as well as by other means such as percussion sounds, gesture, and contact. Some have a great variety of sound at their disposal which even we recognize. The Pig, the Cat, and the Dog may be named as eminently conversational, but the whole subject needs more study. Many have also scent-glands, or other means of producing odours useful as signals. This, with their keen sense of smell, enables them to recognize, avoid, or follow each other and, in some, the habit of visiting agreed places to gather the news has been formed. These scent-glands have also their dangers, making easy the task of the pursuer, and it is often hard to see how the advantage can offset this peril.

The social life of animals varies from the extreme loneliness of the Hares, who are rarely together except during the breeding season, to the pack or flock habits of the Dog and the Red Deer. Few animals do much to help each other, though hunting in common is frequent among the flesh eaters, and many grass eaters herd together for better protection.

The marriage laws of the animals are also very variable. There seems to be a gradual progress from promiscuity, by way of polygamy, to monogamy. In some polygamous animals (e.g. Horses) a marked preference is shown for certain mates, while in others (such as Red Deer) there seems to be complete indifference. Such preferences are doubtless the first step towards monogamy, and there are animals (like the Otter and the Roe) who choose one mate probably for life. Monogamy, and the presence in the home of both parents to train the young, leads to the highest state of mental development.

Man's relation to the other Mammals is almost wholly that of slayer. The question whether an animal is useful to Man or not from a purely practical point of view is rarely easily answered. There is a good and a bad side to almost every species. Of some the only good lies in their meat or skins: the Deer, the Hare, and the Rabbit have nothing else to be said in their favour, while the farmer's crops cry out against them. This merit, while pleading strongly for the preservation of the species, condemns the individual to death.

The Fox destroys a vast number of Field Mice, but raids the hen-yard. The Mole saves our crops from hordes of insect larvae, but hampers machine mowing and annoys the gardener with its hillocks. The Bat is of great utility with its insect diet, but, in large colonies, is malodorous and verminous. The Stoats and Weasel take toll of Hares, Rabbits, and Birds, but help in the battle with Rats and Mice.

Only the defence of the small Rodents (Rats, Mice, and Voles) would test the ingenuity of any would-be advocate, though even their fur is used in some countries.

Nevertheless, however innocent, or even helpful, a species may be, the result is much the same. All the surviving wild species owe their existence either to their nocturnal or evasive habits, or to their small size, or large birth-rate. Almost all those wild beasts which were large enough to be dangerous have been exterminated.

In addition to killing the wild animals, Man keeps many of his domestic animals for the purpose of killing them. Of the seven species not kept to be killed for food (the Horse, the Ass, the Goat, the Guinea-pig, the Dog, the Cat, and the Ferret) the last three help him to kill other animals.

To the above reasons for the survival of our Mammal fauna one must add the protection given by Man for the sake of sport. This is often forgotten by those who claim the greatest interest in saving them. Apart from any profit derived from killing them, the skill needed to do so, either by hunting with hounds, or shooting, affords Man a pleasure for which he pays sums which form a large part of the revenue of considerable areas of the country, and maintains a system of protection which alone enables certain species to survive. The abolition of the gamekeeper and his traps would mean a great increase in the numbers of Rats, Stoats, and Weasels, with very serious effects upon bird life, and if hunting and shooting were also abolished it would mean the extermination of the Red Deer, the Fox, the Hare, the Otter and, in all thickly populated districts, of the Rabbit.

Before turning to the classification of the Mammals and the separate species, there is one subject which must be treated briefly—*Heredity*. So far as our knowledge goes, this is in no way peculiar to the Mammals, or indeed even to animal life as distinct from plants. Most of our knowledge comes from experiments upon plants and insects (as being the quickest and most fertile breeders under our control), though these results are confirmed by the facts ascertained about animals. The subject must here be taken as an excursus relating to life in general. It has been treated with the utmost brevity, and so far as possible without the terminology which makes it so difficult to follow.

Certain physical and mental characteristics are inherited from their parents by all creatures having life, animal or vegetable. It is not possible here to consider what, or to embark upon the question as to whether such qualities as are acquired by the parents, but not inherited, can, or can not become hereditary in the offspring. This is one of the battle-fields of modern science. It is enough to deal only with what is known, namely, that some things are inherited—like begets like.

The process by which this is effected was discovered during this century as the result of research based on the work of the Abbé Gregor Johann Mendel (1822–84), whose experiments had passed unnoticed until 1900. It is as follows:

Each new generation comes into existence by fertilization, which is the union into one cell[1] of two cells[2] contributed by the parents. One of the uniting cells[2] (which we may call 'half-children') comes from each parent and the two blend in

---

[1] Called a Zygote.   [2] Called Gametes.

the united cell[1] (or fertilized egg) which begins at once to grow, by subdivision, into the myriad cells which make up the body of the embryo, the child and the adult. In each 'half-child'[2] there are a countless number of tiny things, each one of which affects the subsequent development of the child in regard to everything which it will inherit from its parents. Thus it will have 4 limbs, 10 toes, 2 eyes, &c. There are also points upon which individuals of the species vary. It may have blue or brown eyes, a good or bad temper, or hair of different colours. Each 'half-child' will have in it something which determines each of these points, whether liable to vary or not. These tiny things are called Factors,[3] and, as there is one such factor for each characteristic in each 'half-child', there are two in each fertilized egg. These factors are not themselves visible, but they are collected in bundles[4] which are seen under the microscope. The number of such bundles in the united cell[1] is the same in every member of the same species, though it differs in different species.[5]

In regard to things in which variation occurs, the two factors must either be harmoniously pulling the same way (e.g. both for straight hair or both for curly) or they must be pulling in opposite directions (one for straight and one for curly). In the former case the creature is 'pure-bred'[6] for that particular character. In the latter it is 'hybrid'[7] for that character. The results of such a tug-of-war differ greatly in different cases. Sometimes an intermediate type appears. Thus Cattle inheriting the 'red' factor from one parent and the 'white' from the other, will be roan or red and white. Sometimes one factor seems completely to master the other. Thus Cattle inheriting the 'red' and 'black' factors will be black; though hybrid for colour, the beast will be indistinguishable from a pure-bred black. In such a case the factor winning the tug-of-war is known as a (Mendelian) dominant,

---

[1] Called a Zygote. [2] Called a Gamete. [3] or Genes.
[4] Called Chromosomes, or Colour-bodies, because they take up colour and become visible under the microscope only if the cell is dyed.
[5] In Man the number is 64. Some species have only 4.
[6] or Homozygous. [7] or Heterozygous.

the loser as a recessive. In Cattle 'black' is said to be dominant over 'red', 'red' recessive to 'black'.

Now as every creature of a particular species has the same number of these bundles of factors, and as these bundles are doubled in number at each fertilization, it is clear that at some time between one generation and the next the number must be halved. Such is the case. This halving takes place when the new cells are formed which are to go to the making of the next generation—those which have been here called the 'half-children'. These cells, unlike all others in the body, are single-factored and not double: they have only half the number of bundles present in the other cells. Thus, in Man, 32 instead of 64. They each have only one factor relating to each thing instead of two. This halving corrects the doubling at fertilization and keeps the number of bundles constant in every individual of every species. In the history of each species we thus have in every generation a repetition of the process of halving and again doubling the bundles of factors. The process of doubling needs no more explanation—the new child takes all the factors in the two 'half-children'. That of halving is less simple. Each new 'half-child' is so formed as to have one complete set of factors relating to every characteristic, but not two sets. One bundle of each pair is omitted and only one retained. The parent passes to each of his offspring either the bundle of factors he had from his father or that from his mother, not both. Further, each bundle of factors is selected quite independently of any other. It is an even chance which of the two bundles containing the factors which govern (e.g.) the colour of the eyes will pass to any 'half-child,' and this is equally true of all others. Pure chance seems to rule the selection. It is, of course, possible for such a division to result in every factor coming from one of the original grandparents, but the odds are many millions to one against it. The factors of neither grandparent are likely to pass *in toto* and, even if they did, there are those of the other 'half-child' to affect them before they produce characteristics in the child. In fact, in regard to each separate character, the father discards either his father's or his mother's contribution to his own make-up when forming the cell which is his contribution to the next generation, and the mother does the same. Thus, at each new generation, one half the total number of factors derived from the four grandparents are finally and irretrievably lost.

The fact that it is the bundles, and not the separate factors, that are rejected or retained in the process of halving above described, results in what is called 'linkage'—that is, that some factors are found to hang together and either all or none retained. This is when they are in the same bundle.[1]

To return to the cases of hybrids in which one factor is dominant and the other recessive, we have seen that such hybrids look like pure-bred dominants. This is so: but as breeding stock they are totally different. The pure-bred dominant has no recessive factor to pass on to his offspring. The pure-bred black bull, or cow, can never have a red calf. But the hybrid black beast will pass the factor for 'red' to half its calves, producing red beasts whenever that factor meets another 'red' factor from the other sex. Thus, if crossed with a red beast, half the calves will be red, for the red (recessive) can have no 'black' factor; and, if crossed with another hybrid black, 25 per cent. of the calves will be red, wherever that is, the 'red' factor from the one meets that from the other. These facts make it easier to maintain a pure breed of a recessive character than one of a dominant. The breeder is safe if he mates apparent recessives—they must be pure and will breed true. If, however, he mates apparent dominants, it may be many generations before he finds that a recessive strain lies hid in his apparently dominant stock. The quickest way to make sure is to cross each apparently dominant beast several times (say 6 or 8) with recessives. If none of the

[1] There are exceptional cases of occasional separation of usually linked factors which, by their comparative rarity, have led to remarkable deductions as to the actual position of a given unseen factor in (or on) a particular bundle, with a greater or lesser chance of its being rubbed off or otherwise shifted to another bundle.

offspring shows the recessive type, he may be fairly sure that his dominant is pure bred.

It has been found that one pair of the bundles of factors in every animal is concerned with the question of sex and that those two bundles differ in appearance in the males only. All factors for attributes which differ in the two sexes are in these bundles and are said to be sex-linked. The females have two similar bundles, the males one like those of the females and one different in form. Thus the father's 'half-child' determines the sex of the offspring, which has an equal chance of inheriting maleness or not, so that, in the long run, the sexes will be equal in number.[1]

If we think not of any special characteristics but of how many of the traits of any particular ancestor an individual will be likely to have, it will appear that he must inherit half of his factors from each parent, that he will, probably, inherit about a quarter from each grandparent, an eighth from each great-grandparent, &c.

The distinction between inheriting factors and inheriting characteristics must be remembered. Of the factors inherited, some only will be developed as traits, namely, (1) those also inherited in duplicate from the other parent, and (2) those which are dominants to recessives inherited from the other parent. All others will either remain as hidden recessive factors or else will take a part in producing an intermediate compromise condition due to a tug-of-war with a contradictory factor when neither dominates. Nevertheless the above rule accounts for the potency of 'in and in' breeding. It gives a greater chance of reproducing the traits of the individual whom it is desired to reproduce.

The following diagram gives all possible combinations of breeding if we consider only one pair of factors. There are

---

[1] The bundles of which every female has two and every male only one are called the X chromosomes: those of which the male alone has one, the Y chromosomes. A male has the bundles XY, a female XX. The Y behaves as a Mendelian dominant crossed with the X, a recessive.

In Birds, alone, the situation is reversed. It is the hen, not the cock, which has and transmits the single sex-determining bundle.

six possible varieties of mating between the three types (two pure and the hybrid between them) and the diagram gives their various results.

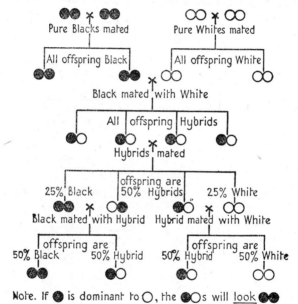

Note. If ● is dominant to ○, the ●○s will look ●●

TABLE OF ALL COMBINATIONS OF ONE PAIR
OF TRAITS

The next diagram shows the working of two pairs of contrasted factors relating to two different things which are not linked but in separate bundles. They are, as we have seen, liable to be separated at every new halving of bundles in each generation. This separation (or 'segregation of characteristics'

45

HEREDITY

as it is called) is one of the great Mendelian discoveries and has led to the modern science of breeding, enabling the breeder to collect from his stock the characteristics he wants, and to eliminate those he does not want.

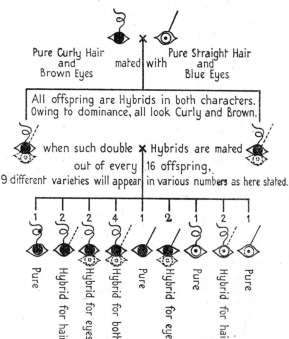

Note. There will be 4 pure bred, 2 of which are <u>new</u>.

TABLE OF TWO GENERATIONS OF TWO PAIRS OF TRAITS, ONE OF EACH BEING DOMINANT

CLASSIFICATION

The classification of Mammals takes notice of similarities of form and structure. Each species differs from every other, but the various species fall into groups which have characteristics in common. Where the likeness between species is great, two or more species are said to belong to the same Genus. Genera are grouped into families, and families into Orders. Sometimes groups of families are classed together in a subdivision of an Order to which the name of Sub-order is given.

Although there are differences of opinion as to the degree of likeness which constitutes a species or a genus, it is easier to agree upon these smaller groups than to arrange the major groups in such a series as to show their probable relationship to each other, or origin in a common stock. The members of some orders seem clearly to hang together and apart from others. Thus the Bats are readily distinguished from any other creatures by their hand-wing; yet Linnaeus placed them with Man, the Monkeys, and the Lemurs in his Order of Primates. Cuvier took the limbs as the main basis of his classification, while Owen based his division upon the differences in the brains.

No attempt is here made to improve on any scientific classification, but merely to adopt an order convenient to the reader who is trying to follow the various groups and is presumed to have some knowledge of the human body. Certain groups (sometimes Orders, sometimes Sub-orders, and sometimes Families) will be considered separately, with a single species chosen as an example to represent them. In choosing the Dog as example of the Carnivora, it is not implied that he is more carnivorous than, say, the Cat (he is not), or even that he is less like any other member of any other group. Still less does it mean that the other members of the group, the Weasel, the Fox, or the Badger, are Dogs (they are not). It merely means that it is easier to grasp the characters common to a group by thinking of one example than by trying to think of all its members at once.

CLASSIFICATION

The following are here taken as examples of the ten groups which together make up our Mammals: Man, Dog, Shrew, Mouse, Pig, Sheep, Horse, Bat, Seal, and Porpoise.

Here the groups are distinguished only by reference to their limbs and toes, teeth and diet, skulls and brains.

MAMMALS   *MAMMALIA*

LAND MAMMALS

BIPED. Omnivorous teeth, brain very large and folded.

MAN

QUADRUPEDS.
  With CLAWS.
    Animal eaters.

      Slicing and killing teeth. Brain large and well folded.

        CARNIVORA FISSIPEDIA

DOG

      Crushing teeth. Brain small and smooth.

        INSECTIVORA

SHREW

    Vegetable eaters.
      Gnawing front teeth. Brain small and smooth.

        RODENTIA

MOUSE

With Hoofs. Brain small but folded.
UNGULATA

Cloven Hoofs.
ARTIODACTYLA

Omnivorous teeth. Not chewing cud.
SUIDAE

PIG

Herbivorous teeth. Chewing cud.
RUMINANTIA

SHEEP

Central toed.
PERISSODACTYLA

Herbivorous teeth. Not chewing cud.
EQUIDAE

HORSE

AIR MAMMALS. WINGED.

Hands developed as wings.

Crushing teeth. Brain small and smooth.
CHIROPTERA

BAT

WATER MAMMALS. FLIPPERED.

Swimming.

4 limbs, with claws, hind legs a mere tail.
Brain large and folded.
CARNIVORA PINNIPEDIA

SEAL

2 limbs, without claws, boneless fins.
Brain small, but folded.
CETACEA

PORPOISE

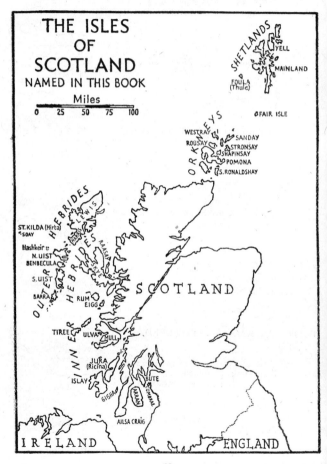

THE ISLES
OF
SCOTLAND
NAMED IN THIS BOOK

Miles
0   25   50   75   100

SHETLANDS
YELL
MAINLAND
FOULA
(Thule)

ØFAIR ISLE

WESTRAY
ROUSAY
SANDAY
STRONSAY
SHAPINSAY
POMONA
S.RONALDSHAY

ORKNEYS

HEBRIDES
LEWIS
ST.KILDA (Hirta)
SOAY
Hashkeir
N.UIST
BENBECULA
S.UIST
BARRA

OUTER   HEBRIDES

RAASAY
SKYE

INNER   HEBRIDES

RUM
EIGG

SCOTLAND

TIREE
ULVA
MULL

JURA
(Ricina)

ISLAY

BUTE
GIGHA
ARRAN
CUMBRAE

AILSA CRAIG

IRELAND   ENGLAND

50

THE PRIMATES

Order *PRIMATES*

Man is classed in this Order with the Apes, Monkeys, and Lemurs. Though the Apes are in many ways man-like, the others differ greatly. No other species has the large and highly developed brain of Man, and in some it is small and of low type. None have more than 36 teeth. All but one have 5 fingers and toes on hands and feet. Their thumbs are opposed and can grip and (except in Man) the big toes also. All usually produce only one at a birth. Here we are concerned with Man alone.

MAN

Homo sapiens

Habitat. Species, world-wide except the extreme polar regions. Our races have spread by emigration to North America, South Africa, Australasia and, in smaller numbers, throughout most of the globe.

Description. Sexes differ. Men grow hair on face and, to a greater extent than Women, on the body, and are generally larger and stronger. Women have larger hips, more prominent mammae (2) and smoother, softer skins.

Stands erect and, alone of our Mammals (except the Bats), has the limbs free of the body from the shoulder-blades and hips downwards. More nearly naked than any Mammal except the Whales. Our races are pale-skinned, hatchet-faced, and have hair long and only moderately wavy. Average Man stands about 5 ft. 9 in. tall, Women some 4 in. less.

Teeth. $\frac{2-1-2-3}{2-1-2-3} = 32$. Mouth is small. Teeth covered with enamel which remains intact. Incisors small, vertical and chisel shaped. i^1 is half as wide again as i_1 so that each tooth in the mouth, except i_1, bites upon two others. Canines very slightly longer and rounder than incisors. Man's use of his hands prevents his needing fighting-teeth. The cheek teeth have raised hillocks and hollows adapted for crushing rather than grinding. The milk teeth (20) are retained for about 7 years and m^3 and m_3 'wisdom teeth' appear at the age of about 20 years. See p. 19.

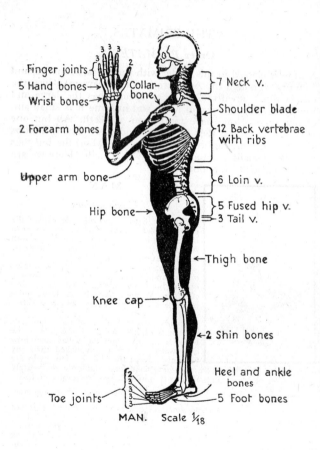

Finger joints { 3 3 3 3
5 Hand bones
Wrist bones →
Collarbone
2 Forearm bones
Upper arm bone
Hip bone →
Knee cap →
Toe joints { 2 3 3 3 3

7 Neck v.
Shoulder blade
12 Back vertebrae with ribs
6 Loin v.
5 Fused hip v.
3 Tail v.
← Thigh bone
← 2 Shin bones
Heel and ankle bones
5 Foot bones

MAN.   Scale 1/18

52

Limbs. The erect position has freed the hands and their form has given them wonderful dexterity. The forearm and shin each have 2 separate bones. Those of the arm rotate upon each other, so that the hand can be turned palm up or down at will. The hands (with 5 nailed fingers) are used only for work, play, or combat, rarely for crawling. The thumbs have only 2 joints and are opposed to the other fingers, so as to grip. The feet (5 nailed toes) have the big-toe not opposed and are used only for locomotion.

Structure. Vertebrae 7–12–6–5–3. The 3 tail vertebrae are small and fused into 2. No visible tail. Shoulders wide, and with collar bones.

Life history. One child at a birth (twins not uncommon, up to 5 recorded) born at any season of the year after 9 months' gestation. Open-eyed, but completely helpless Suckled for 6 months, crawl in about 8 months, walk erect in about 14 months, and learn to talk in about 2 years. Males are adult at 14, females at about 12. Growth continues till about 20. Normal span of life about 70 years, extending to over 100.

Yearly life. There is no special mating season, though perhaps a greater inclination thereto appears in spring. Overcomes winter cold by wearing clothes, using fire, and building houses.

Daily life. Diurnal. Sleeps (lying down) usually from about 11 p.m. to about 7 a.m. Habitually sits on a raised seat. Feeds on waking, about midday, and in the evening. Social. Man is wholly dependent for his food upon the harvesting of sown crops, the flesh of birds and animals and their transport and storage. He does not get each meal by his own effort of hunting or browsing. He eats what other Men have garnered or killed. A Man usually produces nothing for his own use, very rarely much. He gets everything as the result of a highly complex system of ownership, contract, payment, and credit. This enables him to exchange his work for that of others, or for property which he or his children can exchange. Those who can neither work nor pay are kept at the public expense, whether young or old, sick, criminal, or insane. The only way to lose this right is to commit wilful murder.

A few words must here suffice to suggest the variety of civilized Man's interests: they clothe, shave, paint and adorn themselves; they sow, reap, cook, brew, and distil; they use tools, weapons, wheels, ships, machines, fire, water,

53

MAN (cont.)

explosives, gases, and electricity; they build, tunnel, and mine; they speak, sing, make music, draw, paint, and record by writing, photography, phonography, and wireless, so as to inform and mislead, soothe and excite, amuse and annoy; they think, read, reason, and pray; they tame birds and beasts for their food, clothing, transport, labour, and pastime; they regulate their behaviour by custom, public opinion, law, and occasional devastating wars; they dig for relics of the past, and play childish games even when adult.

Food. Almost omnivorous, but eat very few raw foods, such as oysters, salads, fruits, and nuts. Cannot digest grass, even cooked.

Gait. Erect; biped. Walk (2–6 m.p.h.) upon the whole foot, heel and toe, keeping one foot on the ground until the other is also down. Run upon the toes only, with heel up, raising one foot before the fall of the other. Can run 100 yards in 10 seconds, a mile at about 13 m.p.h. Cannot swim without tuition.

Voice. Man has the power of speech understood by all who share the same language. The voice of the Males is louder and deeper, of Females higher pitched and, perhaps, less usually silent.

Varieties: Albinos are uncommon, but exist.

The whole Human Race is classified as a single species, named, with little modesty, *Homo sapiens*. There are a great number of widely differing local varieties, but no sub-species have been named. We are left with a number of terms in common use, such as Briton, Englishman, Yorkshireman, Swede, Laplander, Swiss, Walloon, Basque, Hindoo, Jew, Nomad, Red Indian, Negro, and hundreds of others. A glance at these shows that they are based on different lines of thought—political, geographical, linguistic, religious, occupational, racial, and physical. We know so much more about the history and mind of Man (his ancestry, character, habits, thought, and language) than of any other creature, that bodily differences (measurements, hair, and skin colour) seem less important. All races can interbreed and produce fertile hybrids. They are constantly mixed by invasion, commerce, and world-wide transportation. Man exercises no such control over his own breeding as he does over that of the domestic animals. All this has made the preservation of 'pure breeds' difficult and classification still more so. Yet the 'races' of Man are more like the 'breeds' of domestic animals than any other animal varieties.

All the Men of our islands belong to the pale-faced, wavy-haired branch of Humanity to which the name of Caucasian has been given.

The story of Man in the U.K. is briefly as follows:

Prehistoric peoples, small, dark-haired, and long-skulled (*dolichocephalic*), traceable back to Palaeolithic times, appear to have been over-run by successive waves of conquerors. Firstly, in the early Bronze Age, by a broad-headed (*brachycephalic*) black-haired folk, matriarchal, and armed with halberds (the Picts) who came by sea, probably from Spain, and, seeking tin and gold, occupied Ireland, Cornwall, and parts of S. Wales. About the same time, a broad-headed, red- or brown-haired race from the Rhine valley (known from decorated beakers found in their tombs as the 'Beaker People') speaking a Celtic tongue (now Gaelic and Erse) invaded England from the south-east and later (towards the end of the Bronze Age) spread over Ireland and imposed their language, with the help of bronze swords.

In the Iron Age, the Britons, tall, fair-haired, broad-headed, and more highly cultured (with iron swords), speaking a different Celtic dialect (now Welsh) followed from Belgium, landing in the south-east and spreading north and west. Though Celtic in speech, these were probably mainly Teutons in blood.

When the Romans came, the Celtic speech and arts had been imposed upon the whole country, except, perhaps, a part of the extreme north.

How far the various invaders had exterminated, or how far been absorbed by, earlier races is doubtful.

The invasion of Rome, which dominated the greater part of Britain from about A.D. 50 to 350, is less important racially than might be expected, for after A.D. 150 the legions began to be recruited from Britain itself and many of their descendants were slain by succeeding invaders. Their contribution to us was cultural and disciplinary rather than racial. During their occupation an influx of hostile Scandinavian and Teutonic people, though repulsed from the Empire, increasingly menaced the north and, after the collapse of the Empire, continued in successive waves until the eleventh century, by which time they had overrun the Romanized Celtic peoples and driven them to the mountains and western extremities (the present 'Celtic Fringes') of Britain. These waves were made up of many different tribes, Angles, Saxons, Jutes, Danes, Norwegians, and many others. With few exceptions they were tall, long-skulled, very fair-haired, blue-eyed men with narrow, prominent noses, and belonged to what is called the 'Nordic' race. The previous inhabitants, called from their language the Celts, though conquered, driven off and killed, were not exterminated. Few conquerors kill pretty women. The survival of dark-haired people, even in the eastern counties, attests this. The Celtic strain is, however, stronger the farther one goes from the eastern coast. This blend of mixed Nordic and Celtic peoples, in which the former predominates, made up the Englishman and the Lowland Scot, together called the Anglo-Saxons.

Other important infusions of blood have been few. The following alone need be noticed.

(1) That of the Normans (Scandinavians who had rested a few years in Normandy) brought ideas and some linguistic changes rather than any racial change. They were merely more Nordics.

MAN (*cont.*)

(2) That of the French Huguenots (after 1685), small (perhaps a quarter of a million) but culturally important.

(3) That of the Jews (17th–19th centuries). They are mainly town dwellers in London, numbering some 300,000 adherents of the Jewish faith, and racially perhaps twice as many.

It would be possible to make a long list of local types, of the nature of breeds, but their history is so doubtful, and the confusion between them so great, that it is enough here to divide our people into Anglo-Saxons and Celts, remembering, as is clear from the above history, that both are inextricably mixed in themselves, and greatly mixed with each other. This division corresponds with common speech and is convenient. In all, there are some 50 million inhabitants of these islands.

The Anglo-Saxon is mainly tall, with narrow skull, fair hair, pink skin, and blue eyes. In character calm, taciturn, slow to move, and hard to stop. Cautious, obstinate and practical, conservative, proud and distrustful of heroics or bragging. Outspoken, tactless, and illogical, he shows a marked tendency to compromise. They have evolved National Churches in both England and Scotland, to which the majority belong. They have created popular government and show great ability in adapting and working it. They are law-abiding. They made the English language and all use it, with but slightly differing dialects. They are far the more numerous race (some 43 of the total 50 millions) covering almost the whole of England, more than half Scotland, including Caithness, the Orkneys and Shetlands, a large area in North Ireland (with about a quarter of the people of that island), the coastal districts of the Isle of Man, and Pembrokeshire in Wales.

The Celtic races of these islands are mainly smaller, black- or red-haired and, with even fewer exceptions, long-skulled. They once spoke languages which have much in common. They are quick-witted, vivacious, excitable, talkative, and eloquent in speech and song. They are anxious to please, avoiding unpleasant truths. They are quarrelsome, easily stirred to tumult, intolerant of order, discipline or coercion, and lack cohesion. They are unforgiving, and their dislike of the Anglo-Saxon has resulted in the retention, or adoption, of forms of faith other than those of the established Churches. They are mystical and 'gifted' with second sight. English is the language of the great majority of our Celtic people. Celtic languages survive in Wales, the Highlands of Scotland, and Ireland. In south Ireland an attempt is being made to revive and learn Erse. In Wales about a third of the people speak Welsh, and 78 thousand Welsh only. In Scotland 140 thousand speak Gaelic, and 7 thousand Gaelic only. In Ireland an eighth of the people can speak Erse and 16 thousand speak Erse alone. Cornish finally died out in the 18th century. Our total Celtic population is about 7 millions. In England and Wales there are perhaps 2½ millions, mostly in Wales, Cornwall, the centre of the Isle of Man, the Lake district, Liverpool, and London. In Scotland (in the Highlands, in Glasgow, and the Western Isles) there are perhaps 1½ million. In Ireland there are over 3 million.

THE FLESH EATERS

Order *CARNIVORA*

Sub-order *FISSIPEDIA*

These form a large Order varying greatly in the degree in which they are purely carnivorous. The Seals, which are carnivora, will be treated separately.

All their bones, although slender, are strong. The two shin and forearm bones are separate. Generally speaking, the lower jaws are short and so articulated with the skull as to have little or no sideways motion. The muscles used in biting are powerful and the skull is so shaped as to give suitable points and ridges for their attachment. The cheek bones are large and prominent. The collar bones are absent, or purely rudimentary. All the toes have claws.

In the family of Cats the claws are retractile, the toes separately movable, and the two forearm bones, as in Man, capable of so twisting upon each other as to turn the palm up or down at will.

The true hunters among our Flesh Eaters (i.e. all except the Badger) have a double edge at the back of the ear, forming a small pocket which probably helps in gathering sound. They also walk upon the toes only, but not the tips. None have thumbs opposed so as to be able to grasp.

The teeth are of all the four kinds, completely covered with enamel retained throughout life, and they vary in number from the Cat's 30 to the Dog's 42. In all, the canines are strongly developed as weapons and the cheek teeth mainly formed for cutting flesh rather than crushing or grinding. Two teeth (the last upper premolar and the first lower molar) are larger than all the others, are commonly called 'Flesh teeth',[1] and have shearing edges which slice, one inside the other, scissor-wise. There are always 20 vertebrae for the back and loins (variously divided as the number of ribs differs) and three fused hip vertebrae, while the number in the tails varies greatly.

---

[1] Carnassials.

The Flesh Eaters are represented here by the following: Cats, Fox, Dog, and the Weasel Family (Otter, Badger, Stoats, Weasel, Marten, Polecat, and Ferret).

WILD CAT

Felis silvestris

Sub-spe. *F. s. grampia*

Habitat. Species: Wild regions of Europe from Scotland to Asia Minor. Sub-spe.: Wilder parts of the Highlands, mainly in Ross, Inverness, and Perthshire. Almost extinct in 1900. Has lately increased. Often mixed with Tame Cat blood.

Description. Sexes alike, males (Toms) slightly larger, about 22–5 in. plus tail 11–14¾ in., weight about 10–15 lb. 10 oz. Hair makes the tail club-shaped, marked with 2–4 complete black bands and black tip. The new (Oct.) fur of Toms is often reddish, fading to buff later. Tiger-like pattern varies in distinctness, and sometimes the black stripes break up into spots, especially on thighs. Long, sensitive moustache and eyebrow hairs. No eyelashes. In bright light the pupil of the eye narrows vertically, thus: ● ◗ ▮. Eye colour a greenish yellow. 8 teats. The Tom makes water backwards. *F. s. g.* is darker and more distinctly marked than the Continental type.

Teeth $\frac{3-1-3-1}{3-1-2-1} = 30$. Of all teeth the most wholly carnivorous. Incisors small and weak, canines large, sharp, and powerful. No tooth has any grinding surface. No sideways movement in the jaw. m^1 is useless and small. All other cheek teeth are narrow, trenchant blades, which shut scissor-wise, the lower within the upper. See figure on p. 24.

Limbs. Walk on the toes from ball of foot downwards, with wrists and heels high. Forearm bones about the same size, that from elbow to 5th finger (*ulna*) being longer and bigger above, while the other is thicker below. These bones swing across one another, as in Man, so that the paw can be turned palm up or down. There is a small bare callous at the wrist. Forefoot has 5 clawed toes (thumb very small). Two separate shin bones. Hind feet, 4 clawed toes (no big toe). As well as the wrist callous, there are on both paws large bare pads under the ball of the foot, and smaller pads under each toe. There is no pad on the heel. On all feet the claws are fixed to the last bone, and with it are normally bent up backward by means of an elastic ligament and so sheathed. They are pulled down and out when wanted by a tendon passing under the toe. They leave no mark in the track.

WILD CAT
Scale ⅛

59

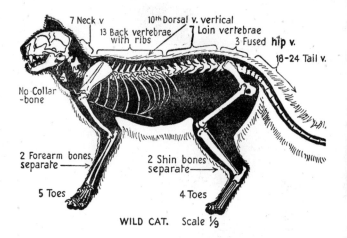

7 Neck v

13 Back vertebrae with ribs

10th Dorsal v. vertical

7 Loin vertebrae

3 Fused hip v.

18-24 Tail v.

No Collar -bone

2 Forearm bones, separate →

2 Shin bones separate

5 Toes

4 Toes

WILD CAT. Scale 1/9

Structure. Vertebrae 7–13–7–3 and in the tail 18 to 24. 8 pairs of ribs join the breast bone direct. The chest is narrow and lungs small, so that speed can be kept up for only a short distance. The stomach holds only $\frac{1}{2}$ pint (that of the smallest lap-dog holds $1\frac{1}{4}$ pints) and the guts are short—not more than $3\frac{3}{4}$ times the length of the body. No collar bone. Tongue rough.

Life history. 2–5 kittens in a litter. Gestation 68 days. Usually born in May. Perhaps a 2nd litter in Sept. Young born with hair, but blind and deaf. Eyes open 9th day. They need 8 weeks' suckling and thereafter are fed by the parents and follow them for about 4 months.

Yearly life. In winter sometimes approach farms to steal poultry, otherwise keep to the wilds. Abroad live mainly in trees: here, in treeless deer-forests.

Daily life. Frequent wildest rocky and mountainous areas of the Highlands. 'Catamount.' Make lairs in a Fox's earth or under tree-trunks or in thicket or, in open moorland, in screes or rock caves. Sometimes nest in bracken or deserted Buzzard's nest. Hunt chiefly at dawn or sunset, stalking stealthily by sight, in slow gliding movements, and then charging, at tremendous speed, in swift bounds. If cornered or trapped, show great ferocity and agility. Untameable.

Food. Purely carnivorous. Anything living, up to the size of Lamb or Roe Fawn. Mainly Blue Hares, Grouse, and Black Game.

Gait. Walk and trot, placing the hind feet in the tracks of the fore. At speed, bound in long leaps. Usually avoid water, but sometimes swim voluntarily.

CAT'S BOUNDING GALLOP

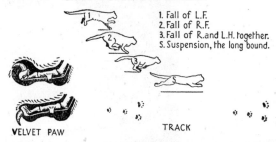

1. Fall of L.F.
2. Fall of R.F.
3. Fall of R.and L.H. together.
S. Suspension, the long bound.

VELVET PAW

TRACK

Voice. Said to give a loud scream when charging. Spit and growl as Tame Cat. A 'wild unearthly howl' is reported, probably the Tom's love song.

NOTE.—In the language of medieval sport, many Cats together were called a *clowder* of Cats, or a *kyndyll* of young Cats. Strutt's *Sports and Pastimes* gives other such collective nouns for our beasts, thus : a *herd* of any Deer, a *bevy* of Roes, a *dryft* of tame Swine (a *sownder* if wild), a *harras* of Horses, a *rag* of Colts, a *stud* of Mares, a *flock* of Sheep, a *tribe* of Goats, a *skulk* of Foxes, a *cete* of Badgers, a *richness* of Martens, a *husk* or *down* of Hares, a *nest* of Rabbits, and a *labour* of Moles. Also, for foreign beasts : a *route* of Wolves, a *sloth* or *singular* of Bears, a *lepe* of Leopards, and a *pride* of Lions.

TAME CAT
Scale ⅛

TAME CAT

Felis catus

Origin. Domesticated since prehistoric times, probably from the European Wild Cat (*F. s.*) and a very similar Egyptian species (*F. ocreata*). Not found with savage races of Man, but remains are found in cave-dwellings. Said, but on doubtful evidence, to breed with 8 different wild species. Our Cats to-day have doubtless Wild Cat blood.

Uses. Cats have two uses, as mousers and as companionable pets. Egypt, as the granary of the ancient world, worshipped the Cat.

Description. Similar to Wild Cats. Said to be smaller, really more variable. They have scaled 17 lb., which is more than any recorded Wild Cat. A fairly large one measured 19 in. plus 11 in. tail. Tail hairs usually diminish to a point instead of being club-shaped. Some races have much longer hair. In colour there is much greater variety: black, white, sandy, tortoiseshell, dun, grey, and orange. Almost every Tame Cat is marked with 1 of 2 different patterns, either the striped pattern of the Wild Cat or a peculiar blotched pattern. These 2 patterns are shown on the 2 half skins sketched here. There is no doubt as to the type to which a given Cat belongs because the 2 patterns do not blend, but remain distinct. The pattern can usually be seen even in pure black or white Cats, and even if not in adults, appears clearly in kittens. The 'stripy pussy' type differs from that of the Wild Cat only in a less distinct ringing of the tail. It shows the same break up of the stripes into spots as is found in Wild Cats. The origin of the 'blotchy pussy' type is unknown. It was probably a variation of the other which occurred and remains. Its origin is probably European and it is later in date than the stripy type. As well as wholly white Cats there are many which have white patches, often unsymmetrical.

Colour of the eyes, usually as Wild Cats. All kittens born with blue eyes. White Cats may keep blue eyes through life, and, if they do, are almost always deaf. Black Cats have clear yellow eyes and usually some white hairs under the chin and at tail tip. The true tortoiseshell (brindled sandy and black, without white) is always a female. Orange Cats are almost always Toms.

Teeth, Limbs, and Structure, as Wild Cat. The guts are longer, but not more than 5 times the body length.

TAME CAT (*cont.*)

Life history. 4–6 kittens at a birth (up to 9 on record) after 65 or 66 days' gestation, otherwise as Wild Cat. Female can breed at a year old and have 2 or 3 litters a year up to her 9th year. Usual life about 12 years—24 recorded.

Yearly life. No yearly variations in their lives except such as are forced upon them by their owners, who too often leave them to forage for themselves, unfed, during a 'holiday'.

Daily life. Solitary, hunting alone, and, where there are Mice, Rabbits, or small birds, largely self-supporting. Will kill, but seldom eat, Rats and Shrews. Will eat 20 Mice a day, kill many more, and frighten away still more. Devoted mothers. Home-loving, orderly, clean (burying dung and constantly washing fur), and sensitive. Never forget a blow. Largely nocturnal. Pair at night. As kittens play with movable objects, and always with prey after capture. This habit gives dexterity. Marked 'homing' instinct. Fall on their feet.

Food. By nature purely carnivorous. Trained by Man to take other foods, particularly milk. Cat's meat is none the less their true food. Crave fish in a way which suggests some fish-eating ancestor.

Voice. Great variety of 'mewings', plaintive and conversational. Like Man, but no other Mammal, has a song of pleasure—'purring'. Spits, hisses, and growls in rage, waving the tail. The amorous Tom utters horrible howls—'caterwauling'.

Varieties. Owing to the habit of nocturnal vagabondage, it is hard to create, or maintain, any separate breed of Cat. Specimens of foreign Cats showing special types, such as the long-haired Angora, or Persian, or the blue-eyed Siamese (cream coloured with dark chocolate ears, face, legs, and tail) are imported and, by rigorous imprisonment, kept apart, with great difficulty, for a time. But sooner or later all such go to swell the long list of types contributing to the mixed blood of the Domestic Cat. The so-called Manx Cats have only 3 tail vertebrae. The most important distinction is that between the Striped and Blotched types above mentioned.

FOX

Vulpes   Sub-spe. *V.*² *crucigera*

Habitat. Species: Throughout Europe. Sub-spe.: Same range, except in the Peninsula and Scandinavia. Common throughout U.K., but absent from Orkneys, Shetlands, and the Isles except Skye. Owes its survival in U.K. to Fox-hunting.

Description. Sexes generally alike, the females, 'Vixens', have a shorter, greyer coat, and are smaller. Size variable, length about 2 ft. to 2 ft. 8 in. plus tail, 'Brush', of 12–18 in. Males, 'Dog-Foxes', vary from about 15 to 29 lb. weight, 12–14 in. in height. Mountain Foxes are larger, longer-legged, and darker; those of low lands smaller, redder, and whiter. Has a strongly scented gland under the tail, the smell repelling many animals, and enabling hounds to follow. Eyes, cat-like: ● ◗ ❘. Usually 8 teats. The sub-spe. differs from the Scandinavian type (*V*³) in having less robust teeth.

Teeth $\frac{3-1-4-2}{3-1-4-3} = 42$. Teeth generally long and slender: canines very long. p^4 a narrow 3-pointed, flesh-cutting tooth: m_1 has the largest area, 2 cutting points and a crushing surface at the back: all the other molars are crushing teeth.

Limbs. Fore-feet, 5-toed; hind, 4-toed; both with non-retractile claws, furred between and sometimes on pads. Forearm and shin bones as Dog.

Structure. Generally as Dog, q.v. Back bone suddenly thins at the hips, 22 tail vertebrae. Forehead without air cells, a concave bone behind the eye socket. Brain highly developed and convoluted.

Life history. 3–8 cubs in a yearly litter, born after about 2 months' gestation in March or April (even Jan. in S. England). Born blind, seeing after 9 days; suckled for a month in the 'earth' and then begin to come out and are fed by Vixen (a model mother) with Rats or Mice. She will move cubs if disturbed, or when half grown, to new hiding-place nearer convenient hunting-ground, seldom going far until they can follow. Cubs born with grey-brown woolly coat and small pointed tail. Coat changed for yellow-brown fur about Sept., when they can forage for themselves. Adult in 12–18 months.

Yearly life. Solitary, though the same covert may shelter several Foxes. Dog and Vixen rarely together except during breeding season (mid-winter and early spring) when several Dog-Foxes will follow a Vixen and fight fiercely, snapping, wolflike, not holding, doglike. Does not usually dig own 'earth' except in very sandy soil, but adopts those of Badgers or Rabbits, closing all but one hidden entrance. Earths are often changed in accordance with food conditions. Have been found living with Badgers or Rabbits and even both.

Daily life. Mainly nocturnal, lying up all day and hunting all night. Their guile is proverbial. Countless instances, thus: floating down stream to Ducks with nose covered by mass of weeds: hunting far from home while sparing neighbouring warren or poultry farm: rolling and gambolling, dissimulating interest, and then when Rabbits gather, reassured and curious, pouncing on them. Concealing scent when hunted by taking to water, climbing trees, doubling and leaping sideways, mingling with Sheep, rolling in muck, and putting up another Fox. When hunting Rabbits, they quarter the ground as a Setter does, then point and rush in, bite neck, eat head, and then skin them, using teeth and feet. Kill wantonly, and far in excess of food needs. Will bury surplus food, returning later, sometimes with a friend. Hard to trap and will bite off a trapped leg. Subject to hydrophobia. Doubtful whether crosses with Dog.

Food. Purely carnivorous. Fish, flesh, and fowl, dead or alive. All Rodents, Hens, Ducks, Swans, and Turkeys, Pheasants, Partridges, Frogs, Fish, Crabs, Molluscs, Insects and Worms, Lambs, and even Pony foals. The Highland Foxes live mainly on Blue Hares, Ptarmigan, and Grouse.

Gait. Walk, trot, and gallop on toes, holding the brush clear of the ground. Can climb trees, and can (particularly the young) climb in or out of almost any enclosure. Swim well and readily.

Voice. Usually silent, but the peacock-like, yapping scream of the Vixen, and the yelping bark of the Dog-Foxes (uttered twice and repeated after a gap) are heard at night in winter.

Varieties. The underparts vary in normal Foxes from dark grey to white and the upper parts from yellow-red to greyish-brown. Black, pied, and white Foxes are on record.

FOX
Scale ⅙

DOG

Canis familiaris

Origin. Uncertain: probably derived from the Common Wolf (*Canis lupus*) but possibly from several wild species, including the Jackal (*C. aureus*). Probably the first animal tamed by man. Fossil remains prove comradeship back to Neolithic Age, and, if, as is likely, the Australian Dingo (*C. dingo*) is an escaped domestic Dog, it goes back to Pleistocene times. There are probably over 4 million Dogs in Great Britain. 3 million are licensed, drovers' and shepherds' Dogs are exempt, and young puppies must be added.

Uses. Originally tamed to defend Man and his property and to help in the capture of other beasts, the Dog to-day serves very many purposes. This breeding for various ends has produced the greatest diversity, both of body and mind. So much so that all the breeds cannot even be named here, and where breeds are named, it is only to illustrate their uses. Many of these uses are obsolete (as for bull-baiting) or foreign (as for draught), but the types bred for them survive or are here for other purposes.

I. The first great use of Dogs is the Defence of Man, his home, property, and cattle. Dogs were bred to fight in his battles (**Mastiffs**) and to defend him against dangerous beasts (**Wolfhounds**): to protect his house and to guard his flocks (the shepherds' watchdogs). These are all powerful fighters. Others serve similar ends by acting as sentinels and barking an alarm (as the **Lupetto** over the Italian wine-cart and the **Schipperke** over the Dutchman's barge). Many small Dogs are valuable in this way. Other Dogs have been trained to save human life in snow (**St. Bernards**) or water (**Newfoundlands**).

II. The second use of Dogs is to help in the Chase. This may be done in many ways according to the prey pursued: thus (*a*) some Dogs hunt mainly by sight and kill. These usually act individually, and include the swiftest of Dogs, like **Greyhounds, Deerhounds, Lurchers,** and **Whippets.**

(*b*) Others, who also kill, hunt by scent, usually in packs, displaying sagacity and endurance rather than speed: the 'Hounds', **Staghounds, Foxhounds, Otterhounds, Harriers, Beagles,** and **Bassets.** Others have been trained for the special purpose of tracking Men by scent (**Bloodhounds**) working alone on a leash.

(*c*) Small Dogs are used to dislodge some beasts from their holes. They are ready to go to earth to bolt, or hold until dug out, Foxes (**Foxterriers**), Otters (**Dandie Dinmonts**), and Badgers (**Dachshunds**). Similar Dogs of quick sight, good nose and tried courage (the large class of **Terriers**) have been bred to destroy Rats and other vermin.

(*d*) Other sporting Dogs are trained to suppress the natural instinct to kill and, while tracking by scent, to remain at a distance and show the presence of game by their attitudes—**Setters** and **Pointers**.

(*e*) Others, also tracking by scent, find and retrieve game after it has been shot (**Retrievers** and **Spaniels**).

III. The third use of Dogs is to help Man in his Daily Work. Thus those bred for draught (the **Esquimaux** and **Belgian Dogs**), those trained to hunt for truffles, and those who turned the roast (the **Turnspit**). Perhaps the most highly intelligent class of all are those which, as distinct from merely guarding flocks, guide, herd, and control other domestic animals (the working **Collie** and other **Sheep Dogs**, and the **Drover's Dog**). A little known example of these is the **Heeling Dog**, or **Ci Sawdl**, rather like a short-headed Collie, which, on the Welsh hills, is taught to throw, by a tweak of the flying fetlock, the half-wild ponies so that his master may catch them.

IV. Dogs have been bred to provide meat and fur (**Chows**).

V. The fifth use of Dogs is the Amusement of Man, either by a display of their physical powers and courage in fighting other beasts (**Bull-dogs**) or other Dogs (**Bull-terriers**), in coursing or racing (**Greyhounds**), or of their almost human mental powers as 'performing Dogs' (**Poodles**).

VI. Lastly, there are those Dogs which may be regarded as merely ornamental and useless or, looked at from another angle, as giving Man the supreme gift which no other animal can—Comradeship. These are either drawn from the breeds above mentioned which have lost their former occupations (**Bulldogs, Wolfdogs, Chows,** &c.) or diminutive specimens of similar breeds (e.g. the French **Bulldog,** Italian **Greyhound,** Toy **Spaniel, Pug, Pekinese,** &c.) or types of Dog bred for their looks alone (as the **Mexican Hairless Dog** and the **Yorkshire Terrier**. In this connexion the true status of some breeds becomes a matter of history. Thus the **Pom,** to-day a noisy lap-dog, started his career as a Wolf dog. It will soon be hard to recall that the **Dalmatian Spotted Dog** used to be the guardian of the carriage and the companion of the Horses at whose heels he ran.

Description. Naturally, long noses, legs, and tails, and pointed ears. The variety produced by breeding is such that little can be said of Dogs in general. The females (Bitches) are somewhat smaller, by from $\frac{1}{8}$th to $\frac{1}{10}$th. In size Dogs may vary from over 5 ft. in length to 7 in.: from the size of a small pony to that of a large rat. The shape of the head varies from the long and narrow form of the Greyhound or Borzoi, to the broad or undershot shapes of the **Clumber Spaniel, Pekinese,** and **Bulldog.** These same breeds illustrate the variety of general form, while the coat may vary from that of the **Bob-tailed Sheep Dog** to those of the **Skye Terrier, Bull-terrier,** or **Mexican Hairless Dog.** In colour, there appears to be but one rule: that if there is any white on the Dog, it appears on the tip of the tail. The pupils of the eyes are round, contracting under light to a smaller circle.

Teeth $\frac{3-1-4-2}{3-1-4-3}$ = 42. Incisors larger than those of Cat, having two

WORKING COLLIE DOG
Scale ⅛ (on right). Repeated smaller (on left)

notches in the cutting edges of each. Canines thicker and shorter than those of Cat or Fox. p^4 and m_1 are the big flesh teeth. There is a large grinding surface on m^1 which works upon the inner and hinder part of m_1. Abnormalities of teeth are fairly common.

Limbs. Stand and move on the toes only, wrist and heel high. The forearm bones are separate, but do not revolve upon each other, so that the paw can not be held palm up. There is a small callous under the wrist. There are 5 toes, the thumb small and off the ground, a pad under each toe and a clover-shaped pad at the ball of the foot; thus 5 toes, 7 pads, of which 5 touch ground. Hind legs have two separate shin bones, 4 toes and 5 pads, all touching ground. The missing (big) toe is represented by two rudimentary bones near the heel, and, in some Dogs, by a dew-claw. The claws are blunt and cannot be withdrawn. Hair between all toes.

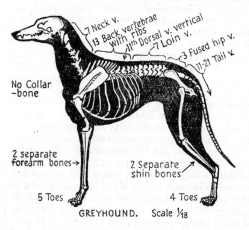

7 Neck v.
13 Back vertebrae with ribs
11th Dorsal v. vertical
7 Loin v.
3 Fused hip v.
11-21 Tail v.
No Collar -bone
2 separate forearm bones→
2 Separate shin bones
5 Toes
4 Toes

GREYHOUND.   Scale 1/18

Structure. Vertebrae 7–13–7–3, and in the tail 11 to 21. The 11th dorsal is vertical, 8 ribs join the breast bone direct. Usually the snout of the skull is longer than in the Cats. Eyeballs not enclosed. No collar bone, merely a loose cartilage. Guts 6–7 times the length of the body (increased by domestication). 6–10 teats.

Life history. 3–12 puppies at a birth. Gestation 62–8 days, usually 63. Born blind and helpless, but with hair. Eyes

DOG (*cont.*)

open on 9th day. Suckled for about 6 weeks. For some time after this mother Wolves disgorge food for the young and some Dogs retain this habit. Young Bitches do not breed until 2 years old. Normal span of life about 12–16 years.

Yearly life. When living a quasi-wild life, the female is usually in season early in spring, so that the puppies are self-supporting by autumn.

Daily life. Despite their variety, some habits are common to almost all Dogs. They are naturally sociable, running in packs and resenting strangers, but many breeds have lost this instinct. They show chivalry, a Dog rarely attacking a Bitch. Excellent mothers. Turn round before lying down, as if to smooth the coat on grass. In fighting, bite and hold, rather than snap. Have a strong sense of property: a big Dog will respect the premises or bones of a smaller. Set aside and secrete food. In anger, walk stiff-legged and with crest erect. Wag tail in pleasure. Intensely sensitive to smell, establish signal posts where urine is left as record. Will also leave urine or dung as a mark of scorn. The dung is not buried, but left away from home: easily 'house-trained'. Show self-sacrificing devotion to their masters.

Food. Naturally purely carnivorous, but, accustomed by Man to other foods, has become almost omnivorous.

Gait. Walks, trots, ambles, canters and, at full speed, gallops with a rotatory gallop (see p. 36) having two periods of suspension in each full stride. The gallop of a heavy dog has only one suspension (with legs bunched under) as the first foreleg falls before the second hind leg rises. Greyhound's full gallop covers a mile at about 31 m.p.h. and the stride may measure 9 ft. 6 in. Swims well and readily. Cannot climb.

Voice. Barks. This is an acquired habit, known among wild Canidae only in the Coyote (*C. latrans*): it can be lost by Dogs which run wild, and again resumed. The bark is varied to express all emotions. The different races vary, according to their training, from almost complete silence to extreme loquacity. Yelp with pain, whimper with excitement, and howl under the influence of music or when 'baying the moon'.

Varieties. Albino and black colouring appear in many races (and in Wolves) and the bow-legs, and underhung jaws, of some breeds certainly originated in varieties.

DOG'S ROTATORY GALLOP

R.F. and L.H. leading

1. Fall of R.H.
2. Fall of L.H.
Sa. First suspension, outstretched.
3. Fall of L.F.
4. Fall of R.F.
Sb. Second suspension, bunched under.

Track →

Next No. 1

OTTER

Lutra[2]

Habitat. Europe, North Africa, and east into Asia. On most streams, swift or sluggish, throughout U.K. Also on the remoter coasts and inlets and all islands.

Description. Sexes alike. Length very variable, usually about 25–30 in. plus tail 16–20 in. Males (Dogs) larger than females (Bitches). Usual weights, Dogs 20–25 lb., Bitches 15–18 lb. Body long and lithe, legs short and strong. Tail (rudder) large near the body, long and tapering. Nostrils can be closed. Ears short and closing under water. Small foetid glands under tail. Numerous oily glands in skin. Fur thick and close. 6 teats, in groin.

Teeth $\frac{3-1-4-1}{3-1-3-2} = 36$. Large: the cheek teeth sharp-pointed and interlocking, with very little grinding surface.

Limbs. Walks on toes. 5 rounded toes on all feet, web footed, with short, pointed claws. Forearm and shin bones separate.

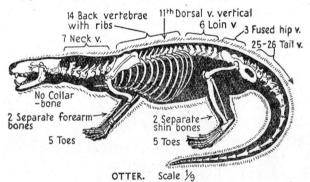

14 Back vertebrae with ribs
11ᵗʰ Dorsal v. vertical
7 Neck v.
6 Loin v.
3 Fused hip v.
25–26 Tail v.
No Collar-bone
2 Separate forearm bones
2 Separate shin bones
5 Toes
5 Toes

OTTER. Scale 1/9

Structure. Skull broad and flat. Intestines long. Vertebrae 7–14–6–3 and 25–6 in tail. 11th dorsal is vertical. 10 ribs direct to breastbone.

Life history. 1 to 3 'Whelps' (4 and 5 on record) born once

OTTER
Scale ⅛

75

in a year in any month, but mostly in early spring, after 63 days' gestation. Born with fine, silky coat, blind for 35 days. Suckled for 6 months, but soon taught to eat fish brought by both parents. Before the eyes open taken by mother and carried under water. Later, about 8 weeks old, taught, though reluctant, to swim (this takes a week) and, gradually, to hunt for themselves. Fully adult at 8 months.

Yearly life. Neither hibernate nor store food. Some live all the year by sea-coast and never ascend streams except during storms: the majority spend the year by streams or tarns, going to the sea in dry summers and returning up stream for the breeding season in autumn. Sexes are together from breeding season until whelps are able to feed themselves, when dog goes away. Bitch stays with whelps, prolonging their training till autumn. A 'holt' is sought as a permanent resting- and breeding-place. Holts are usually in stream banks, under roots or in old hollow trees, with an under-water entrance and, often, also an exit above ground. There is usually one chamber used as an earth closet. Where much hunted, their holts are larger and deeper. On the Norfolk Broads they build large 'nests' of dry reeds. In Devon, Scotland, and on the coast, holts are usually under rocks, or in holes in peat-banks.

Daily life. Nocturnal rovers. Very shy, elusive, agile, and strong. Rarely seen save when hunted. Rest all day in holt, sleeping, curled up doglike. Come out for night hunt about sunset. Keen of scent, sight, and touch. Cunning and resourceful. Work a pool in circles from centre, driving fish to the shores. Often hunt in couples. Can chase, tire, and kill a salmon of greater weight than themselves. Kill by biting backbone; take prey to land to eat; often leave after a small meal; never eat the tail or return to a kill. Dig, head in mud, for eels, &c., which are eaten from the tail up. Said to hunt under water by scent (?). Working up stream, land and trot across bends or to avoid rapids. Make long land journeys up to 15 miles. On coming out of water, drag on belly, then shake dry before lying up. The Bitch, when in season, will carry a straw in her mouth as if for nest building. Fight fiercely in defence of whelps. No serious enemy except Man. They, but not their whelps, are hunted.

Food. All kinds of fish, molluscs, and crustacea, above all, Eels and Crayfish. Failing fish, will eat Rabbits and Frogs (which they skin), Ducks, Moorhens, Snakes, Worms, and even Grouse and Sheep. Has some value, even to the fisherman, for killing eels and old cannibal and sick fish.

Gait. On land, a swift trot or gallop, leaving web-footed 'spur' or tracks. In snow, footmarks are erased by the low-swung body, so that the track seems that of a dragged log. In water, swim very fast and perfectly, entering water noiselessly. Swim on the surface with 4 feet, under water with fore-feet only, steering with hind feet and tail, showing merely a line of bubbles.

Voice. Short, sharp whistle as call to mate or young. Hiss when playful or scared. Squeal when angry. Whelps squeal much.

Varieties. Albinos, cream-coloured, and spotted Otters known.

BADGER

Meles[2]   Sub spe. *M*[3].

Habitat. Species: All Europe up to S. Sweden, eastern limits unknown. Sub-spe.: As above except Spain. In the U.K. somewhat scarce, but generally distributed. Rarer in the north and absent from Caithness and the Isles, save, by introduction, in Jura and on Ailsa Craig. Frequents mostly deep woods on sandy soil.

Description. Sexes alike. Female ('Sow') usually slightly smaller than male ('Boar'). Length 28 in. plus 8 in. tail. Weight very variable; average, boar about 25 lb., sow 22 lb., but recorded up to 40 lb. Thickset, bear-like, round-backed, very powerful. Fur coarse, long, and loose. Foetid gland under tail. 6 teats.

BADGER
Scale ½

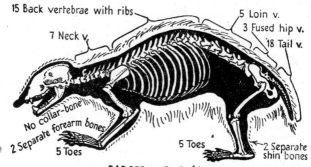

15 Back vertebrae with ribs

7 Neck v.

5 Loin v.

3 Fused hip v.

18 Tail v.

No collar-bone

2 Separate forearm bones

5 Toes

5 Toes

2 Separate shin bones

BADGER. Scale 1/9

Teeth $\frac{3-1-4-1}{3-1-4-2}$ = 38. Fairly large, prominent canines. m^1 and m_1 are very large, with considerable areas for crunching.

Limbs. Short and very strong. Shin and forearm bones separate. Cannot turn palm up. 5 toes with claws on each foot. Soles naked. Claws on forefeet large for digging.

Structure. Head large and powerful, with strongly developed bony crest, and jaw so articulated to the skull that it cannot be removed after death without breaking the bone. No collar bone. Vertebrae, 7-15-5-3-18. 9 rib pairs join the breast bone. The 13th back vertebra vertical.

Life history. 2–4 'Earth Pigs' (6 recorded) at a birth in spring or summer. It is said that young are produced only once in 3 years. Gestation usually 4–6 months, but very variable, instances being recorded of births in captivity after 12 or even 15 months. Cubs are born a silver-grey colour, blind till 10th day, and helpless. Later turn brownish-yellow and lastly like adults. Cubs do not come out for 2 months. Mother tends young most carefully, cleansing them.

Yearly life. In colder climates (e.g. Sweden) hibernate completely from Nov. to March. With us, partially hibernate, in deep chamber in the earth ('Set'), bedded with fermenting leaf mould, and with its access blocked up, but come out in mild weather and sometimes even with snow on ground. The set consists of one or more chambers, 10 or more feet below the surface, having usually several entrance passages and many workings on various levels. At the main entrance, often distributed round it, is a huge mound of excavated soil. Sets are sometimes very large, with as many as 40 exits, holding many families, and also Foxes and Rabbits. Rabbit warrens are often adapted. A regular spring cleaning takes place about March, the bedding being dragged out into the sun. New chambers are made and lined with fern and grass, in preparation for the breeding season. The Boars keep, or are kept, for a time away from the growing young.

Daily life. Nocturnal, sleeping all day, usually near exit from the set, and rarely abroad until after dark. Then they emerge (the parents carefully scouting before allowing the cubs out) and go hunting. During the night walks (when they may cover as much as 6 miles) they are in constant restless action, playing, working, seeking food, rolling and scratching (Monkey-like). Very keen of scent and hearing, intelligent, resourceful, courageous, acquisitive, and pertinacious. Some become difficult to trap. They are said to approach a gin only to snap it, by rolling on it (the coarse back hairs protecting the body) and then to eat the bait. Very clean, burying dung in an 'earth closet' dug far from the set. Clean their claws (Cat-like) on a tree before entering set. Sometimes play in the sun on special playgrounds. A few Highland Badgers live an undisturbed life in stone cairns on the high summits. No enemies except Man, to whom they are useful.

Food. Fairly omnivorous: roots, fruit, honey, slugs, snails, wireworms, wasp grubs and comb, beetles, and insects of all kinds, Moles, Snakes, young birds, and Rabbits.

Gait. A slow, rolling, bear-like shuffle, with the head and tail low. Walk on the flat feet (heels and wrists down). Feet in the track almost in a line.

Voice. Usually silent. Clucking sound in pleasure. Growl in anger. Loud chatter in discomfort. Grunt when hunting, digging, and as alarm. Scream loudly in pain or terror.

Varieties. Albinos are not rare.

STOAT or ERMINE

Mustela erminea

Habitat. Species: Europe from the Arctic coast to the Pyrenees and from Great Britain east into Asia. Abundant throughout Britain and on most of the Islands except Arran, Harris, N. and S. Uist, and the Orkneys. Not in Ireland or Isle of Man.

Description. Sexes alike. Size very variable, males larger (length about 10½ in. plus tail 4½ in., weight 10 oz.) than females (length about 9½ in. plus tail 3½ in., weight 8½ oz.). Body and neck cylindrical and long, legs short. Black tail tip marks all Stoats all the year. The winter change to pure white (except the tail tip) is rare in this country, especially in males, and depends on local temperature. Last parts to turn white are 'spectacles' round eyes. Some become white in S. England, but the change is rarely complete there. Stoats on the tops of Ben Nevis are always white all the year. 8 teats. Foetid glands by tail. Emit an evil stench as protection from enemies.

Teeth $\dfrac{3-1-3-1}{3-1-3-2} = 34$.

Limbs. Forearm and shin bones separate, but forefoot not reversible. 5 clawed toes on all feet.

Structure. Elongated. Vertebrae 7–14–6–3–18. 10 rib-pairs join the breast bone; the 10th back vertebra spine points back, the 11th forward. See p. 84.

Life history. Usually 5–8 young at a birth (2–13 recorded). Gestation probably about 40 days. Blind for 9 days. Then soon become active and follow mother when hunting.

Yearly life. No hibernation or food storing. The colour-change varies in date with temperature. Pair early, often February, the young being born April or May.

Daily life. Less nocturnal than any other British Flesh-eater. Frequent, and nest in, hollow trunks, mole-hills, walls, banks, thickets, or rough ground near cultivation, or in wood, high mountain or moor. Hunt prey relentlessly by both sight and smell, finally rushing in to seize the throat or artery behind ear. Do not suck blood. Drag victims to nest to be eaten, pulling and pushing beasts even four times their own weight.

STOAT. Summer

STOAT. Autumn

STOAT. Winter

IRISH STOAT
Scale ⅙

Roll eggs, holding them under the chin. Burrow in snow, climb trees, and enter any Rat's or Mole's burrow. The dung is often found outside the nest entrance. A 'stoated' Hare or Rabbit seems paralysed with fear and awaits death, motionless and screaming. When moving in packs, Stoats will sometimes attack Dog or Man. Will return boldly to prey if driven off. Very inquisitive. Mobbed by birds. Will live and play with Rabbits, on whom they prey when hungry. Tumble and writhe, snake-like, to attract birds within range. Savagely destructive, killing when no longer hungry. A trapped Stoat has been found eaten by her suckling young. Man is their chief enemy, but they are eaten by Foxes, Cats, Owls, and even Pike. Though destructive to poultry and game, they do much good by destroying Rodents. Hard to tell why so numerous. Birth-rate, and smaller size, seem their main advantages over the Polecat.

Food. Purely carnivorous: Voles, Mice, Rats, Rabbits, Hares, birds, eggs, and, perhaps, a few spent fish. Sometimes carrion.

Gait. Creep, wriggle, run in long, low jumps (as Rabbit) at considerable speed. Climb trees with great agility, descending backwards. Bold and strong swimmer, head well up. Has been seen 4 miles from land. Often crosses great rivers. When swimming will not be deterred from chosen landing place.

Voice. In play, a crowing sound, 'Curoo curoo curoo!' Angry, a loud chattering. 'Bark' when hunting in parties.

Varieties. Rarely, true albinos are found, with white tail tip. One black and white recorded. Our sub-species are:

BRITISH STOAT. *M. e. stabilis.* Full change to white rarer than in Continental type $(M. e.^2)$. Skull lengths of males 48·8 to 52·4 mm., widths 28·4 to 30 mm. *Habitat:* In Britain only, as above for species, except Islay and Jura.

JURA STOAT. *M. e. ricinae.* Differs from *M. e. s.* as follows. Slightly smaller, but wider at the cheeks. Skull lengths of males 47 to 50 mm., widths 28·4 to 31·2 mm. *Habitat:* Islay and Jura.

IRISH STOAT

Mustela hibernicus

Habitat. Ireland and Isle of Man.

Differs from the British Stoat (*M. e. s.*) as follows:

(1) Average size smaller, that of the males being as British females. Skull length, male 44·2 to 50 mm.

(2) Summer coat has the dark colour usually over a larger area, particularly on the upper lip.

(3) Winter coat rarely even partly assumed. This is climatic.

(4) Usually 10 or 12 teats.

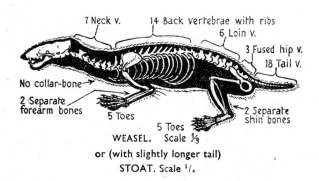

WEASEL. Scale ⅓

or (with slightly longer tail)

STOAT. Scale ¹/₄

Male   Female

Scale $\frac{1}{6}$

WEASEL

Mustela nivalis

Sub-spe. *M. n.*[2]

Habitat. Species: all Europe. Not Ireland. Typical sub-spe.: As above except Spain, Italy, Mediterranean Islands, and SE. France. Common throughout Britain. Not in the Isles, except Islay, Bute, and Skye.

'As the Stoat's totally different, you easily know it from the Weasel', but the Weasel is best described by the differences.

Description. Smaller, length of males 8–8½ in. plus tail 2½ in., weight 3½ oz., females markedly smaller than males, length 7 in. plus 2 in. tail, weight 3 oz. Tail relatively shorter than Stoat's, less bushy and without black tip. Legs shorter: head narrower. Paler in winter. In colder climates assumes a white winter coat, but not in this country.

Life history. 4–6 young born about April or May (May or June in Scotland). Young are dark in colour. Sometimes 2 or 3 litters a year.

Other differences. Owing to smaller size, less destructive to game and very valuable in keeping down Mice, Voles, and Rats, which form its main food. In ratting, courage even greater than Stoat's. Can enter a Field Vole's hole. Has been known to kill Hares, Rabbits, and adult birds of all sizes.

WEASEL (*cont.*)

Eats Frogs and, occasionally, Toads. Makes its final charge with tail erect. The nest, of grass or leaves, in hole in wall, tree stump, or stack. Also recorded in odd places, as in the body of a dead beast. Burrows through stacks and pounces out at the top to seize and kill Sparrows.

Voice. Young, a high whimper, later, a hiss.

Gait. Swift scamper with straight body, also a series of bounds. Though able to climb trees, and swim when hunting, does so less often than Stoat.

Varieties. Albinos rarely recorded.

MARTEN

Martes[2]

Sub-spe. *M.*[3]

Habitat. Species: Entire wooded region of Europe. Sub-spe.: The same, except Mediterranean area. In U.K. almost extinct but a very few survive in Lake District, Scotland, Wales(?), and Ireland.

Description. A large, long-tailed Stoat, less the smell. Length 16–22 in. plus tail 12 in. Weight about 3 lb. 2 oz. Males are the larger. Tail glands have only a faint, agreeable, musky smell. 'Sweet Marten.' Fur thick and fine. No seasonal variation to white. 4 teats.

Teeth $\frac{3-1-4-1}{3-1-4-2} = 38$. Canines large and prominent. p^4 has little or no grinding surface. The other flesh tooth (m_1) has cutting and grinding parts about equal.

Limbs. 5 toes on all feet, walking on the toes. In winter, feet are thickly furred; in summer, only between pads. Shin and forearm bones separate, but the palms do not turn up.

MARTEN
Scale ⅛

MARTEN (*cont.*)

Structure. Vertebrae, 7–14–6–3–18. Generally as Stoat.

Life history. 2–5 cubs at a birth (7 recorded). Possibly 2 litters in some years. Young born white in colour, with fine, short hair; blind for about 3 weeks. Gestation about 100 days.

Yearly life. Though abroad mainly arboreal (and even here named 'Pine Marten'), they live in screes or cairns in Wales, Ross-shire, and Lake District. In Ireland, and sometimes in Scotland, take over Crow's, Buzzard's, or Squirrel's nest. In Lake District some stay on open fells till April or May. Then come to wooded valleys and nest in Magpie's or Squirrel's nest. Others remain on high tops.

Daily life. Lives either on remote boulder-strewn hill-sides, or else in thick fir woods. Perhaps the wildest and shyest of our beasts. Very rarely seen. Even if living in the open, is apt to get up a tree if pursued. Leaves little scent for a dog. Fierce, gallant fighter. Easy to trap. Mobbed by birds.

Food. Rabbits, Squirrels, Moles, Lizards, Frogs, birds, including poultry, and eggs, fruit, berries, beech-mast, honey (robbed from hives), and wasps. Can kill young Roe and Lambs. Hunt by sight and smell, slowly, with final rush.

Gait. Active, graceful, swift: in forest, climbs with perfect agility along and over branches. Wriggles through amazingly small hole. In haste, travels in long leaps of 6 or 7 feet. Track as Hare.

Voice. Spits and hisses, cat-like: a shrill, sharp, loud cry.

POLECAT

Mustela putorius

Sub-spe. *M. p.*[1]

Habitat. Species: Europe from Great Britain eastwards and from central Scandinavia to Mediterranean. Typical sub-spe.: Same except west of the Peninsula. In Britain almost extinct, but still survive in yearly lessening numbers. Extinct in Ireland.

Description. Sexes alike, but males distinctly larger, length about 22 in. plus 8 in. tail, weight about 2¾ lb.: female about 20 in. plus 6½ in. tail, weight about 1¾ lb. Fur long, almost black with purple sheen, showing buff undercoat. Coat changed early May. Glands near tail give out disgusting smell, which never leaves fur. 'Foumart' = foul marten. 8 teats.

Teeth $\frac{3-1-3-1}{3-1-3-2} = 34$. Flesh teeth ($p^3$ and m_1) are almost mere blades.

Limbs and structure. As Stoat. Fore-claws are partly retractile.

Life history. 4–5 young born about April or May, after 40 days' gestation. Probably 2 broods a year. Born very pale in colour, gradually darkening to full colour in 8 months. Begin to eat when 3 weeks old, come out of nest on 39th day. Fully grown in 3 months.

Yearly life. Sexes live together for greater part of year. During mating season (Feb. to April) males make long night journeys. A nest is made in some hole, Fox's earth, Rabbit's burrow, hollow tree, or rock crevice, and consists of two chambers, one leaf-lined for the young, the other a larder stored with food. In this, Frogs and Toads have been found not dead, but stunned by a bite on skull. In winter will sometimes nest in a deserted building.

Daily life. Frequents woods and hilly thickets. Mainly nocturnal. Sleeps all day in nest. Ranges for food at night. Does not travel so far as Marten, usually only to visit neighbouring farm or Rabbit warren. Goes to streams for eels or trout. Kills for pleasure far more than it eats. Attacks skull of small victims, the throat or back of ear of large. Has been

POLECAT
Scale ⅛

known to attack Man. Easy to trap. Uses scent gland as defence if wounded or annoyed.

Food. Mainly Rabbits and poultry, but also game birds, eggs, fish, Frogs, Toads, Snakes. Even Geese, Turkeys, and Hares.

Gait. Much as Stoat, but poor climber. Fine, bold swimmer.

Voice. Said to be deeper in tone than the Marten's.

Varieties. In Tregaron Bog, Wales, a pale reddish variety is found.

Scale ⅙

FERRET

Mustela furo

Origin. An albino of some species of wild Polecat, probably the Asiatic Polecat (*M. eversmanni*).

Uses. Bred to assist in the killing of Rabbits and Rats. For rabbiting they have been used since the 1st century, and are mentioned by Pliny. They are muzzled and put into the burrows, from which the Rabbits bolt to the gun or into nets. For Rats they are usually released in couples, unmuzzled, the Rats being bolted to be killed by gun or Terriers. Recently they have become of great value for scientific experiment, having proved liable to take Dog's distemper and Man's influenza.

Description. Sexes alike. The males (bucks, dogs, or hobs) are slightly larger than the females (does, bitches, or jills). Yellowish-white in colour. Size about 14 in. plus 5 in. tail. Generally resemble the wild Polecat. Have the evil-smelling tail glands, using them when seriously annoyed or distressed.

FERRET (cont.)

Teeth, limbs, and structure. As Polecat. The flesh teeth are smaller and, in the skull, the hollows behind ear are deeper, and there are other minor differences, all of which are shared by the Asiatic species.

Life history. 6–9 young in a litter, 2 litters a year. Jills usually in season April–May and July. Gestation 42–45 days. If the young are looked at by Man in their first 2 or 3 weeks, there is danger of the mother eating them.

Yearly and daily life. They should be kept in a dry, clean, and well ventilated hutch. Scrupulously clean in their habits, usually deposit dung in the furthest corner of their yard. When unmuzzled, grip their prey fiercely and hold on. Dislike water. Will rarely come out onto wet ground, and work badly in wet weather. Can be safely handled by one they know, but often vicious with strangers. Cannot fend for themselves if lost, but soon die.

Gait. As polecat.

Food. Fed twice daily, on bread, milk, and meat. The habit of giving entrails is bad. The young instinctively attack Rabbits and Rats.

Voice. Chatter when annoyed. Hiss in anger.

Varieties. Have been crossed with wild Polecats and the cross gives a fertile breed called 'Polecat Ferrets'. These resemble the Polecat in colour, but while smaller than Polecats, are very variable in size, being either distinctly smaller than the pure Ferret, or else distinctly larger. They are said to work more quickly than albinos, but are less readily seen on emerging from warrens.

THE INSECT EATERS

Order *INSECTIVORA*

The Insect Eaters are a large group of usually small Mammals. They are found all over the world except in Australia and in S. America, where they appear only in the extreme N.W. corner. Terrestrial in habit. Brains of a low type, without convolutions. All flat-foot walkers. The forearm bones separate, the shin bones united below. Fossil remains show them almost unchanged since Pliocene times.

Although called Insect Eaters, they are not confined to this diet, and our species will eat any small creatures they can get hold of, alive or dead, and, in some cases, vegetable food. They are not eaters of insects from choice. They are eaters of animal life who are too small, slow, and ill-equipped to catch anything more active than the beetles, larvae, and worms, which are their chief diet.

Their teeth are eminently adapted for crushing the hard cases of Insects. For this the teeth are pointed in shape, each point fitting into a hollow in, or between, the opposing teeth. The cheek teeth, as seen from the biting surface, are usually V- or W-shaped.[1] The canines are often small and hard to distinguish. This, with the presence of a powerful collar bone, and the smooth brain, distinguishes them from the Carnivora. Differ greatly in general appearance and form. Mainly, but not all, nocturnal.

They are here represented by the Hedgehog, the Mole, and the Shrews. Apart from lack of wing, they differ from the Bats in having teats upon the abdomen and (except the Mole) not on the breast.

[1] See page 25.

HEDGEHOG

Erinaceus europaeus

Sub-spe. *E. e.*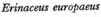[2]

Habitat. Species: Throughout Europe up to S. Scandinavia, eastern limit unknown. Sub-spe.: north of the Alps and Pyrenees. Throughout U.K. except in the extreme north-west and on high land. Not in the Isles, save, by importation, in Mull, Bute, Shetland, and (?) Orkneys.

Description. Sexes alike. Male (Boar) slightly larger than female (Sow). Length 9 in. plus tail $1\frac{1}{2}$ in. Weight 1 lb. 8 oz. to 2 lb. 7 oz. Whole upper part of head and body covered with a thick coat of spines, about $\frac{3}{4}$ in. in length arranged in groups surrounded with fur. 12 teats on the belly.

Teeth $\frac{3-1-3-3}{2-1-2-3} = 36$. i^1 and i_1 are longest.

Molars are strongly pointed and W-shaped. The 4 classes of teeth are not clearly differentiated. Last p and first 2 ms are the largest teeth.

Limbs. Forearm bones are separate, but do not rotate so that the palm stays down; the 'small' bone (*ulna*) is much the larger. Shin bones unite half-way down. 5 toes on all feet. Long, but weak claws. Pads on the soles.

Structure. Vertebrae 7–15–6–3–11. Very short neck. Well-developed collar bones. Large enveloping muscle covers the whole crown of the head and body, and when tightened, rolls the whole animal into a ball, with all the spines erect. If relaxed, the Hedgehog straightens out with the spines laid flat, pointing backwards.

Life history. 2 litters of 4–7 young in May–July, and Aug.–Sept. Born blind, with pale-coloured soft spines, which take 3 weeks to harden. Not above a month's gestation. Said to mate for life.

Yearly life. Late in Nov. or Dec. retire to hibernate in warm bed of moss and leaves, in bank or old wasp's nest. Store fruits and beech-mast, whether to be eaten or to attract insects is unknown. During hibernation the blood alters in character, nearly all the white corpuscles going to the stomach to absorb all bacilli of decay and returning to the blood when this is done. Sometimes come out after settling in for winter

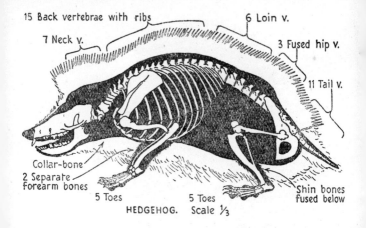

15 Back vertebrae with ribs   6 Loin v.

7 Neck v.   3 Fused hip v.

11 Tail v.

Collar-bone
2 Separate
forearm bones
5 Toes   5 Toes   Shin bones
fused below

HEDGEHOG.   Scale 1/3

(apparently on cold nights!), but rarely after Feb., when winter-sleep becomes complete until April.

Daily life. Usually nocturnal, but if undisturbed, come out soon after sunset, and in mid-summer even before. Hide most of day in thick cover or holes, sleeping and snoring loudly. In autumn often seen by day and sometimes in summer. Sight poor, hearing good. Sensitive to vibrations. When aware of danger, stop, listen, drop head between fore-feet and erect spines. If further alarmed, roll into a tight ball, head to tail. A Fox, Badger, and some Dogs, know how to open and kill Hedgehogs. The Boars fight.

Food. Beetles and other insects, slugs, worms, and Frogs, young birds, Rats, and Mice. Sometimes birds' eggs. There are records of their killing Hares, Rabbits, and Hens, but, as they certainly eat these as carrion, these may be errors. Kill Vipers by biting tail, rolling up, and allowing the Snake to kill itself on the spines. Sometimes eat vegetables: turnips. There is some evidence for a current belief that they suck cows' udders. Taste almost anything, including boot polish!

HEDGEHOG
Scale ½

Gait. Usually very slow, quartering, nuzzling walk. Can run quite quickly. Will roll or drop, ball-wise, down steep slopes, or from high ledges, landing on spines. Good swimmer.

Voice. Usually silent. Give subdued grunt or 'cough-like snort'. Said to scream if attacked by Badger. Young have shrill squeak.

Varieties. Albinos and partial albinos not very rare.

MOLE

Talpa europaea

Habitat. Europe and across Asia to Japan. Omnipresent in Britain. Recently extended to the north and north-west. Not in the Isles, except Mull and Ulva. Not in Ireland.

Description. Sexes alike. Length 140 mm. plus tail 28 mm. Weight about 4 oz. Whole body adapted to burrowing, forelegs thick and strong and set sideways on body. Eyes and ears minute and covered in the thick velvety fur, which stands upright on the skin, lying equally readily in any direction. Body cylindrical, with narrow, pointed, hard muzzle and thin tail. 6 teats, sometimes 8.

Teeth $\frac{3-1-4-3}{3-1-4-3}$ = 44. Very sharp. Molars sharp pointed and W-shaped.

Limbs. Shoulder-blades long and narrow. Upper arm bone very short and thick. Shoulder-muscles immensely powerful. 5 toes on each foot, claws curved, and, on forefeet, flattened.

MOLE. *Scale ½*

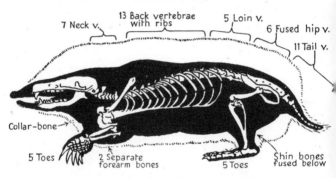

7 Neck v.

13 Back vertebrae with ribs

5 Loin v.

6 Fused hip v.

11 Tail v.

Collar-bone

5 Toes

2 Separate forearm bones

5 Toes

Shin bones fused below

Structure. Vertebrae 7–13–5–6–11. Skull long and narrow. Short neck. Short and thick collar bone.

Life history. Once a year 2–7 young are born, naked and pink-skinned. Skin darkens and becomes hairy in about 10 days. Eyes open in 3 weeks. Gestation 4 weeks or rather more. Young, born about May, leave home June or July when about 5 weeks old.

Yearly life. No hibernation, but deeper digging in winter. Burrow in search of food, making, from their nests, long tunnels just under the surface, and throwing up small 'mole-hills' at short distances. The runs dug by the adult males (who live apart) radiate from a main highway and are usually straight. Those dug by the females (who, with the young, are more sociable) are curly and meandering. The nests are circular cavities the size of a football, lined with grass and leaves and covered by a dome of earth about a foot high and a yard across. The main highways are betrayed by the yellowing of the grass above them. Nests usually have one or more bolt holes, starting downwards and then turning upwards, which may also serve for drainage. The largest nests seem to be dug by the males for the winter. In wet, marshy ground nests are found on the surface. They are used year after year and 7 have been found one above another. In the breeding season (March to early May) the males fight fiercely, biting at the throat. Open trenches are used for pairing.

Daily life. Almost wholly underground: a constant, active, food and flea hunt. (They have a special, blind flea.) Whether they see is disputed, but there is probably some sight. Can spread out the hairs around the eyes. Senses of smell and hearing very acute. Two strange Moles meeting fight to the death. Stoats and Owls will not touch them. Foxes kill, but do not eat.

Food. Purely animal, no vegetable substance. Chiefly worms and insect grubs. Very voracious. Adults require constant supplies of food, dying of starvation if unfed for 10 or 12 hours. A captive will eat 60 worms a day. The Mole bites off the tail, turns the worm round, takes the head in its mouth and squeezes all earth out at the tail end. Also eats Lizards, Frogs, Larvae, and small Mammals or birds. Is said to eat eggs (?).

Gait. On the surface a mere swimming, clumsy, but not very slow (2–3 m.p.h.). When burrowing get out of sight in half a minute. Travel just below the surface at about the same pace, excavating with forefeet and advancing with hind. Will sometimes jump out of the ground to seize a worm. Can swim, even long distances, high in water, tail up.

Voice. Chiefly heard in spring. Loud squeak in anger. Also 'purring'.

Varieties. Albino, ashy, and cream-coloured Moles known.

COMMON SHREW

Sorex araneus

Sub-spe. *S. a. castaneus*

Habitat. Species: Europe and Asia from Britain east and from the Arctic to central Spain and central Italy. Sub-spe.: Mainland of Britain and a few islands. Not Ireland.

Description. Sexes alike. Length 62–78 mm. plus tail 38–43 mm. Weight $\frac{1}{3}$ oz. Flexible, pointed snout. Close velvety coat of 3 fairly distinct colours (on back, sides, and underparts) especially in winter when back is darker. Sub-spe. paler than *S. a.*[2] Gland on each flank emits foul musky odour. Tail covered with minute fine hairs, longer at tip. 6 teats.

$Teeth \; \dfrac{3-1-3-3}{1-1-1-3} = 32.$ The tiny teeth are remarkable: all tipped with red-brown and sharply pointed. i^1 big (for him) and 2-pointed, overhangs i_1, still bigger, horizontal and 4-pointed. Canines like the smaller incisors. Molars of crushing W-pattern. See p. 105.

Limbs. Forearm bones separate; shin bones united below. Collar bone present. All feet have 5 toes, with fine, needle-like claws.

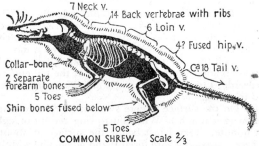

7 Neck v.
14 Back vertebrae with ribs
6 Loin v.
4? Fused hip v.
Ca 18 Tail v.
Collar-bone
2 Separate forearm bones
5 Toes
Shin bones fused below
5 Toes

COMMON SHREW.   Scale $\frac{2}{3}$

Structure. Vertebrae 7-14-6-4 and about 18 in tail. No cheek bones.

Life history. 5–7 (10 recorded) in a litter, born naked, pink, blind, and deaf. Probably several litters a year. Young stay at home, fed by parents, till almost fully grown.

Yearly life. No hibernation. In early March they fight

Common Shrew

Pigmy Shrew

Water Shrew

SHREWS
Scale ½

Scilly Shrew

fiercely (killing) and breed in all months from April to Nov. In summer live in grass or thick cover where they form runs or use those of Mice or Voles. A cup-shaped breeding nest, woven of dry grass, with loose lid, is built under a log, in a tree hole, or bank. In autumn migrate to other ground. In winter take to hedgerows, gorse, leaves, or sticks. Heavy autumn mortality is now attributed to their normal life span being 18 months. Many are said to die in thundery weather.

Daily life. Constantly foraging for food, day and night, with brief recurrent intervals of sleep, snout tucked in between forepaws. Very voracious, eating with febrile energy. Can eat 4 times their own weight in 36 hours. Die if not fed for a few hours. Lick fur, but do not sit up to wash as Mice do. Sight weak, hearing keen. Can dig in soft ground. Prefer to use Rodents' holes. Will sham dead. Dogs and Cats kill but do not eat them. Moles, Stoats, Weasels, Owls, and Kestrels kill and eat. Wholly useful to Man.

Food. Insects, worms, slugs, snails, and carrion. Kill small Rodents and the young of ground-nesting birds.

Gait. Walk on the whole flat foot. Run (on a lawn) at about 2½ m.p.h. Can move by leaps of 2 ft. each (!), taking off from all 4 legs. Climb in search of insects. Swim.

Voice. High squeal (inaudible to many) in fight, in alarm, or when crossing another's trail.

Varieties. Pied, white, and albinos known. Black rare. Those of E. Anglia, brighter and darker.

Note. There have existed many odd superstitions all reflecting dread and horror of the Shrews—that they kill Men and Cattle with poisonous bites, or even by running over their feet: die if they cross a human trail: give curative properties to trees by being sacrificed and buried in them with due ceremonies, and the like. Modern writers have wondered how so useful and harmless a beast can have earned such hatred. I once caught two Short-tailed Voles and a small Shrew together in a box-trap which did not injure them. When opened in the morning, the trap contained the Shrew and the bodies of the two Voles, each of which was twice his size. Both had been killed by bites behind the ears and formed a bleeding mass which the Shrew, with frantic voracity, continued to devour. The whole trap (and room) reeked of the Shrew. I felt such disgust as fully explained to me the view of the seventeenth-century writer who spoke of the Shrew as 'a ravening beast, feared of all'.

ISLAY SHREW

Sorex granti

Differs from Common Shrew as follows: Greater contrast between dusky upper parts and light flanks. p^2 disappearing. Lacking in about half.

PIGMY SHREW

Sorex minutus

Sub-spe. *S. m.*²

Habitat. Species: N. Europe and Asia from Ireland east, and southwards to Pyrenees and S. Italy. Sub-spe: As above except S. Italy. Probably throughout England and Wales, but distinctly rarer than Common Shrew. Also in Scotland, Ireland, and almost every island. Recorded from the top of Ben Nevis.

Differs from Common Shrew as follows:

Description. Smaller and more slender. Length 50–60 mm. plus tail 30–50 mm. Weighs $\frac{1}{8}$ to $\frac{1}{6}$ oz. Feet never exceed 12 mm. 1st and 5th toes relatively longer. Colour of two shades only, without different side colour. Relatively longer tail, thicker and hairier.

Teeth differ minutely. Thus the 2nd prong of i^1 is relatively longer, thinner, and sharper, and the 2nd prong of i_1 more clearly divided from the 1st. See p. 105.

Structure. Brain-case is relatively longer.

Life history. Probably only 2 litters a year.

WATER SHREW

Neomys fodiens

Sub-spe. *N. f. bicolor*

Habitat. Species: Europe from Norway and England to Pyrenees, N. Italy and W. Siberia. Sub-spe.: Britain. Local throughout England and Wales, more local in Scotland, and absent from Ireland and most of the Isles.

Description. Sexes alike. Size unusually variable. Length 72–127 mm. plus tail 50–70 mm. Weight about $\frac{1}{2}$ oz. Fur close, shiny and velvety, remaining dry under water. Colour above varies from blue-black to dark brown. Tail has a 'keel' of stiff hairs on the under side. Eyes brighter than those of the Common Shrew. Ears are not seen and can be closed when under water. Whiskers black and white. 8 teats. The under parts are said to be darker than in the continental type (*N.f.*²).

Teeth $\frac{3-1-2-3}{1-1-1-3}$ = 30. Generally similar in type to those of *Sorex*. All teeth coloured red at the tips. i^1 more vertical than in *Sorex*. i_1 not serrated. See p. 105.

Limbs. Toes as *Sorex*. Feet broad with a fringe of long hairs at edges of toes and soles, which act as webbing.

Structure generally as *Sorex*.

Life history. 5–8 young born in May after 3 weeks' gestation. Probably 2 litters. Soon play about on the ground near the hole.

Yearly life. No hibernation. They nest in small, Mole-like galleries in the banks of streams, with entrances above and below water. The nest is a ball of grass, moss, roots, or oak leaves, deep in the burrow. They travel in autumn and sometimes live away from water. They are subject to the same autumn death-rate as the Common Shrew.

Daily life. About by day and night, winter and summer. Mainly aquatic. Frequent clear, slow streams and backwaters rather than muddy or swift waters. Seek food under stones at the bottom, turning them over as does a Dipper. They come up every half minute to breathe, and rarely venture far from the bank. On land stay near the hole. Probably store food. Form Mole-like runs in the mud to get worms. They are eaten by Kingfishers.

Food. Fish spawn, small fry, caddis-flies, and other insects and larvae: on land, slugs, insects, and worms. Will even kill and eat each other.

Gait. Unlike most Mammals, they do not use all 4 legs in swimming, as when running on land. They have a special swimming gait, high in the water, wriggling the body, fish-like, and using the forelegs only to steer. Dive with a 'plop'.

The air-bubbles show like silver in the fur. On rising to

the surface they often leap clear of the water. Gait ashore as *Sorex*. A great jumper.

Voice. High, cricket-like chirp.

Varieties. Sometimes there is no white on belly or ear-patches, which are dark brown or black. Piebald specimens are recorded.

SCILLY SHREW

Crocidura cassiteridum

One Shrew from an uninhabited isle of the Scillies, caught in 1924, was found to belong to this Continental genus, though differing slightly from any known species. Specimens since obtained indicate that all Shrews of the Scillies are these. Differs from Pigmy Shrew as follows: Teeth white instead of red-tipped. $\frac{3-1-1-3}{1-1-1-3} = 28$. i_1 has only one point. See below. Size 58 mm. plus tail 33 mm.

TEETH OF OUR SHREWS

The following profiles, enlarged about $2\frac{1}{2}$ times, give the teeth of 4 of our species of Shrews and the differences described in the text.

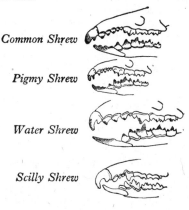

Common Shrew

Pigmy Shrew

Water Shrew

Scilly Shrew

THE RODENTS or GNAWING MAMMALS

Order *RODENTIA*

The Gnawing Mammals are the most numerous and wide-spread of any. They are distinguished by their teeth. There are 2 front teeth in both the upper and lower jaws (i^1 and i_1 on each side). These 4 working teeth are large, prominent, and chisel-shaped, and grow continuously throughout life. They have a hard enamel surface on the front and little or no enamel on the sides and back, so that with use they wear each other into constantly sharpened chisels. To keep them in condition all Rodents must gnaw. If one of these teeth is lost, the opposite tooth continues to grow, unopposed, until it leads to the death of the animal, either by preventing it from feeding, or by turning a full circle and piercing the brain. There are no canines, and a wide gap separates these incisors from the cheek teeth. Into this gap the cheeks close, forming two hairy pads which help to keep out of the mouth the filings of such things as are not eaten. The cheek teeth are adapted for crushing or grinding, and are entirely without cutting-edges. In many cases they are also rootless permanent teeth. The Hares and Rabbits have an extra pair of small incisors (i^2 on each side) behind (not by the side of) the large incisors of the upper jaw. The Rodents are all small land Mammals, mainly vegetarian, and some living on the toughest of vegetable substances. Their brains are smooth. In the midst of countless enemies they hold their own by their wariness, insignificance, power of concealment, and enormous birth-rate.

This very large Order is divided into two Sub-orders—the SINGLE TOOTHED RODENTS (*SIMPLICIDENTATA*) which have only the four front teeth, and the DOUBLE TOOTHED RODENTS (*DUPLICIDENTATA*) which have six, as above described.

SINGLE TOOTHED RODENTS. *SIMPLICIDENTATA.*

These include all our Rodents except the Hare family. They have only the four rodent front teeth with no enamel except on the front. There are no milk incisors. The width of the lower jaw is the same as that of the upper, so that the cheek teeth on both sides meet and the movement in chewing is mainly from back to front. They have the two forearm bones separate, so that they can use the forefeet as hands for feeding as well as for locomotion.

The number and nature of the cheek teeth vary in different species, as does the form of the shin bones, and these variations afford a basis for classifying the countless species belonging to this large sub-order. So far as ours go, they belong to five groups—the Squirrels, the Dormouse, the Mice, the Voles, and the (imported) Guinea Pig.

The Squirrels have milk teeth $\left(\frac{1-0-2-3}{1-0-1-3} = 22\right)$. The cheek teeth are rooted and retain an unbroken enamel surface showing a central depression. The shin bones are separate throughout their length. The collar bones are complete. The forefeet have 4 toes and a small thumb, and the hind feet 5 toes. The muzzle is naked.

The Dormouse has fewer milk teeth $\left(\frac{1-0-1-3}{1-0-1-3} = 20\right)$. The cheek teeth are rooted, with an unbroken enamel surface showing many cross ridges. The shin bones are separate above but united below. The collar bones and toes are like those of the Squirrels: so is the muzzle.

The Mice (*Murinae*) have no milk teeth $\left(\frac{1-0-0-3}{1-0-0-3} = 16\right)$. The cheek teeth are rooted and their enamel wears off the hill tops, showing a partial grinding surface. The shin bones, collar bones, toes, and muzzles are like those of the Dormouse. Our members of this group are the Harvest Mouse, the Wood Mice, the House Mice, and the Rats.

The Voles (*Microtinae*) and Guinea Pig are described on pages 131 and 142 respectively.

RED SQUIRREL

Sciurus vulgaris

Sub-spe. *S. v. leucourus*

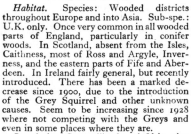

Habitat. Species: Wooded districts throughout Europe and into Asia. Sub-spe.: U.K. only. Once very common in all wooded parts of England, particularly in conifer woods. In Scotland, absent from the Isles, Caithness, most of Ross and Argyle, Inverness, and the eastern parts of Fife and Aberdeen. In Ireland fairly general, but recently introduced. There has been a marked decrease since 1900, due to the introduction of the Grey Squirrel and other unknown causes. Seem to be increasing since 1928 where not competing with the Greys and even in some places where they are.

Description. Sexes alike, length $8\frac{1}{2}$ in. plus tail (with hair) $8\frac{1}{2}$ in., weight about 12 oz. Colour varies much during the year owing to 2 moults, (*a*) complete moult in Oct., (*b*) moult of all except tail in May. Tail starts dark and gradually bleaches and thins through the year. General effect of changes is that the coat in mid-summer is red, with no ear-tufts, and soles naked: in winter as in plate, with soles hairy. Muzzle naked. 8 teats. Our sub-species, described above, differs from the type (*S. v.²*) in colour.

Teeth $\frac{1-0-2-3}{1-0-1-3} = 22$. Incisors brown in colour. p^1 very small. The cheek teeth are rooted, generally square in plan, hollowed in their centres, with transverse ridges. Their enamel surface is retained in wear.

Right Upper Cheek Teeth × $2\frac{1}{2}$ ←

p^1 p^2 m^1 m^2 m^3

Limbs. Shin and forearm bones separate, but palms not reversible. Feet very hand-like: forefeet have 4 long, flexible, sharp-clawed fingers and rudimentary thumb, with nail: hind feet, 5 similar 'fingers'. Rest on whole soles of feet.

Structure. Vertebrae, 7-13-6-3-20. Complete collar bone.

Life history. 2–3 (sometimes 4) young born in March or April (sometimes even earlier); often a 2nd litter in August. Born naked and blind, soon resembling adults, but with short-haired red tails and ear-tufts. Mother carries young in her mouth. Also brings them food in mouth.

RED SQUIRREL
Scale ½

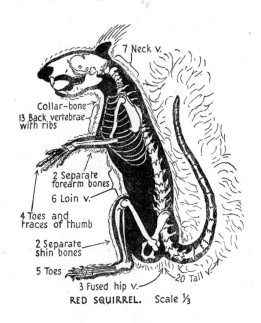

7 Neck v.

Collar-bone
13 Back vertebrae
with ribs

2 Separate
forearm bones

6 Loin v.

4 Toes and
traces of thumb

2 Separate
shin bones

5 Toes

3 Fused hip v.

20 Tail v.

RED SQUIRREL.   Scale ⅓

Yearly life. No true hibernation, but long periods of sleep in winter. Suffer much from wet and cold. Pair in early spring, when males fight much. New nests ('dreys') are built of sticks, bark, and moss, in Feb. or March by both sexes. Usually in conifers. Built like birds' nests. Sometimes as Magpie's nest, with roof and side entrance. Sometimes in hollow tree and sometimes an old Crow's, Sparrowhawk's, or Wood Pigeon's nest is used as basis. Dreys are used for breeding and also as resting-places. Additional (neighbouring) nests are built to which the young can be taken on threat of danger. In autumn they collect provisions for winter in holes in ground or tree, the sites of which they often forget.

Daily life. Diurnal, living in trees. Very timid, dart behind trunks, climb up the far side, and travel from tree to tree. Flippant, pert, and full of play. In autumn, much on the ground to pick up food. Very wasteful feeder, destroying much never eaten. Very destructive to conifers, peeling bark and cutting the 'leaders'.

Food. Mainly acorns, nuts, beech-mast, haws, pine seeds and bark, fungi, bulbs, fruit, seeds, and berries: but also (exceptionally) small birds, young and eggs of birds. Holds food in hand when eating.

Voice. A great variety of barks and cries: when scared, scolds and chatters 'Ski-wow-wow-wow!'

Gait. Sits up, shaded by tail. When on ground, jumps with both hind and forelegs (see p. 37) at all speeds, with tail down. Progresses by long leaps from branch to branch. Runs down trunks head first. Sleeps with head covered by tail. An unwilling, but strong, swimmer.

Varieties. Albinos recorded and, once, a black squirrel.

SQUIRREL'S JUMPING GAIT

1. Fall of fore legs.
2. Fall of hind legs.
S. Suspension, the jump.

Track →

GREY SQUIRREL

Sciurus carolinensis

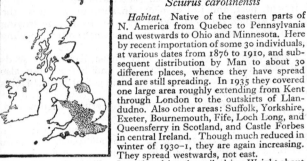

Habitat. Native of the eastern parts of N. America from Quebec to Pennsylvania and westwards to Ohio and Minnesota. Here by recent importation of some 30 individuals, at various dates from 1876 to 1910, and subsequent distribution by Man to about 30 different places, whence they have spread and are still spreading. In 1935 they covered one large area roughly extending from Kent through London to the outskirts of Llandudno. Also other areas: Suffolk, Yorkshire, Exeter, Bournemouth, Fife, Loch Long, and Queensferry in Scotland, and Castle Forbes in central Ireland. Though much reduced in winter of 1930-1, they are again increasing. They spread westwards, not east.

Description. Sexes alike. Length 11½ in. plus tail 9½ in. Weight about 21 oz. The grey colour is made up of hairs black at base, then light brown, then black and tipped with white. No tufts on ears. 8 teats. Has strong gamey scent.

Teeth $\frac{1-0-2-3}{1-0-1-3}$ = 22. Incisors are a dirty yellow. Generally as Red Squirrel.

Limbs and structure. As Red Squirrel. Nails long and black.

Life history. 3-5 young at a birth (often 6 in America), normally born between March and May. Some 2nd litters in June and July and some (3rd?) in August or September. Young are born naked and blind. Suckled for some time after they are able to feed. Can breed when a year old. The young of a litter spend their first winter together in one nest after ejectment by the parents.

Yearly life. No hibernation or long sleep. Are limited in number by scarcity of winter food. Males fight with tooth and claw in early spring. The nests are made of leaf-bearing twigs, usually in deciduous trees, sometimes in conifers. Domed structures, with hidden entrances at side. Sometimes in hollow trees.

Daily life. Generally as Red Squirrel. Mostly about early and late in the day. Unlike the Red, prefer deciduous wood-

GREY SQUIRREL
Scale ½

land. Spend much time away from wood in hedgerows and on fields, particularly in autumn. Will run some distance on ground. Sometimes hide, and even live, in Rabbit burrows. Even more destructive to all kinds of trees and gardens, tearing off much more fruit, ripe or unripe, than is eaten. Hide food when plentiful, often never returning to it. Fight and drive away Red Squirrels and kill them and their young. Kill by a neck bite, as Stoats. There is one record of the two races living in harmony. Have few enemies except Man.

Food. Buds and young shoots of all trees. Bark of deciduous trees. All stored grain, nuts, seeds, and fruit. Also birds' eggs, young birds, young Rabbits, carrion and, possibly, adult Rabbits and Rats.

Voice. Indignant scolding 'Chur-urr!'

Gait. Much as Red Squirrel, perhaps less active in foliage, but quicker on the ground, running in short leaps. Climb with tail straight out behind and feet widely separated. Descend head down and feet wider apart. Feed sitting up with food in hands.

Varieties. Black only once recorded, though common in America. Albinos in districts south and east of London.

Several sub-species have been differentiated in America. Ours are probably mostly *S. c. leucotus* from the eastern U.S.A.

DORMOUSE

Muscardinus avellanarius

Habitat. Central Europe. England eastwards and central Sweden to Pyrenees and Rome. Not Scotland or Ireland, but throughout England and Wales in wooded country. Commonest in the south, somewhat local, and rare north of a line from Suffolk to Cheshire. Frequents woodland borders, hedgerows, thicket, and copse.

Description. Sexes alike. Length 70 mm. plus tail 63 mm. Externally much like Squirrel. Short-haired, bushy tail: no scent glands. Muzzle naked. 8 teats.

Teeth $\frac{1-0-1-3}{1-0-1-3} = 20$. p^1 and p_1. small: all cheek teeth with a grinding surface of cross ridges of enamel folds. The enamel surface does not wear off.

Right Upper Cheek Teeth × 5 ←

$p^1 \quad m^1 \qquad m^2 \qquad m^3$

Limbs. Forefeet: 4 fingered, with rudimentary, clawless thumb; hind feet: 5 finger-like toes, the first clawless.

Structure. Two forearm bones. The 2 shin bones united at the lower end. Collar bone developed. Vertebrae 7–13–6 (or 7)–3 and some 20 in the tail. The neck vertebrae are very short (6 mm.) and those of the loins long (20 mm.). The stomach is complicated and (alone of all Rodents) it has no blind gut.

Life history. 2–4 young (up to 7 recorded) in a litter born in June. Newly born young are also found in autumn, but these probably do not survive the winter. Young born blind and naked. Soon see, and grow quickly. 1st coat grey, with red only on head and flanks, adult colour after 18 months.

Yearly life. Hibernate from mid-Oct. to mid-April, curled in a ball, sleeping very soundly, without perceptible breathing and becoming so cold and rigid that they can be rolled on a table without waking. Sometimes wake in warm weather to eat up food, stored in considerable quantities before retiring. Winter nests are usually underground or

DORMOUSE (*cont.*)

among roots of shrubs, though adapted birds' nests are re-corded. After waking they remain lethargic for some days. In spring build small nests for daytime rest, about 3 in. across, near (rarely on) ground in thicket or hedgerow. These and the breeding nests (twice as large) are built of grass, moss, and honeysuckle bark strips, lined and covered with leaves.

Daily life. Arboreal in habit, frequenting copse (particularly hazel) and hedgerow, often near houses, and gardens. Strictly nocturnal: usually sleep until evening. Less nocturnal in spring and autumn, particularly in cold or damp weather. Sluggish in thunder. During the summer they put on much fat, which is used up during the winter sleep.[1]

Food. Apples, cherries, other fruit, haws, acorns, and nuts: also insects and grubs and, probably, small birds and eggs.

Gait. Wonderfully agile, but not so graceful as Squirrel. More Mouse-like. Jump well. Tail used as a balance, not prehensile. Feed with hands, sitting up, as Squirrel.

Voice. Faint squeaks.

Varieties. White-tipped tail not uncommon. Albino known. Will cross with House Mouse.

St. Kilda

HOUSE MOUSE

Mus musculus

Sub-spe. *M. m.*[2]

Habitat. Species: Cosmopolitan. Wher-ever Man dwells or stores food. Typical sub-spe.: In Europe, north of the Mediter-ranean area. All over U.K.

Description. Sexes alike. Length 78 mm. (70–100 mm.) plus tail of equal length, tapering, naked, and not prehensile. Skull length, 19·8–22·4 mm. Hind foot 18 mm. Weight ½ oz. Ear long (13 mm.), reaching eye if pulled forward. General colour grey-brown above, shading gradually, without contrast, into greyish-buff below. 10 teats.

Teeth $\frac{1-0-0-3}{1-0-0-3} = 16$. Incisors smooth,

[1] Weight of a female before hibernation has been recorded as 510 grains (= 1¼ oz.) and on awaking 300 grains (= ⅔ oz.).

DORMOUSE
Scale ½

HOUSE MOUSE
Scale ½

narrow, and with brown enamel: i^1 meets i_1 in such a way as to become notched in profile. The molars are rooted and have hill-like points. There are 3 transverse rows of these points on each tooth. As the enamel of the points wears off with use, a pattern and partial grinding surface is formed. The molars of the upper jaw slope backwards, those of the lower jaw forwards. See p. 26.

Right Upper Molars × 5 ←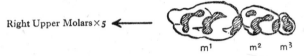

m^1 m^2 m^3

Limbs. Forearm bones separate, but not revolving, so paws cannot turn palm up. 4 clawed fingers with a mere nail for thumb. Shin bones fused at lower ends. 5 clawed fingers on hind feet.

Structure. Vertebrae 7–13–6–3 and about 27 in tail. Complete collar bone. Generally as Brown Rat, see p. 122.

Life history. 5–7 young at a birth (12 on record), 4–5 litters a year and more if food is ample. Gestation 19–21 days. Born helpless, blind, and naked. Fur grows in 10 days, eyes open in 14 days, and at 21 days can shift for themselves. Can breed in 10–12 weeks. People have amused themselves by ciphering the huge numbers of Mice which one pair might produce with unlimited food and no casualties. In the second year it runs to millions. Though this does not happen, it is only by a determined effort at extermination that their numbers are kept within bounds.

Yearly life. In country villages, take to the cornfields in summer and to the stacks in winter, which they riddle with runways. The domed nests are made of anything soft (wool, paper, linen, straw, &c.) gnawed up and placed in any convenient spot, preferably a hole in the wall near stores of Man's food.

Daily life. Dependent on Man for its food supply. Not found where Man is not. In houses, largely nocturnal owing to timidity, but will appear by day if they think themselves safe, and sometimes become bold and familiar with Man. The prisoner's friend. Males fight fiercely. Females fight for holes, but the possessor is said to have an advantage due to recognition of the rights of property. Unknown how far the male has any interest in the family or whether purely promiscuous. They hoard and store food throughout the year in their holes.

Food. Omnivorous: mainly grain or scraps of human food, but do not disdain insects, gum, or carrion.

Gait. Walk on the flat foot, with gliding motion; trot and, at full speed, proceed by bounds of the hind legs and skips of the fore, as Cat. Sit up to eat (food held in forepaws) and to wash. Jump high and can climb a vertical wooden surface.

Voice. Various squeaks, chiefly in fear or anger.

Varieties. Many colour varieties: albino, sandy, black and tan, and black Mice are common and, in captivity as pets, these and other colours are bred. There are also two odd varieties, the 'Singing Mice', whose squeaks are said to run up a full octave, and the 'Waltzing Mice', which run round in circles. These abnormalities are hereditary.

The comparative width of hindquarters places the hind footprints outside the fore

House Mouse Walking Track. Scale ⅓.

BROWN RAT
Scale ½

ST. KILDA HOUSE MOUSE

Mus muralis

Habitat. Island of St. Kilda. Possibly extinct since the abandonment of the island in Sept. 1930.

Differs from Common House Mouse as follows:

Feet and tail less slender. Under parts more often distinctly buff white. There are also slight differences in the shape of the bones of the palate, which are more wedge-shaped, narrowing forwards.

BROWN RAT

Rattus norvegicus

Habitat. Throughout the globe. Shipborne by Man. Present in myriads in town and country.

Description. Sexes alike. Size very variable. Usually about $8\frac{1}{2}$ in. plus tail $7\frac{1}{2}$ in., but varying from total (with tail) of $12\frac{1}{4}$ in. to 23 in. Weight 14 oz. (up to 1 lb. 13 oz.) Generally like a large Mouse. Skull arched, 46 to 54 mm. long. Fur fine and soft. Tail scaly and fleshy, the separate scales hiding the rings. Has a repulsive smell. Usually 12 teats, 8 to 14 known.

Teeth $\frac{1-0-0-3}{1-0-0-3} = 16$. Very similar to those of House Mouse; the upper incisors are not worn into a groove, but merely chisel sharpened. The pattern made by the worn molars differs slightly and m^1 and m_1 are relatively smaller.

Limbs and structure. As House Mouse, with fewer tail vertebrae—about 20. See next page.

Life history. Appallingly prolific. 1–20 in a litter, usually about 8: litters every 6 weeks all the year: the female (Doe) breeds at 3 months old. Gestation 21 days.

Yearly life. Active all the year. In cities frequent sewers, docks, and warehouses; in the country hedgerows, ricks, and coverts; on the coast rocks and banks. Infest ships. They migrate in hordes when fire, food scarcity, or danger threaten

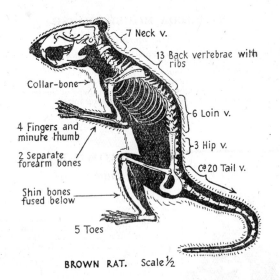

BROWN RAT. Scale ½

their homes. An incredible menace to poultry, grain stores, crops, game, &c. Nests formed of any soft material—1,728 shredded napkins were found when the old Gaiety Restaurant was destroyed.

Daily life. Sociable. Mainly nocturnal. Burrow, forming small towns underground in city or country. The old males (Bucks) drive off other males from their neighbourhood. Will run away from Man or Dog unless cornered, when they will attack *en masse* and, individually, will attack even a Hedgehog. Clean fur carefully, but seem to neglect tail. Leave dung everywhere. Highly intelligent. Help each other in difficulties. Very hard to trap, and, if trapped, will bite off a leg to escape. Most small food is taken to the nest to be stored or eaten. Eggs are rolled between the chin and forepaws. Chief enemies are Man (with trap, Ferret,

Dog, gun, and poison), Fox, Weasel, Tawny Owl, and Hawks. Every effort should be made to exterminate them, not only as competitors for Man's food, but as bearers of deadly diseases—bubonic plague, trichinosis, equine influenza, and foot and mouth disease.

Food. Omnivorous. Believed once to have nibbled the toes of Elephants at the Zoo! When eating turnips, bite off the skin all round and leave it. Need much water and will gnaw through a 2 in. lead pipe to get it.

Gait. As House Mouse. Swims well.

Voice. Loud squeaks.

Varieties. Black, white, fawn, pied, and also hairless Rats occur. All tame Rats are of this species and not R^2.

BLACK or LONG-TAILED RAT

Rattus[2]

Habitat. Species: Originally North Temperate zone of the Old World; now anywhere, seaborne by Man. Here has been largely replaced by Brown Rat (*norvegicus*), but is still the ship rat. Survive in London Docks, Yarmouth, and a few other places, and appear from time to time elsewhere. Has increased since 1900. Differs from the Brown Rat as follows:

Description. Smaller, length $6\frac{5}{8}$ in. to $9\frac{1}{4}$ in. plus tail, which is relatively longer, being equal to, or longer than, body and head. Eyes larger and less protuberant. Head relatively larger and ear longer. Fur less soft, mixed with some grooved bristles. 10 teats.

Teeth $\frac{1-0-0-3}{1-0-0-3} = 16$. As Brown Rat, but enamel pattern differs slightly.

Structure. Skull broader, particularly behind, than that of Brown Rat.

Other distinctions. Neither so bold nor so carnivorous. It is said that their voice is 'more twittering'. Smarter,

BLACK RAT
Scale ½

and less smelly. More inclined to take to the higher parts of buildings, and less to the sewers. For that reason the modern custom of building kitchens in the upper stories of buildings, and making cellars rat-proof, has favoured them in their fight for existence against the Brown Rat. They are particularly at home on board ship. Regret has been expressed at the extermination of the noble old English Black Rat by the Hanover (*norvegicus*) Rat—the Brown. The Black Rat has not been exterminated; he is not noble, but a nuisance second only to the Brown Rat, which did not come from Hanover (or Norway), and the only matter for regret is that they did not behave as *Felis kilkennicus*.

Varieties. Brown and other colour varieties of these long-tailed Rats are often seaborne to our shores. Before ships carried and mixed them, there were, doubtless, many races of Rats. The darker specimens lived in the north, and the whitish-bellied, brown ones in the Mediterranean area. The Black Rats got to us first, the Brown (short-tailed) Rats later, and began to kill them off. The stock of Black Rats is still replenished from time to time from ships, and as there are brown Black Rats (called *R.² alexandrinus* by some) and black Brown Rats (called *R. n. hibernicus*) there is much confusion. *R.²* and *R. n.* do not interbreed.

LONG-TAILED FIELD MOUSE

Genus *Apodemus*

Habitat. All temperate Europe, Asia, and N. Africa. Divided into many species and sub-species. The fertility of the Mice has spread to their nomenclature. If any rocky islet has no sub-species bearing its name, it is probably because no man has yet measured some Mice from its soil. Here the whole genus will be dealt with as if it were one species and the subdivisions will be relegated to the heading Varieties.

Present in large numbers throughout U.K.

Description. Sexes alike. Long tail, not prehensile. Ears mobile and long enough to reach eye if pulled forward. White feet, heels brown. Upper dark and lower light parts clearly separated. Usually an orange spot between forepaws. Length about 100 mm. plus tail of same length. Weight, male ¾ oz., female ½ oz. 6 teats.

Teeth. Formula and type as House Mouse. Slightly more complex.

Limbs. As House Mouse. Hind feet longer and more slender.

Structure. As House Mouse. Skull larger and less flat.

Life history. Litters of 4–7, sometimes 5 times a year. Breed continuously all summer. Gestation 3 weeks. Females breed at 5 months old. Young born blind and naked. First coat in 9 days, darker and greyer. Eyes open in 14 days. The young will cling to the mother if she is disturbed from the nest.

Yearly life. No hibernation, but less active in winter. Devastate gardens in spring and crops in summer. Dig burrows (down to 3 ft. deep) with 3 entrances to a nest-hole lined with grass, usually in hedgerows or growing crops. Also nest in the open and sometimes high in trees (e.g. old Rook's nest). Families remain together and thus burrows are often shared. For winter they store food in holes or burrows, sometimes in old nest of Thrush or Blackbird.

Daily life. Omnipresent. Our most numerous Mammal. From sea-level to mountain top. Seldom in houses or stacks. Have been found living (on insects) in deep disused mines. Nocturnal. Only about by day if ill. Short-sighted. Sit up and 'wash' thoroughly all over, especially if scared. Very easy to trap. Have countless enemies: Weasels, Stoats, Cats, Foxes, Dogs, Moles, Owls, Crows, Rooks, Gulls, Kestrels, Vipers, and Bank Voles.

Food. Omnivorous; mainly vegetable, seeds rather than grasses. Acorns, nuts, corn, peas, bulbs, roots, haws (the seeds, not the pulp), fruit, leaves of peas and bark: also insects, carrion, and young birds. Probably cannibal.

Gait. Run jerkily; in haste, hop. Swim well. Can jump out of a 10 in. vertical-sided biscuit box. Skilled climber.

Track. Hind feet (black) on top of fore (light).

Voice. A quiet chuckling; in anger, high-pitched.

Varieties. Albinos extremely rare, black specimens still more so. Our FIELD MICE are divided into the following species and sub-species. The sizes given are the lengths (in mm.) of head and body plus tail. They are averages, fractions over a half being taken as 1 mm.

Apodemus sylvaticus. Found throughout U.K. and islands, except where replaced by the following species. Yellow-brown above with russet tinge, below white or whitish, usually with chest spot. Divided into:

> *A. s.²* Common LONG-TAILED FIELD MOUSE. As above described. Small and long-tailed. Size 88 plus 86.
>
> *A. s. butei,* BUTE MOUSE. Darker, shorter tail. Size 91 plus 79.

A. fridariensis. Fair Isle and Shetlands. Large, dark, long-tailed. Sub-spe.:

> *A. fr.²,* FAIR ISLE MOUSE. Blue-white belly, often no chest spot, small ear. Size 109 plus 106.
>
> *A. fr. granti,* SHETLAND MOUSE. Yell and (?) Mainland. Shorter tail, slight skull differences. Chest spot. Size 101 plus 92.
>
> *A. fr. thuleo,* FOULA MOUSE. Larger foot. Size 96 plus 94.

A. hebridensis. Almost all the Isles except Orkneys, Shetlands, and Skye. Larger. Shorter tail and ear. Skull larger, but shorter behind molars. Divided into:

> *A. heb.²,* HEBRIDEAN MOUSE. Outer Isles and Eigg. Colour much as *A. s.²,* varying locally. Size 96 plus 88.
>
> *A. heb. hamiltoni,* RUM MOUSE. As largest *A. heb.²* Skull even larger. Size 104 plus 96.

LONG-TAILED FIELD MOUSE
Scale ½

HARVEST MOUSE
Scale ½

A. heb. maclean, **MULL MOUSE**, also Islay and (darker) Jura. Darkened by long black hairs, faint chest spot. Narrower cheek bones. Size 97 plus 87.

A. heb. cumbrae, **CUMBRAE MOUSE**, also Gigha and Tiree. Pale, rufous, few black hairs, belly silver, faintest chest spot. Small. Skull shaped as *A. heb.*, but size of *A. s.* Size 93 plus 90.

A. heb. fiolagan, **ARRAN MOUSE**. Dark rufous, belly silver, faintest chest spot. Skull of medium size, long behind molars. Short foot. Size 98 plus 84.

A. hirtensis, **ST. KILDA FIELD MOUSE**. Largest of all. Skull specially large. Size 111 plus 100. Largest recorded 129 plus 109.

A. flavicollis wintoni. **YELLOW-NECKED MOUSE**. England and Wales, commonest in the south and west. Does not replace, but overlaps, and possibly (?) interbreeds with, *A. s.*[2] Chest spot extends right across neck, forming collar, and down to greyish-white belly. Colour more brilliant, but less so than continental type (*A. fl.*[2]). Skull more angular, particularly in old mice. Large. Size 109 plus 107.

HARVEST MOUSE

Micromys minutus

Sub-spe.: *M. m. soracinus*

Habitat. Species: Central Europe and Asia from Britain east. North to Scotland and Denmark. South to Italy and S. France. Sub-spe.: As above save in Hungary and Rumania. In U.K. confined to England and a few counties of SE. Scotland. Local and becoming rarer, least rare in south.

Description. Sexes alike. Very small, length 63 mm. plus tail 60 mm. Weight ¼ oz. Tawny and white parts clearly separated. Tail prehensile, scaly, ringed, and thinly haired, especially upon the upper side.

Teeth, limbs, and structure. Generally as House Mouse. Incisors reddish-yellow, narrow, and smooth.

Life history. Breed several times a year, 5–9 young at a birth. Gestation 3 weeks. Born blind and naked. Later a grey colour.

Yearly life. Sleep fitfully during the winter. Become active in mild weather. Before retiring for winter, store quantities of grain in nest. Winter sleeping-nests are of moss inside ricks, or sometimes attached to reeds over water. In summer they frequent growing crops or hedgerows and rough ground near cultivation. The summer breeding-nests are the size of an orange, compact balls of grass, corn blades, or reed leaves, interwoven among shrubs or stalks, placed less than a foot from the ground and lined with chewed grass or reeds. Often, not always, in standing corn. The entrance is at the side, and is closed when the mother goes in or out.

Daily life. Sociable, gymnastic, swinging, and revolving in play. Diurnal. Climb up growing crops and there eat grain. Also cut off the ears to eat on ground. When frightened run upwards, dreading heavier and less active enemies. Bite fiercely, gripping as bulldog, and worrying.

Food. Wheat, barley, oats, seeds, shoots, and tender leaves. Also flies and other insects, caught with hand or mouth, and also by digging. In captivity, cannibal. Lap water.

Gait. Graceful, active, and skilful climbers, but not swift. When eating, revolve a grain of wheat with the hands against the Rodent teeth until the skin is 'turned off', and it is reduced to a white ball. Do not jump, but reach out from stalk to stalk. Tail always coils about anything it touches.

Voice. Low, chirping squeak, almost bird-like.

THE VOLES
Family *MICROTINAE*

The Voles differ from the other Mice (*Murinae*, see p. 107), with which they are grouped (under the name of *Muridae*) in their molar teeth. These are permanent and rootless and the enamel wears off from the whole of the biting area, exposing a grinding surface. The enamel sidewalls are vertical, angular, and zigzagged. The teeth of the Bank Voles and Muskrat become rooted in later life. These typically herbivorous teeth correspond with a difference of diet: in place of the seeds and softer vegetable foods favoured by the other Mice, the Voles can and do eat the toughest of fibres and grasses. See p. 26.

The names of all small Rodents are mere book-learning. Common speech calls the smaller (and the Shrews) 'Mice', and the larger 'Rats'. The word 'Vole' (of Norse origin, meaning a field) was first used in the name 'Vole-mouse'. Vole is now used for the Mice which have the teeth above described.

BANK VOLE

Genus *Clethrionomys* (= *Evotomys*)

Habitat: Europe and Asia from Scotland and central Scandinavia to the Pyrenees and S. Italy and east to China. Also N. America from New Jersey to the Arctic and across the Continent to Alaska.

The genus is here treated as a whole. Our subdivisions are under 'Varieties'.

All England and Wales, particularly where there are ivy-clad banks. In Scotland rarer in north and west, but exist in all low cultivated areas. Not in Ireland.

Description. Sexes alike. Length 81–120 mm. plus hairy, 2-coloured tail 40–59 mm. The most Mouse-like Vole. Ears short, often barely visible. Weight ¾ oz. Colour rufous above, whitish below.

Teeth. Formula as House Mouse. i^1 without grooves. The Voles are distinguished from the rest of the Mice and the Rats by the character of the molars. These have very thin enamel on the grinding surfaces which is at once worn off by use, leaving only the thick enamel of the vertical sides. These sides are zigzagged with more or less sharp re-entrant angles, leaving a flat surface of the softer ivory surrounded by the curly wall of hard enamel. The Bank Voles have the enamel curves of the molars rounded and the adults' *ms* have two fanged roots, the pulp cavities having closed. m^3 takes 2 forms, the simpler with 2 re-entrant angles on the inner side, and the more complex with 3.

Right Upper Molars × 6
m^3 of simple form
or
m^3 of complex form.

m^1 m^2 m^3 OR

←

Limbs. Generally as Mice. Hands: 4 fingers and rudimentary thumb with flat nail (visible only with lens), 5 pads. Feet: 5 nailed toes and 6 sole pads. Claws small and sharp, palms and soles naked.

Structure. Generally as Mice. Heads rounder and tails much shorter.

Life history. Litters of 4–8 after 22 (28?) days' gestation. 2–4 litters yearly. Young blind and naked. Grow blackish down on 5th day, when eyes open, and brown hair (darker than adult's), on 7th. They grow throughout life.

Yearly life. Do not hibernate, but cease breeding in winter and stay more in burrows. Do not seem to breed abnormally in certain years as do Short-Tailed Voles. The term 'Vole plagues' applies to the latter.

Daily life. Generally nocturnal, but also enjoy sunlight, particularly in spring. Dig less than other Voles, but make shallow burrows, partly underground, which form runs in banks under ivy or exposed bush roots. Use Mole-runs. Share these burrows with Mice, other Voles, and Shrews. Drill smaller burrows from these, into which Moles and Rats cannot follow, leading to chambers (sleeping-rooms and stores) some 18 in. deep and lined with chewed grass. Sometimes build straw nests in root clamps. Bite if handled, as do Mice, but not Short-tailed Voles. Gnaw quickly through wood. Very destructive in stripping trees. If undisturbed become bold and take food in sight of Man. Will kill and eat Short-tailed Voles. Easy to trap. If scared, bolt or 'freeze'. Not bold in defence of young. The mothers leave them at the least alarm. Spend much time in washing all over. Hearing very acute. Very quarrelsome. Enemies: Weasels, Stoats, Cats, Dogs, Moles, Hedgehogs, Owls, Rooks, Crows, Gulls, Kestrels, and Vipers.

Food. Mainly vegetable: grain, nuts, roots, bulbs, seeds, green vegetables, bark, and shoots. But also insects, worms, probably snails and flesh. In captivity they are even cannibal in tastes.

Gait. Hop and run actively, carrying tail up. Climb nimbly. More agile than Short-tailed Vole, but much less so than Long-tailed Field Mouse. Restless. Can jump out of a biscuit tin $9\frac{1}{4}$ in. high, with vertical sides. They feed in two different positions, either holding their food down with the hands, or sitting up and holding the food in their hands. Carry nuts with point in teeth. Fight in upright position. Burrow under snow rather than appear on surface. Swim well. Dive for food.

Voice. Short, grunting squeaks. They also grind their teeth in rage.

Varieties. Albinos are very rare.

Our species are as follows. The figures given are averages (in mm.), fractions over a half being taken as 1 mm.

Clethrionomys glareolus britannicus, the British BANK VOLE. Habitat throughout Britain on the mainland and in Skye. Small. Size 93 plus tail 45. m^3 usually simple.

C. skomerensis, SKOMER VOLE. Habitat Skomer Island, off Pembroke, S. Wales. Differs from *C. g. b.* as follows: Larger. Size 109 plus tail 55. Colour paler red-brown and brighter. Under parts strongly contrasted buffy-white. Skull differs materially, particularly in shape of the nasal bones, which are long, and narrow abruptly about the middle, instead of gradually from front to back. m^3 almost always complex. This Vole is the only one on the small island and is found about the farm and in turnip clamps, as well as in banks and fields. It was discovered by Robert Drane of Cardiff in 1897. This was important because it was the first recognition of the existence of 'island species' of Voles or Mice, and has led to the finding of all the many others.

C. alstoni, MULL VOLE. Larger than *C. g. b.* Size 105 plus tail 44. Rather darker, underside rich buff. m^3 complex.

C. erica, RAASAY VOLE. Habitat Raasay, off Skye. Still larger. Size

BANK VOLE

SHORT-TAILED VOLE

ORKNEY VOLE
Scale ½

134

110–14 plus tail 45–50. Longer ears, more robust tail, stronger skull, and larger molars. m^3 complex. There are slight cranial differences.

These three island species appear to belong to an older race, replaced by the smaller *C. g. b.* on the mainland.

SHORT-TAILED VOLE

Genus *Microtus*

Habitat: All Europe, N. Asia, and N. America.

The genus is here treated as a whole. Our species and sub-species are under 'Varieties'.

Very numerous throughout Britain and most of the islands. Not in Ireland, Man, Scillies, or Lewis.

Description. Sexes alike. Length 108–28 mm. plus tail 27–44 mm. Tail scaly or sparsely haired and about ⅓rd of body length. Head blunter and more rounded than Bank Vole, chest broader. Colour variable, but not so red. 8 teats.

Teeth. Formula as House Mouse. Cheek teeth similar to those of Bank Vole, but pattern is much more angular.

Right upper cheek teeth ←
(*M. a. hirtus*) × 6

m^1 m^2 m^3

Note 'bubble' at back of m^2. This and a similar 'bubble' on m^1 are found in some and help in classification. The cheek teeth are permanent, never forming roots.

Limbs and Structure. Generally as Mice. About 17 tail vertebrae.

Life history. Litters of 3–6 (10 recorded), born about April. In mild seasons, as early as Feb. Normally 3–4 such litters a year but in certain years their numbers increase so much that they devastate large tracts. These 'Vole plagues' appear to follow a series of mild winters. Gestation probably 24 days. Young born blind and naked. First fur greyer. Develop slowly. Not independent until 5 weeks old.

Yearly life. Do not hibernate, but sleep for some days in very cold weather. Also migrate in winter from land on which the grass has perished to places where coarser grass survives. Burrow in the ground a vertical hole some 2 ft. deep ending in a small nest cavity containing a tight ball of grass which is food stored for winter. From the entrances to their holes they eat countless radiating passages in the grass, leaving the upper part of the grass as cover over their heads and dipping under obstacles and bare spots. Nests are often above ground, particularly in years of Vole plagues.

Daily life. About by day and night. Inhabit chiefly rough damp grasslands, plantations, and moorland. Never leave the ground. Gregarious, living in pairs or small communities. Fight with strange Voles, but amiable and sociable with those they know. Sit up to eat with food in hands. Have special places as dung heaps. Dread overhead dangers and rarely leave the cover of their runs. When scared, go down hole or 'freeze'. Always wash after fright. If handled, do not bite so readily as Bank Voles. Enemies: as those of Bank Vole. The Short-Eared Owl multiplies rapidly in 'Vole plagues', laying again while the last brood are still unfledged.

Food. Chiefly grass-stalks, also clover, carrots, bark, and roots. Will eat almost any vegetable substance. Drink much. Damage trees, especially where thick undergrowth gives cover. Eat crocus bulbs (preferring yellow-flowering), not snowdrop or daffodil. Probably insects and grubs.

Voice. A high squeak, also a low chatter.

Gait. Run, but do not jump. Least active of our Voles. The width of the chest makes the tracks of the hands coincide with those of the feet instead of being inside them.

Varieties. Colour varieties are rare, but white, buff, black, and pied specimens are on record.

Our species and sub-species are as follows:

Microtus agrestis. Found in W. Europe from the Arctic to the Pyrenees and Portugal. In Britain, not in the Orkneys, Shetlands, Lewis, Man, Scillies, or in Ireland. All have 'bubble' on m^2: some on m^1. Divided into:

M. a. hirtus. Our SHORT-TAILED VOLE. England, Wales, and the Scottish Lowlands. Smaller than the Scandinavian type (*M. a.²*). Size 101 mm. plus tail 36 mm. Back tawny russet, sides buffy, belly ochre-buff. No 'bubble' on m^1

M. a. neglectus, **SCOTTISH SHORT-TAILED VOLE**. The Highlands and Bute. Larger. Size 128 mm. plus tail 40 mm. Longer hair, darker and browner. Sometimes 'bubble' on m^1.

M. a. exul, **HEBRIDEAN VOLE**. Arran, Gigha, Jura, Mull, Skye, N. and S. Uist, Benbecula, and Rum. Not Lewis. Brown, not russet, above: yellower sides. Long and thick hair. Large. Size 125 mm. plus tail 36 mm. Small ear. Usually 'bubble' on m^1.

M. a. macgillivraii, **ISLAY VOLE**. As *M. a. e.*, but with short and thin coat of duller colour. Slight skull differences.

M. a. mial, **EIGG VOLE**. As *M. a. e.*, but longer, shaggy fur. Skull differs slightly.

Microtus orcadensis. Orkneys. No 'bubbles' on either m^2 or m^1. Shape of skulls affected by stronger chewing muscles. All of large size (117 mm. plus 38 mm.). Differ in colour, paler northwards. More aquatic. Swim often and in water dive to escape capture. Quarrelsome; will kill each other. Divided into:

M. o.², ORKNEY VOLE. Pomona and (?) Shapinsay. Rich dark brown above, passing into bright ochre below.

M. o. ronaldshaiensis, (South) **RONALDSHAY VOLE**. As *M. o.²*, but has a longer and narrower brain-case.

M. o. rousaiensis, **ROUSAY VOLE**. Brain-case slightly flattened.

M. o. westrae, **WESTRAY VOLE**. Lighter brown above and ochre buff below, but some dark hairs show. Brain-case short and broad, much flattened.

M. o. sandayensis, **SANDAY VOLE**. Much lighter. Pale greyish-brown above, whitish-grey below, faintly washed with buff, fewer dark hairs show. Brain-case as *M. o. w.*

WATER VOLE or WATER RAT

Arvicola amphibius

Habitat. Species: Britain. Found throughout, but rare in S. Wales.

Description. Sexes alike. Heavier, blunter-nosed, and robuster than Brown Rat. Ear low and barely visible, with a lid to keep out water. Length 6⅜–10 in. plus tail 4⅛–5½ in. Skull 42–4 mm. and hind foot 30–4 mm. Two large musk glands in front of hind legs. Oily skin. 8 teats.

Teeth $\frac{1-0-0-3}{1-0-0-3}$ = 16. Generally similar to those of our other native Voles, but much larger. Incisors brownish-yellow, showing when mouth closed.

Limbs and Structure as other Voles. Feet

WATER VOLE
Scale ½

not webbed. Fore, broad and robust, 4 fingers with rudimentary nailed thumb. Hind, much larger, 5-toed and 'feathered' for swimming.

Life history. 2–8 young, born about June; possibly 2 or more litters. Nest of chewed water plants, generally made in a cavity of the burrow, but occasionally above ground. Mother often moves young with her teeth. Young can swim and dive soon.

Yearly life. Frequent sluggish rivers and dykes, and also, particularly in Scotland, hill streams. Dig burrows in the banks and sometimes at a distance from water. Burrows are long and rambling, usually with several exits above water and the same number below. Do not hibernate, but rest in severe weather, as do all Voles. Store food in autumn.

Daily life. Live in exclusive clans. Diurnal, particularly in spring and autumn, when they feed all day. Bring leaves or other cover from the bottom for concealment when rising to the surface. Very clean. Harmless, except to young osier beds, or to banks undermined by their burrows. Enemies are Otters, Stoats, Weasels, Brown Rats, Herons, Owls, Pike, and large Trout.

Food. Probably almost wholly vegetarian : roots and shoots of flags and other water plants. In hard weather, potatoes, turnips, and carrots. Some evidence of fish- and frog-eating, but the common idea that they live on fish is an error.

Gait. Swim mainly with the hind legs. Fairly fast swimmer (slower than Brown Rat) showing head and back; if scared, only top of head. Dive to avoid pursuit with a loud 'plop'. Also to reach food under water. Usually rise under cover. Dives last about 20 seconds. On land, as Field Voles.

Varieties. Black Water Voles are common in the East and North, rare in the South. Buff, albino, and pied varieties are on record. Our sub-species are:

ENGLISH WATER VOLE. *A. a.*²
  Habitat. England and S. Scotland. Typical sub-species as above.

SCOTTISH WATER VOLE. *A. a. reta.*
  Habitat. Scotland, except in the south. Differs from *A. a.*² as follows: smaller, hind foot 30–2 mm., skull usually less than 42 mm. Darker in colour. Black variety much more frequent.

MUSKRAT
Scale ½

TRACK. Scale ½

140

MUSKRAT

Ondatra zibethica

Habitat. Almost the whole of N. America. There are many sub-species. In Britain first imported (in 1929) for fur farms. Have escaped in many districts: south of the Tay, Dumfriesshire, valleys of the Severn and Arun. A large area in central Europe has been covered by similarly escaped Muskrats.

Description. Sexes alike. Length 11 in. plus tail 10 in. Hind foot 89 mm. Weight 1 lb. 10 oz. Like giant Water Voles with naked, vertically flattened, scaly tails. Feet covered with close, hard, silvery brown hair. Musky scent glands by the anus leave scent with the dung. Dense reddish-brown coat, with thick waterproof undercoat, is valuable as fur. 6 teats.

Teeth. Formula and type as other Voles. Incisors brown, rounded in front and not grooved. Molars become rooted in late life.

Limbs and Structure. As other Voles, but long tails. The hind feet are 'feathered' with hair and partly webbed. Soles naked.

Life history. 4–9 young, born after 30 days' gestation. 3 litters a year. Born naked, blind, and helpless. Suckled for 3 or 4 weeks until one-third grown and covered with dark lead-coloured fur.

Yearly life. Mate about April. Probably monogamous, as males help in housebuilding and even in rearing young. Where the banks permit, live in burrows with several entrances. In July repair old homes or dig new. In August, in swamps, build elaborate stick- and weed-covered dens (completed by Nov.) up to 4 ft. above water. The entrance to both types of den is by under-water tunnel, approached by a deeply cut trench if the water is shallow. Dens are surrounded by 'rafts' built of floating reeds and mud to act as landing-places on which to feed and breathing-places if there is ice. In Sept. often migrate.

Daily life. Prefer stagnant or sluggish waters, but can adapt themselves to trout streams and tidal waters. Do great injury by burrowing, and building obstructions, wherever waters are controlled by embankments. So destructive are they that a special law (22 and 23 Geo. V, c. 12) has been passed to forbid their importation, to try to exterminate them, and to order landowners to report their presence. This has succeeded in greatly reducing their numbers. Except when migrating, they rarely travel more than 100 yds. Nocturnal. Dens are kept clean, dung being left in the water or on special logs or landing-places, visited to learn the news. When on land migrating, they will attack Ox, Horse, or Man: in water they try to escape. Sometimes store food. Easily bite through wire-netting.

Food. Mainly vegetable—rushes and water plants. Also some insects, fish, shell-fish, and young birds.

Gait. On land, slow and cumbrous, hind feet treading just beyond fore, and tail leaving a curly furrow in mud. See track on p. 140. Swift swimmer (3 m.p.h.), going 100 yds. before rising to breathe.

Voice. Low squeak (as Man sucking back of his hand), also loud squeaks and snarls. When alarmed splashes water.

Varieties. Black common (valuable fur); albinos rare (worthless).

GUINEA PIG or CAVY

Cavia porcellus

Origin. Domesticated by Peruvians (before the conquest) from the Restless Cavy (*Cavia cutleri*), a small greyish Rodent, with rounded ears and no tail, vegetarian and partly diurnal, living in burrows. The wild Cavy breeds but once a year with only 1 or 2 young at a birth. First brought to Europe by the Dutch, and to England about 1750.

Uses. Merely pets. Here, at least, rarely eaten, they are useful only for scientific experiment in breeding and inoculation.

Description. Sexes alike, length about 10 in., weight 2 lb. Vary much in size and colour, which may be black, white, tan, cream, chocolate, rufous or almost any blend of these, including what is called 'agouti', which is gold or silver mixed with dark hairs. Coat may be short or long. Tail a mere trace; ears small, naked and rounded; muzzle hairy: upper lip not cleft. Only 2 teats. They belong to the large and varied Porcupine Group, which is almost wholly S. American.

Teeth $\frac{1-0-1-3}{1-0-1-3} = 20$. Incisors white. The milk teeth preceding the

GUINEA PIG
Scale ½

RIGHT UPPER CHEEK TEETH
Biting Surfaces ×1½

p¹ m¹ m² m³

143

premolars are shed before birth. The cheek teeth are all rootless and permanent. Grinding is from front to back, the grinding surfaces sloping downwards towards the tongue. See p. 143.

Limbs. Forefeet 4 toes, hind 3, all with broad claws, covering their sides as well as tops. Shin and forearm bones separate. Foot not reversible. Walk on wrist and heel.

Structure. Vertebrae 7–13–6–4 and 5 to 7 minute tail vertebrae which do not reach beyond the hip bones. 6 rib pairs join breast bone. Minute traces of collar bone.

Life history. Remarkably fertile. Litters of 6–8 young (12 recorded) born, after 65 to 70 days' gestation, in a high state of development, furry, open-eyed, and able to feed themselves the day after birth. Can breed at 2 months old, though for fancy breeding it is wiser to wait until 9 months, when they reach full growth.

Yearly and daily life. In captivity they live a dull life, usually shut up in small hutches, where feeding and breeding are their only occupations. Hardy; can look after themselves in the open, under dry, warm conditions.

Food. Naturally vegetarian. In captivity mainly bread, milk, and green food. Also roots and oats.

Gait. Jerky and shuffling. Do not use the feet in eating.

Voice. Faint squeaks and grunts.

Varieties. Apart from the many colour varieties, three types are known: (1) *English.* Short, smooth coats on a small cobby body. (2) *Peruvian.* Long, silky coats. (3) *Abyssinian.* Short, harsh coats with 'rosettes' of long hair dotted about all over the body. All types may be any colour.

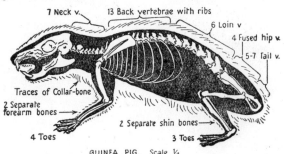

GUINEA PIG. Scale ¼

144

DOUBLE-TOOTHED RODENTS
Sub-Order *DUPLICIDENTATA*

Only one Family, the Hares and Rabbits, are found in the U.K. They have a second pair of small incisor teeth in the upper jaw behind the two large front teeth. At birth there is a third pair of front milk teeth between these two pairs, but these are soon dropped. They have long ears, upturned tails, long hind legs, and no eyelids.

Teeth $\frac{2-0-3-3}{1-0-2-3} = 28$. The incisors are grooved and there is enamel all over them, but much thinner on the inside so that this gets worn away. The upper jaws are wider than the lower, so the cheek teeth of one side only can engage at a time and they chew by moving the lower jaw from side to side. All teeth are permanent and rootless. Cheek teeth have the surface enamel thin and soon worn off, leaving a grinding surface. See Fig. on p. 154.

The two shin bones are fused together. Forearm bones closely connected, the smaller in a groove along the larger. On forefeet 5 toes, on hind 4, all with claws, and the soles cushions of fur. Very small collar bones free at both ends. Narrow skulls with broad foreheads. Vertebrae of loins are long, giving power and suppleness. Long intestines.

BROWN HARE
Lepus europaeus
Sub-spe. *L. e. occidentalis*

Habitat. Species: Europe west of Russia and south of the Baltic, excluding the Peninsula. Sub-spe.: Britain wherever there is cultivation (rarely high on the hills and moors), Isle of Wight, Anglesey, Isle of Man, Inner and Outer Hebrides, and some isles of Orkneys and Shetlands. Several times introduced into Ireland.

Description. Sexes alike, male (Buck) has slightly smaller body, shorter head, and redder shoulders. Length (head and body) about 22–4 in., weight 7–13 lb. Ears 4½ in. Eyelids short. 6 teats. The winter coat is thicker and of a pale, smoky grey. *L. e. o.* (as above) is smaller than the Continental type—*L. e.*[2]

Teeth, Limbs, and Structure. See above and p. 146.

Life history. Young ('Leverets') are born, 2–5 (8 on record)

145

BROWN HARE
Scale ⅛

12 Back vertebrae with ribs
7 Neck v.   7 Loin v.   4 Fused hip v.

No collar-bone

12 Tail v.

2 Forearm bones
closely connected→

Shin bones fused→

5 Toes   4 Toes

Scale 1/12

146

at a birth, after 30 days' gestation. Are covered with thin hair, open-eyed, and able to run. Completely independent at 1 month. Resemble adults, but more russet. Young females ('Does') begin to breed at about a year old. 3–4 broods in the year.

Yearly life. Main courting season, Feb.–March (March–April in Scotland). The Bucks run about all day in pursuit of Does, kicking, bucking, and jumping. The 'Master Buck' fights off all rivals from his Doe. 'March Hares.' Do not pair permanently. Leverets may be born at any season. Does are good mothers, fighting to defend their young. The young are born in the open, and soon after the mother finds separate 'forms' for each Leveret, carries them there in her mouth, and visits them during the night to suckle them.

Daily life. An unsocial, lonely animal. Selects convenient places ('forms') and spends almost all day and night couched in them, crouching and shrinking when alarmed.[1] Prefers low, rolling ground. Forms are chosen to give a view, or to have shade, sun, or shelter from wind, according to the weather. Feed mainly at night. Sleep with eyes closed, but very lightly. Hearing and smell acute, sight straight ahead defective, owing to position of eyes. Hares pant when pleased, raising their temperatures, and sneeze, silently, when warm Will drive Sheep or Cattle away from their forms by 'boxing'. When leaving or returning to the form, will take two very long leaps (some 15 ft.) to baffle scent. When forced to leave, run to a safe distance and then sit up on hind legs, listening and watching intently. Swerve to elude a swifter pursuer. The long hind legs favour it up hill. When hunted, has all the cunning of the Fox with an added trick—doubling back on its tracks and then making a number of long, sideways leaps. The poor sight ahead, and a habit of following regular runs, makes it easy to snare and net. Its survival is due to its being protected for sport, but it is so destructive to crops that the farmer has been given an inalienable right to kill it under

[1] *Note.* The following Yorkshire story gives a useful hint. My friend J. Ll. Davies was walking a field with an old keeper (Cooper of Sledmere) and asked 'Is that a Hare?' He answered 'Wha noo then, ef it gets lartler (= flatter) an' lartler it's 'owd 'Are; ef it gets bigger an' bigger it's nobbut a bit o' moock.'

Summer

Autumn

Winter

BLUE HARE

Scale ⅛

148

BROWN HARE (*cont.*)

the Ground Game Act. Particularly destructive in gardens in spring, eating all tender shoots, which it can reach to a considerable height.

Food. Wholly vegetarian. Chiefly grasses and roots. In eating turnips, tear down and leave the outside. Of wheat, leave the ears, eating the stalks and leaves. All food passing from the bowel is instantly re-swallowed and passed again.

Gait. See p. 152. Can jump on to a 5-ft. wall. Swim well, crossing wide rivers to reach favourite pasture.

Voice. On the whole very silent. Has (1) a grunt or hiss when courting or fighting; (2) a clicking, caused by grinding the teeth, as an alarm; (3) a feeble bleat, or piping, when suckling; (4) 'oont' uttered softly as a call to the young or a mild protest; and (5) a scream, like a child in agony, when wounded.

Varieties. White, pied, albino, and (rarely) silver-grey and black.

BLUE HARE

Lepus timidus   Sub-spe. *L. t. scoticus*

Habitat. Species: Scandinavia, Scotland, and the Alps. Sub-species: Scotland. Common above the level of cultivation in the Highlands. Recently extended south of the Forth and now well established there. Also in Mull, Skye, Raasay, Lewis, and Harris. Not in Shetlands or Orkneys. Introduced, more or less successfully, into N. England, Wales, and Ireland.

Differs from Brown Hare as follows:

Description. Smaller, length about 20 in., ears 3¼ in., weight 5–7 lb. (maximum 8½ lb.). The colour changes in autumn to pure white, except the black ear-tips. 'Variable Hare.' The change is due not to a moult, but to the action of cells which, at low temperatures, absorb the colour of the hair. They are thus protected, by matching the snow, until the growth of the new brown coat in spring. This change varies, thus the Blue Hares of Harris and the Lewis are said never to become fully white. Skin is thin. Flesh is inferior in flavour to that of the Brown Hare, and the fur woollier and poorer.

BLUE HARE (*cont.*)

L. t. s. differs from the Scandinavian type (*L. t.²*) in colouring.

Life history. Leverets grow more slowly, not fully grown under 3 months. 2, perhaps 3, litters a year. Can breed with *L. e.*

Yearly life. In very hard winters will descend to low ground and woods.

Daily life. Less cautious and cunning, generally duller and heavier. Do not make a 'form', but hide among stones or under shelter. Its leaps on leaving the resting-place are shorter (6 to 10 ft.) and, with usually a wriggle of the rump, it canters slowly to a hillock some 50 yds. off, where it sits up to look back. As they run up hill when disturbed, they are easy to surround and kill on the tops. Dodge as well as the Brown Hare. Take cover in cairns or Rabbit holes. During the courting season almost ignore Man. Chief enemies are Foxes and Eagles. Crows, Ravens, and Buzzards take many leverets.

Food. Grasses, rushes, young heather, and moss. Said to eat lichens and to chew fir-cones to reach the seeds.

Varieties. A buff type is known, but rare.

IRISH HARE

Lepus hibernicus

Habitat. Ireland, all over mountain area and, sometimes, on low ground. Introduced into Mull and Carnarvonshire.

Classified by some as a sub-species of the Blue Hare, from which it differs as follows:

Slightly larger, averaging about 23 in. and attaining a maximum of 10 lb. in weight. Colour more russet: also variable, but less inclined to become pure white in winter, though some do. Buff variety not uncommon. Doubtful whether it breeds with other Hares. More gregarious. Has been seen in large droves of 200–300.

Summer

Winter

IRISH HARE

Scale ⅛

151

The *Gait* of the *Hares* and *Rabbits* is, at all speeds, even the slowest, a series of jumps with the hind legs and skips with the fore. They do not walk. Speed is attained by the jumps being longer. The quicker the pace, the farther forward are the footprints of the hind legs in relation to those of the fore, until, at speed, they fall well in front of them. At full speed the heads are outstretched and the ears laid flat. The use of their white sterns and upturned tails (so dangerous since Man with his shotgun has become a main enemy) has been variously explained as (1) a conspicuous alarm signal, and (2) since many of their natural foes hunt by night and see them from below, a means of camouflage—blending with the sky. Ingenious, but contradictory.

RABBIT

Oryctolagus cuniculus

Sub-spe. *O. c.*[1]

Habitat. Species: Central Europe to the Carpathians and, by recent introduction, in Australia, New Zealand, and elsewhere. Sub-spe.: As species save for Mediterranean area and Azores. Throughout U.K., abundant wherever there is grass. Not in U.K. until 12th century.

Description. Sexes alike, the male ('Buck') has shorter and rounder head. Length, head and body 16–18 in., ears 3½ in. without black tip common to all Hares. Weight 3–3½ lb. Some are heavier owing to crosses with tame Rabbits. 6 or more teats. Coat thicker in winter. Fur is much used for clothing, dyed to imitate other furs. Also used for 'felt'. 4 Rabbits make 1 felt hat.

1. Fall of L.F.
2. Fall of R.F.
3. Fall of both hind legs.
S. Suspension, the long jump.

Track

GAIT OF HARES AND RABBITS

RABBIT. Female and Young (8 weeks)
Scale ⅛

RABBIT (cont.)

Teeth and structure. See p. 145. Head relatively larger, and hind legs shorter, than those of the Hares. No change of structure seems to have resulted from its burrowing habit. The following sketch of the right upper cheek teeth gives the pattern of the grinding surface, in which enamel (black), ivory (shaded), and cement (dotted) all appear.

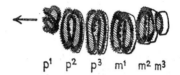

$$p^1 \quad p^2 \quad p^3 \quad m^1 \quad m^2 \quad m^3$$

Life history. 4–8 yearly broods of 3–9 young, after 28–30 days' gestation. Born naked, blind, and with closed ears. Eyes open 11th day; ears 12th. The litters are markedly smaller in Oct.–Nov. Maximum in June. Fur as adults. Can run in a fortnight and are self-supporting in a month. Pair at 6 months. The female ('Doe') before breeding usually leaves burrow and digs a new breeding hole with nest, some 2 ft. long, lined with fur plucked from her own body, leaves, and fern fronds. Rarely a nest is made in the open. Doe leaves the young in the nest, closing entrance after every visit. She will fight even a Stoat to protect her unweaned young. Live 7 or 8 years.

Yearly life. Usual breeding season Feb. to Sept., but young are born in all months. Promiscuous. Does alone attend to young. Bucks sometimes help with nesting materials. Gregarious, digging large burrows. Main entrance usually dips 4–8 ft., then rises to central chamber, from which radiate small bolt-holes to surface. Several burrows may be connected in one warren.

Daily life. Spend most of the day under ground or under thick cover such as bracken, gorse, turnips, &c., except in fine, warm weather, when they lie out in forms. Come out to feed at nightfall and early morning. Come out cautiously along well-trodden paths, watching to see if all is clear. Then rush out in a line to feed and play. Intensely timid. Usually, when pursued by Stoat, will run only a few yards, then close eyes and await death, screaming with terror; but there are records of their showing fight (with the hind legs) and routing the Stoat. Will sometimes come to the scream of a wounded comrade. Bucks carry the tail higher and constantly scratch the earth; Does feed more in daylight in summer. Where Rabbits abound weeds replace grasses and grain. So prolific and destructive that farmers are given the inalienable right to kill them by the Ground Game Acts. As a valuable source of human food and clothing, they are snared for market by the thousand in winter. A hard winter does more than anything else to reduce their numbers, and their enemies include Man, Foxes, Stoats, Weasels, Badgers, Rats, Cats, and birds of prey.

Food. Mainly grass. Also almost all vegetable matter. Gnaw tree bark in hard winters. Very few plants are 'rabbit-proof'. When eating turnips, do not strip, but eat the whole, beginning at the side and eating through. Re-swallow their dung, as do Hares.

Voice. Usually silent, having (1) a low 'Huck', repeated in pleasure; (2) a low growl; (3) a stamping thump of the hind legs, above or underground, as alarm signal, and (4) a scream when wounded or attacked.

Gait. See p. 152. Unhurried, a loping shamble. When hurried, ears back, and tail jerking up and down with each jump. Very fast for 50–80 yds., but then tire. Do not swim as readily as Hares.

Varieties. White, fawn, black, and silver-grey are not uncommon.

TAME RABBIT

Oryctolagus cuniculus domesticus

Origin. All tame Rabbits are descended from the common wild Rabbit. They have been long domesticated and are greatly varied from the parent stock.

Uses. (1) Food, and (2) fur. They also make agreeable pets for children.

Description. The breeds kept for food have become much larger than the wild Rabbit; some others are even smaller. The largest may be 25 in. in length, plus tail, and may weigh 21 lb. To meet the increased size, the skeleton has increased in strength even more than in length, except in the skull. Here, the brain having actually decreased, the skull has lengthened and remained narrow. In lop-eared varieties the weight of the ears has also altered the shape of the skull.

Colour. Advantage has been taken of the natural varieties of colour shown by wild Rabbits to produce breeds of almost every known animal colour.

Life history. That of tame Rabbits has not, generally speaking, changed, though the time of gestation seems to be more usually 30 or 31 days than 29, and the young open their eyes somewhat sooner—usually on the 8th or 9th day.

Yearly and daily life. Their adult life has completely altered into a stationary, feeding, caged existence, which has removed all watchfulness, fear of Man, or need to look after themselves. They have ceased to burrow and have become mere machines to turn vegetable food into meat and fur.

Varieties. Since the War the relative importance of fur and 'fancy' Rabbits in this country has been completely reversed. Those bred so largely abroad primarily for meat have never been common here, except as fancy breeds, because the Wild Rabbit is so common. In fact, while size for meat is valued abroad it is actually a drawback here, where the market is attuned to demand a small (wild-sized) Rabbit.

The fur-bearing Rabbits generally resemble the wild Rabbit in form, and many varieties have recent crosses of the wild Rabbit. Its variegated fur is found to help in giving characters inimitable by mere dyeing.

Fur Rabbits. The range of colours attainable in the fur is remarkable. Rabbits may be white, black, blue, lilac, rich red-brown ('Havana'), tan, and greys of many shades.

In addition to the above self-colours there are also a number of 'broken' colours, of which the following are examples: black and tan, blue and tan, and chocolate and tan. In these the darker colour shades off into the tan on the lips, round the eyes, and under the belly and tail. A 'Marten Sable' Rabbit is a dark brown shading off to a pale yellow in the same black and tan pattern. A 'Siamese Sable' has a rich Havana body, shading to black on head, ears, back, tail, and feet.

Next to these come coats in which longer hairs of a different colour (called 'ticking') are interspersed with the main body colour. Where the

Siamese Sable

Chinchilla

Blue Beveren

Angora

Belgian Hare

Polish

Dutch

Himalayan

English

Lop-eared

TAME RABBITS
Scale 1/12

ticking is white the Rabbit is said to be 'silver'. Such are **Silver Greys** (white on blue-black), **Silver Fawns** (white on orange), **Silver Browns** (white on brown). Similar Rabbits bred from French imported stock, having rather longer fur, are called '**Argentes**': **Argente Silvers** (or **Argente de Champagne**), **Argente Blues**, **Creams**, **Clears** and **Browns**. In these, there is a great quantity of ticking which almost conceals the under colour, so that in the **Argente de Champagne** (white on blue-black) the appearance is that of a general skimmed-milk colour. The Argentes have also a small number of long, black hairs. Many different Rabbits (e.g. **Belgian Hares,** see below) have a black ticking, darkening the backs.

These silvered Rabbits have, by taking advantage of the broken coloured patterns described above as the black and tan pattern, been bred to simulate the Silver Fox fur, both black (white and black) and blue (white and slate blue). In these the white pattern gradually shades off by more infrequent ticking into the un-ticked dark colour.

The most remarkable and valuable (because of the impossibility of imitation by dyeing) of all Rabbit furs are those of the **Chinchilla Rabbits.** This name was once applied to some of the Silvers (white on pale grey), but is now used for a recent breed in which the coat is composed of black and white hairs intermingled almost exactly as in the South American Chinchilla (*Chinchilla laniger*), a Rodent of the Jerboa family. They should be small, to perfect the illusion, though large ('Giant') Chinchilla Rabbits are also bred. Texture and quality of fur are considered, as well as colour. The first Rabbits imported for their fur, and still popular for their long and close coats, were the **Beveren** breed. These, as **Blue Beverens,** are a pale, even blue throughout, and should have no white hair, even under the tail. They weigh 5–6 lb. and have erect ears and deep blue eyes. They have recently been bred in Black and Brown. Others, larger (6¾–11¼ lb.) are known as **Viennese,** and are white, also with blue eyes. Recent additions to the fur Rabbits are known as **Rex** Rabbits. The fur of these is unlike that of any other Rabbit, being very short, velvety, and close, without ticking or longer hairs anywhere, and resembling a close plush or the fur of a Mole. They look as if they had been closely clipped. The type arose from accidental sports, born in France in 1927, and every Rex variety since bred is the descendant of a single pair. A still later, British, sport, derived from Rex Rabbits, has the fur wavy, like astrakhan fur, from which they have the name of **Astrakhan** Rabbits. Though at first all these were Does, they have now been bred pure of both sexes. Of these, and of **Rex** Rabbits, practically all colours exist from black to white, including chinchilla.

After the fur Rabbits one breed requires special mention, a wool Rabbit—the **Angora Rabbit.** These produce hair of great length (up to 10 in.) with an undercoat of wool of remarkable fineness and abundance, which gives them the look of exaggerated powder-puffs. They are of medium size (6–8 lb.) and are white, blue, grey, or fawn. The ears are short and erect, the eyes large and red They are bred for the wool, which commands a high price (18s. a pound in 1933), and are scissor-clipped every 3 months or so, when the wool is about 3 in. long, and the clip weighs some 3 oz.

The remaining breeds, in this country, are mere Fancy Rabbits, bred as pets and for the show ring. The following will give an idea of their variety:

Belgian Hares. These are pure bred Rabbits, having no cross of Hare. They have been, ever since the 16th century, bred, with increasing success, to be as like the Brown Hare as possible. Orange-brown, with a ticking of black hairs of varying length on the ear-tips and back, white only on the belly and under tail. Long, muscular, and lithe in body and limb. Length about 16 in., weight 8 lb.

Flemish Giants. Bred on the Continent for meat and here prized for fancy, for their great size. The largest of all Rabbits, attaining here from 11 to 21½ lb. in weight and, in length (at full stretch from toe to toe) as much as 40 in. Foreign specimens are even bigger. Dark steel-grey in colour, with white only on belly and under tail. Head large and rounded, eyes dark brown, and ears erect.

Polish Rabbits. These come at the opposite end of the scale—the smallest breed. Not more than 3½ lb. in weight and often much smaller They are albinos, having ruby-red eyes and a pure white, short, close, velvety coat. Form rounded and cobby, heads round with short ears held closely together and erect. Delicate and hard to rear, rarely more than 5 at a birth.

Dutch Rabbits. These and the next two breeds named are distinguished by characteristic patterns. The Dutch pattern is white and a darker colour (which may be black or almost any other shade, e.g silver), arranged as seen in the plate. Small, weighing 5–6 lb., hardy, easily reared, and such good mothers as to be the best foster-mothers for other breeds.

Himalayans. This breed was 'made' by accidental crossing of other colours, and is now fixed. They are albinos, having red eyes and white coats with the peculiarity of black 'points', on ears, nose, tail, and feet. Very delicate. The black points do not appear until some time after birth.

English Rabbits. These have the most unusual pattern of any breed, see plate. The darker colour may be of almost any shade, and much attention is devoted to the symmetry and shape of the 'chain' marks. Large, weight about 9 lb., dark-eyed, and hardy.

Lop-ears. Large, up to 22 in. in length. The ears hang down, having lost the power of erection or movement, and have been grown to a length of 28½ in. measured from tip to tip when spread out laterally. (The corresponding measure of a Wild Rabbit's ears is under 8 in.) The ears can be 7 in. in width. The Rabbits are self-coloured, in many shades, or of 'broken' colour, usually in the pattern described above as that of Black and Tans.

HOOFED BEASTS

Order *UNGULATA*

This order is composed of beasts of many different kinds, from gazelles to bisons. In Britain the Deer alone survive as wild animals, all the others being domestic: the Pig, Ox, Sheep, Goat, Horse, and Ass.

These are all of fairly large size, of terrestrial habit, and almost all eat solely vegetable food. They have no collar bones and they walk upon the tips of the toes. These are provided with hoofs which cover the last joint. Hoofs, like claws or finger-nails, grow from the outer layer of the skin. The number of toes varies and gives a classification into two groups, according to whether that number is odd or even.

Their teeth are very complex. Some of the milk teeth are usually retained until the beast is fully grown. The teeth differ markedly in different parts of the mouth and generally are adapted to vegetable feeding. Among them are the most complex examples of grinding cheek teeth, which take two distinct types. One of these has the biting surface covered with rounded hillocks, which, when worn, show round spots of ivory surrounded by circles of enamel as in Pigs. The other type has the biting surfaces marked with deep crescent-shaped pits filled with cement, which, when worn, give a grinding surface of three materials, enamel, ivory, and cement, as in Cattle and Horses.

As to their limbs, the small bones of forearm and shin are either reduced to a mere rudiment, or more or less fused with the large bones. The hand and foot bones are lengthened, reduced in number, and sometimes fused. Their brains are small, but highly developed and convoluted.

EVEN-TOED HOOFED BEASTS
Sub-order *ARTIODACTYLA*

The **mark of** these animals is that the 3rd and 4th toes divide the weight evenly, the central line of the leg falling between them. The hoofs are cloven. They are walkers on moist ground. No toe is, in itself, symmetrical, but the 3rd and 4th form a symmetrical pair and have been equally developed at the expense of all others. The 1st (thumb and big toe) have disappeared, and the two remaining outside toes (2nd and 5th) are more or less obsolete, and are useful only on soft ground. The vertebrae of the back and loins rarely exceed 19 in number. These include all our Hoofed beasts, except the Horse and the Ass, and are divided into three distinct families, the Swine, the Bovine beasts (Cattle, Sheep, and Goats), and the Deer.

The first of these groups, the **Swine** (*Suidae*), differs greatly from the other two.

Of Swine (*Suidae*) we have only the domestic pig. The Wild Boar, which still survives on the continent of Europe, has been extinct in this country since the 17th century. Pigs have all 4 toes with distinct hand, foot, and toe bones. They are omnivorous and they have a full set of Mammal's teeth (total 44) with canines developed into tusks, and molars with rounded hillocks on the biting surface. They are **not** ruminants—do not chew the cud—and have a single stomach.

PIG

Sus domesticus

Origin. Probably various wild species, including the European Wild Boar (*Sus scrofa*) and the Chinese Pig (*Sus indicus*). Wild Boars survive on the Continent, but are extinct here. Tame Pigs differ from Wild chiefly owing to having been bred for fattening qualities, and not having to hunt for food. The skull has been broadened, heightened, and shortened. The young have lost the lengthwise black and tan stripes which mark piglets of all wild species.

Uses. Minor matters apart (pigskin, bristles, &c.), pigs serve two uses only, meat and manure. The flesh is eaten as pork when fresh, as ham or bacon when salted and cured, and the fat is boiled off as lard. It absorbs salt more readily than the flesh of any other animal and therefore, until recently, salt pork was the staple diet of crews on long voyages and of men in remote places. Pigs are unequalled scavengers. They turn into meat the gleanings on the stubbles, the leavings of cattle, and kitchen refuse. This, and the proximity of markets, results in the greatest numbers being found near the large towns and on the arable farms of East Anglia, the fewest in the northern and hilly counties. There are some 4¼ million Pigs in the U.K., of which 3 are in England and Wales, and over a million in Ireland. Scotland has only 166,000.

Description. Sexes differ little. Boars have more prominent tusks, coarser bristles, and the Sow in milk looks different owing to the long row of 14 teats along the belly. The size differs greatly according to race,

THE COMMON BOAR. 1790.
(after Thomas Bewick)

162

but the largest Sow may be 7 ft. 7 in. in length and may weigh as much as 11 cwt. In practice the size of Pigs depends on their age as, nowadays, few are allowed to grow to full size. A Pig can, and roughly, should, add 1 lb. to its weight daily. It is usual to de-sex both males and females about 6–8 weeks after birth as they then fatten more readily. To enable them to dig for food there is a round disk of gristle at the end of the snout, backed by two extra bones in the nose.

Teeth. Pigs have the full Mammal's mouth of $\frac{3-1-4-3}{3-1-4-3} = 44$. In-cisors project forwards. Canines are rootless, of continuous growth, strongly developed as tusks (particularly in Boars) the uppers (c^1) turning up when outside the mouth and serving to dig and fight. The cheek teeth are suited to omnivorous feeding, the premolars having slicing edges, while the molars are of rounded hillock type (see pp. 20 and 25).

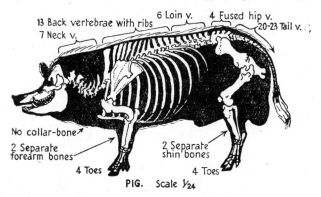

13 Back vertebrae with ribs   6 Loin v.   4 Fused hip v.

7 Neck v.   20-23 Tail v.

No collar-bone

2 Separate forearm bones

4 Toes

2 Separate shin bones

4 Toes

PIG. Scale ½₄

Limbs. The two forearm bones are present but closely connected; the two shin bones are separate. Each foot ('trotter') has four hand (or foot) bones, complete toes and hoofs, the outside pair small and not touching on hard ground.

Structure. Vertebrae 7–13–6–4 and 20–3 in the tail. In improved Pigs the number of back and loin vertebrae is sometimes increased from 19 to 22. No collar bone. Small, simple (not ruminant) stomach.

Colour. Improved Pigs are white, black, or reddish-brown, or a combination of these colours in spots or large patches. Recently the presence of any colour has been discouraged. They tend to lose coats if kept too warm.

Life history. Litters of any number from 6 to 8 (usual for a first litter) up to as many as 22 are born, after about 16 weeks' gestation. Young are born open-eyed and are able to follow the Sow in 7–10 days. They can suck only with the Sow's consent (given with a low grunt), and each has its own teat, though theft occurs. Litters of over 12 are of doubtful value. They begin to eat at about 3 weeks and are weaned in from 6–8 weeks. Young Sows may be mated at 6 months and Pigs are full grown at 2 years.

Yearly life. Sows are in season every 3 weeks and can be paired from 3–7 days after the young are weaned. Thus, if the young are taken from the Sow at 2 or 3 weeks old, it is possible to get 3 litters a year. Two are usual and, as the young are easily injured by excessive heat or cold, it is better to time the litters for spring and autumn. Before the Sow produces her young ('farrows') she will pick up straws and make a rough nest. The demand for pork is in winter, so 'porkers' are fattened for slaughter at that time, usually at from 3–4 months old, weighing from 90–120 lb., not exceeding 140 lb. Bacon is marketable all the year, and bacon Pigs are usually killed at about 6 months old, weighing about 180 lb., not over 240 lb.

Daily life. That of most Pigs is one of strict confinement with, perhaps, a few weeks on the stubbles to clear up. The outdoor life of such Pigs as are at large (e.g. in the New Forest) consists of one long hunt for food, rooting in the earth for roots and fungi, picking up acorns, beech mast, seeds, or carrion. Unlike Wild Boars, they are diurnal and gregarious. They are keen scented and are, abroad, trained to hunt truffles. Pigs are not naturally dirty. Left in a sty 8-ft. square, half open to the weather, without drainage, and with all his food slopped into a trough or on to the cobbled floor, even a sanitary inspector would become an offence. Pigs require much rich feeding when being fattened, though breeding Pigs can do with little but what they pick up until shortly before farrowing. If pork is required, the Pig must never be allowed to lose flesh: growth must be continuous from birth to death.

Food. **Omnivorous**: seeds, fruits, green vegetables, grass, roots, fungi, carrion, small living things, also bran, beans, and meal of all sorts. Food may be cooked to save the Pig effort. Some soil and cinders are useful.

Gait. Walks, trots, and canters. Swims well, without suicide.

Voice. Great variety of conversational grunts and squeaks. In pain, shrieks loudly.

Varieties. The improved Pig differs much from the long-legged, long-snouted, knife-backed, bristle-crested Wild Boar, but there is less variety in Pigs than in many domestic animals because all are bred for one purpose—food. For this a compact but long-bodied Pig, quick growing and of early maturity, is wanted. The following points are common to all good Pigs: head small and wide eyed; nose and lower jaw short; cheeks full; eye not too small or fierce; ears (in most breeds) small; neck thick and fairly long; body rectangular, the back and belly lines level, the back not drooping when walking; the ribs well sprung and deep. Small feet on straight, fine-boned legs, with flesh extending well down them (= 'fleshed down'). Tail long and tufted; skin hairy and thin. The Sow should be long.

A variety occurs in which the two main toes are joined under a single hoof.

Certain characters have, in Pigs, been shown to be Mendelian dominants: thus, black hair over red; self-coloured white over all colours; 'belted' pattern over self-coloured; long face over short; erect ears over lop; and small litters over large.

LARGE WHITE BOAR

WELSH SOW

MIDDLE WHITE BOAR

Scale $^1/_{36}$

The following are the main British breeds:

Large Whites (or **Yorkshires**). Hardy, with strong bone, flat sides, drooping rump, long nose, and big ears. (Generally rather like Wild Boar.) The long legs, thick bone, and big ears have been much reduced. They are good makers of lean bacon. Large, a boar of this breed has weighed 9 cwt.

Large White Ulsters—general in N. Ireland—are similar, but shorter in body, finer in hair, and with drooping ears. Coat sparse and skin thin.

Common Whites of Scotland are also similar to Large Whites, but with longer noses and legs. They mature more slowly.

Cumberlands. Also white, though blue spots sometimes appear on adults. Lop-eared, dish-snouted, sparsely coated, and smooth-skinned. Locally prized both as porkers and bacon Pigs.

White Lops (or **Long White Lop-eared Pigs**)—mainly from the S.W. counties and Wales—are pure white, with a moderate quantity of straight, silky hair. Long and deep in body, short in leg, long lop ears covering the face. Excellent mothers, rearing large litters. Good both for bacon and pork. Docile. Now amalgamated with the Welsh breed, which was similar.

Middle Whites. This breed, now the commonest throughout the country, is a cross between Large Whites and an extinct breed of 'Small Whites' (a small, pug-nosed, delicate, sausage-shaped, small-eared, Chinese-bred race), which has served greatly to improve our native races. Middle Whites mature quickly, are hardy, good mothers, and particularly suitable for pork.

Berkshires. Dark brown or black Pigs with black skin. They have some pink skin and white hair on nose, forehead, feet, and tail-tip. Short faces, heavy jowls. Smaller than Middle Whites. The skin should be smooth, hair soft and plentiful. Their ratio of prime parts to offal is a maximum, as is the proportion of lean meat to fat at an early age. They were the first breed of Pigs to be improved, are of special value for crossing purposes to improve other breeds, and hold unrivalled records for carcass quality in both pork and bacon classes. Their black skin enables them to endure the sun to a degree which makes them valuable in hot climates, to which they have been much exported.

Essex and **Wessex Saddlebacks** differ from the Berkshires and each other mainly in the position of the white markings. The Essex (as illustrated) have the white forelegs and belt, and white on the hind feet and tip of the tail. They are hardy in cold climates. The Wessex are very similar, but have white only on the forelegs and in the belt. They have a strain of Neapolitan blood, said to have improved the quality of their flesh.

Tamworths are nearer to the Wild Boar than any of our other improved breeds. Sandy-red in colour, long-nosed, and very hardy. Slow in maturing, but grow large and bear big litters. They make good lean bacon, and for this reason are much crossed with overfat breeds.

BERKSHIRE SOW

ESSEX SOW

TAMWORTH BOAR
Scale $1/36$

Large Blacks. Originally Cornish, crossed with similar Suffolk Pigs. They are hardier than Berkshires, whose place they have largely taken. The black skin, fine and soft, is covered with straight, silky hair. The ears droop so as to cover the eyes, which helps to make them placid grazers, thriving well on grass with but little added food. Prolific, sows often litter 13 (22 on record). They produce streaky bacon and are much used for crossing with Large or Middle Whites.

Lincoln Curly Coated. Hardy, quick feeders, good breeders, attaining great weight. Pork juicy and of fairly good texture. Somewhat fat for bacon.

Gloucester Old Spots. White, with black spots. Since 1933 the spots are no longer essential. Docile, lean, and hardy. Produce fine streaky bacon. Good mothers. Give two large litters a year on meagre cottage fare ('The Cottage Pig') and respond to better feeding.

LARGE BLACK SOW

LINCOLN CURLY COATED SOW

GLOUCESTER OLD SPOTS SOW
Scale $^1/_{36}$

RUMINANTS: *RUMINANTIA*

The **Bovine Beasts** (*Bovidae*) and the **Deer** (*Cervidae*) are both purely herbivorous and together form the **Ruminants** or chewers of the cud. The stomach consists of four parts,[1] of which the following is a diagram, seen from the left side in section:

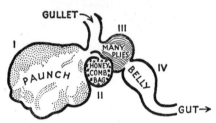

The food is cropped and swallowed, unchewed and in bulk, into the paunch, where it is stored until the whole paunch is filled and the beast begins to ruminate. In this process food passes from the paunch into the honeycomb bag, where it is squeezed into round 'boluses' or balls of 'cud'. The balls are regurgitated, one by one, up the gullet into the mouth, and there mixed with saliva and chewed until they become soft and liquid. Then each is swallowed again and goes direct to the manyplies. The form of the gullet is such that dry, bulky food closes the entrance to the manyplies and opens that to the paunch, whereas liquid and pulpy chewed food follows the other passage and closes the entrance to the paunch. The manyplies allows only well-chewed material to slip between its filter-like leaves into the belly, where the

[1] *Note.* The linings of the four stomachs differ and can be seen by buying tripe at a butcher's. They are:

I. Paunch, like coarse velvet. *Rumen.*

II. Honeycomb Bag, covered with a pattern of muscle like a honeycomb. *Reticulum.*

III. Manyplies, covered with many long folds or leaves, suggesting a book. *Psalterium.*

IV. Belly or Reed, surface smooth. *Abomasum.*

main process of digestion is performed and the residue alone passed on to the gut.

Normally they have horns or antlers, but Man has produced 'polled' breeds of the domestic animals from individuals born hornless.

In the Ruminants the process of simplifying the leg bones has gone much farther than in the Swine. The hand and foot bones of the two working toes (3rd and 4th) have become fused into one (double-barrelled) bone called the 'cannon bone' and the outside toes (2nd and 5th) have become more or less obsolete.

The teeth are adapted to the herbivorous diet. The upper incisors have disappeared and are replaced by a hard pad against which the lower incisors grip the grass. The canines, where they survive, are like additional incisors, and a prolongation of the jaw has left a gap between them and the cheek teeth. These are complex, cemented, and of crescent formation, giving, when worn, a grinding surface of three materials, enamel, ivory, and cement, as do those of the Horses and Voles which serve the same purpose.

The **Bovine Beasts** (*Bovidae*) have horns which are hollow and permanent, growing throughout life over bony cores projecting from the skull. These horns are usually present in both sexes, though smaller, or weaker, and more often lacking, in the females. The disappearance of the bones of the outer (2nd and 5th) toes has gone farther than in the Deer and their cheek teeth grow to a greater length before forming roots. They are represented with us by three domestic species only—Cattle, Sheep, and Goats.

The Deer (*Cervidae*) have antlers of bone, not horn, which are shed and grown afresh every year. They grow from a stump of bone (pedicle), and are covered with a mass of blood-vessels called the 'velvet'. When the new antler is fully grown, a bony thickening (called the 'coronet') develops at its base which cuts off the blood-supply to the velvet, and kills it. The velvet is then rubbed off, leaving the antler hard and 'clean'. This coronet, at a later stage, closes up in the centre and so kills the antler and itself. They are then dropped, to be replaced by the new growth of the following year. In the Deer, horns are almost always the monopoly of the males. Of the 2nd and 5th toes, Deer still have the hoofs and all the three bones of the toes themselves, though they are raised from the ground, but the hand and foot bones of these toes are represented only by small splints. These splints of the Red, Fallow, and recently imported Japanese, Deer, are at the top of the cannon bones and immediately below the wrist ('knee') and heel ('hock'), as in the Horse. In the Roe Deer, on the contrary, it is the lower part which has survived as a splint attached to the toe bones, but widely separated from the wrist and heel. See figure on p. 11. Deer have no gall-bladders. They have large tear-pits, or openings, below the corners of the eyes, which give access to large glands in the face. They have also a tuft of hair on the inside of the hocks, within which is a scent gland. The four species above mentioned are our only Deer.

CATTLE

Bos taurus

Origin. The world's domestic cattle are divided into two groups—those of Europe, and the Humped Cattle of India. These have separate origins. Our own are derived mainly from two sources, the Urus and the Celtic Ox. Possibly also from a third race (*Bos frontosus*), which had a prominence between the horns and of which fossil remains have been found. The Urus or Aurochs (*Bos taurus primogenius*) was a giant beast, standing 6 ft. in height and with long horns. It died out in Great Britain, undomesticated, in prehistoric times but after the arrival of Man, though it survived in Poland until the 17th century. The Celtic Ox (*Bos longifrons*), a small, dark red beast,

standing about 4 ft., was brought to this country, already tamed, by Neolithic Man. These Celtic Oxen were gradually driven, with their masters, to the W. and N. by later invaders who brought with them larger Cattle, tame descendants of the Urus of central Europe. Our modern beasts all share the blood of both races, but Shorthorns and Highland Cattle are perhaps nearest in type to the Urus and Celtic Ox respectively, although they have exchanged horns. There are over 12½ million Cattle in the U.K., of which 6¼ are in England and Wales, nearly 5 in Ireland, and 1¼ in Scotland.

Uses. A mainstay of human life from early times. Naked African tribes still survive whose food is almost wholly milk and blood drawn from living cattle. Their main uses here to-day are to supply meat, milk, and manure. For an analysis of the milk see p. 16. The following list gives some idea of other uses: leather; hair for upholstery, felt, brushes, and plaster mixing; glue; bones for charcoal, manure, and knife-handles; tallow, soap, and glycerine; cat-gut; horn; rennet; ox-gall. Medical use is made of the blood, urine, liver, and glands. Milk gives a substitute for celluloid. Cattle have been trained to carry riders and even to fight for their owners. They are still used for draught in most lands and here in the Orkneys.

Description. Sexes differ much. The 'Bull' is heavier and larger, particularly in the neck and, in horned races, his horns are usually shorter and thicker. Bulls have retained their ancestral ferocity and are almost always dangerous beasts. Therefore, and because one Bull can serve many Cows, it is usual to slaughter almost all bull-calves of the milk breeds, and to castrate those of the meat breeds. De-sexed males (Oxen or Steers), most docile of all animals, grow larger even than Bulls and, in horned races, their horns often grow very large. Castration is usually done in the first 6 months. The numbers of males and females born are equal, though there are years in which one or other sex predominates.

Horns. Unbranched, more or less symmetrical, one on each side of the head, permanent, growing from a bony core and marked with a ring in the fourth, and every succeeding year. Present in most races, certainly in original species, and in both sexes. Some races are hornless ('polled') and have long been so. Absence of horns is a Mendelian dominant in Cattle, though the males half-bred in this respect usually show 'scurs', or vestiges of horns.

Teeth $\dfrac{0-0-3-3}{3-1-3-3} = 32$. Incisors, sharp and chisel-shaped, project and grip the grass against a hard pad in the upper jaw. The mouthful, gathered with a twist of the tongue and gripped, is torn off with a jerk of the head. c_1 is like a fourth i. All cheek teeth are much alike, complex, and covered with cement so as to give a grinding surface when worn. Much shorter than a Horse's. Their surfaces are oblique, the lower teeth being longer inside than towards the cheeks, the upper longer on the cheek side than towards the tongue.

Limbs. Walk upon the 3rd and 4th toes of each foot, and the hand and foot bones of these are fused into single bones (the 'cannon' bones) which resemble the barrels of a double-barrelled shot-gun. There are no toe bones of other toes, but 'dew claws' represent the 2nd and 5th hoofs and there is a trace of the 5th hand bone at the wrist ('knee'). Both bones of the forearm are present, but those of the shin are fused into one.

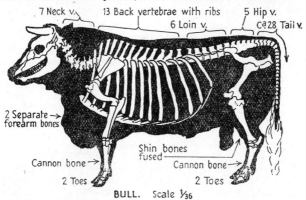

BULL. Scale $\frac{1}{36}$

Structure. Vertebrae, 7–13–6–5 and, in the tail, variable, about 28. No collar bone. They have the large, quadruple ruminant's stomach and

175

a short intestine. The breast bone is broad and flat. 4 teats and two more, usually rudimentary, but effective in some cows.

Colour. Show almost every animal colour known. Sometimes self-coloured, sometimes coloured in patches, and sometimes with mixed hairs of different colours, as roans (red or black and white) or brindles (black and brown). Red roan is a cross, having both red and white hairs. Blue roan has black and white. Black colouring is a Mendelian dominant to red.

Life history. One calf at a birth is usual. Some Cows habitually have twins, which is disliked, as they are usually weaklings. 3 and even 4 have been recorded. Gestation about 40 weeks, but very variable. Where twins are born, one of each sex, the Bull-calf is normal, but the female is almost always sterile and called a 'Free Martin'. Calves are born with open eyes, and hair, can stand at, and, within a few hours, follow the Cow. If left with the mother the calf is weaned in about 5 or 6 months. Young females can calve at the age of about 2 years. They are called 'Heifers' until the birth of their second calf.

Yearly life. Cows are in season every 3 weeks, beginning 3 weeks after the birth of the last calf. Man arranges the time of pairing to suit his chosen system of management. Until everything was altered in the 18th century by the introduction of root-crops and 'cake' and other such foods, the sparseness of winter feed led to the yearly slaughter of many beasts whose meat had to be salted for winter use, while the rest barely survived till spring. Now, herds are kept intact through the winter on food other than pasture, and a supply of milk and fresh meat is got by stall feeding, usually under cover. Cows begin to give milk when the calf is born. The quantity increases for about 2 months, and the full flow continues until, if out of doors, it ceases as soon as the first cold weather sets in. If a Cow is well fed (indoors or out) and is not to have another calf, she will give milk for about 15 months. If she is to breed again, she must be dried (by not being milked) and kept dry for 3 weeks before calving. The quantity of milk given has been vastly increased by skilful breeding and feeding. Whereas an unimproved Cow gives, and a

Calf needs, about $1\frac{1}{2}$ gallons a day, Cows have given over 11 gallons a day, and over 3,600 gallons in a year. Cows give milk as readily to hand, or machine, milking as to the Calf.

Daily life. Cattle suffer from cold, but can endure a damp climate, and require grass. The largest numbers are, therefore, found in the western and midland districts, where the rainfall is greatest, and the climate mild. They will not dig through snow to reach grass. Their daily life is dependent upon the system of management adopted on the farm, which varies with the breed, locality, and object in view.

Speaking very generally, our present system of beef raising is carried out on three different types of farm; (1) the breeding ('store') farms of the hill country in the west, (2) the arable farms of the east, and (3) the grass farms of the midlands. Some of the cattle from the breeding farms are sold in the autumn, after the harvest is gathered, to the arable farms. They are called 'stores' (that is, cattle for fattening) and are fattened (mainly indoors) on the crops harvested, with other food added. They go to the butchers during the winter. Other stores from the breeding farms are sold in the spring to the grazing farms of the midlands, where they are fattened in the fields upon the summer grass, and sold to the butchers during the summer.

Where meat is the sole object, beasts can be left out all the year round, but they are usually housed from Oct. to May, except for a few hours in the day, and when being fattened for slaughter are kept in day and night. Cows should calve in rotation throughout the year. Bull calves are castrated. Under the older system Steers were usually killed in their 3rd year, and cows were used for breeding until about their 10th or 12th year and then fattened for the butcher. It is now usual for beef producers to allow some of their Cows or Heifers to suckle a calf until it is about a year old, and then to sell both together for slaughter. For this ('baby beef') system both mother and calf have to be highly fed. Fattening is hampered by much exercise (walking or chewing) and by cold. Hence the value of warm (if well-ventilated) stalls, and pulping and chaff-cutting machines.

Where milk is the object, if for cheese, the Cows will usually calve in March or April; if for the sale of milk direct to the market, they must calve as nearly as possible in rotation throughout the year. They are habitually warmly housed and those giving milk must be well fed through the winter. Housing all day in the heat of summer is a protection against flies. The opposite system of a wholly outdoor life is also adopted and helps to increase resistance to tuberculosis. The Bull-calves will be sold (for veal and ham pie) at, or just after, birth. The Heifer-calves will be taken from their mothers, either at birth or a week or so later, to be reared by hand with a small part of the mother's milk, soon to be replaced by cheaper substitutes. It is usual to milk morning and evening, sometimes also at midday. At the age of about 10 years Cows are fattened for the butcher.

The above remarks omit all reference to the breeding of pedigree stock. It is rare that either meat or milk is the sole object of a herd.

The value of cattle for manure is due to the fact that a large part of their food is brought on to the land from elsewhere, and not grazed off it. The more the beasts are stall-fed and kept in covered yards to prevent the manure being washed away by rain, the greater the benefit. The local rainfall, the supply of straw for litter, the need for manure on arable land, and the cost of chemical fertilizers, all affect the question of whether open or covered yards are better.

When Cattle are leading a fairly natural life, out at pasture, they feed all day and sleep all night. They rise at daybreak and feed rapidly until the paunch is full, when they settle down to chew the cud. It takes roughly an hour to empty the paunch, and then they feed again. Normally they lie down to chew, but in cold or windy weather will stand with back to wind. At nightfall they lie down and, after chewing the cud, sleep undisturbedly till morning.

Food. Purely herbivorous. Cattle prefer the longer grasses and do not crop as closely as Horses or Sheep. When stall-fed they are given a great variety of foods, including hay, straw, roots, pea and bean straw, ensilage, meal, oil-cake, soaked maize, barley, peas, and lentils. They need frequent access to roots or water. A Cow giving 9 gallons of milk a day will drink 22 gallons of water.

Gait. They walk, and can trot, canter, and gallop much as Horses. They lie down in a position similar to that of a Horse, but resting squarely on the breast bone in front, with the forelegs bent double at the wrist ('knee') so that the hoofs touch the elbows. To lie down, they first kneel. To get up, rise on the hind legs first. Though able to swim, rarely do so voluntarily, but in hot weather like to stand in water.

Voice. Usually silent. Bulls will 'bellow' with rage or desire, and Cows 'Moo' with desire or when distressed by separation from a calf, by pain, or wish to be milked.

Varieties. The differences in the Cattle found in this country appear to be partly the results of climate and of local segregation (increased since the enclosure of the common lands), and partly of the effort of breeders to attain certain standards. Attention was first drawn to this by the remarkable results achieved in the 18th century by Robert Bakewell (1725–95). He first proved the immense influence on domestic animals of judicious pairing, and that the type obtained could be made permanent by close in-breeding. This method also gives a quality desirable in all breeds, early maturity. While it is not impossible to get good beef and abundant milk from the same breed, as a rule the two qualities at their best are not found together.

Of course, the quality of giving a large supply of milk is the one most essential in the milk breeds, but there are some points common to all good Cattle of any breed. These are: The head should be wide-eyed, flat-crowned (except in some polled breeds), flat-nosed and with broad, damp muzzle: the eyes large, full and clear: the ears large, sensitive, and hairy. The neck should be long, full at the body and tapering to the head: in the Bull muscular and arched. The body should be wide and deep in the chest, broad and flat all along the back, the ribs well hooped and extending far backwards in the Ox, while the Cow may have a large, drooping belly, and swelling 'milk veins'. The hips should be large and round; the legs wide in front, with 'brisket' wide and well forward; the tail thin and hanging vertically. The forearm straight, short and muscular; the cannon bones short, strong, fine, and flat; 'legs well under'. The thighs, broad, thick, and well down towards the hocks: the inner thigh ('twist') full and large. The hoofs clear and oily. The skin should be moderately thick, movable, and well covered with fine, soft hair.

CHILLINGHAM BULL AND COW
Scale ¹/₃₆

It is usual to classify cattle into Beef, Dairy and Dual-Purpose breeds,[1] but this order is, for many reasons, inconvenient. Here the Park ('Wild') Cattle are placed first and the other breeds roughly in the order of their numbers in the respective herd-books.

Of our 12½ million cattle, less than 3 per cent. are registered pedigree beasts, though a much larger number are bred to the type of the improved beasts and differ mainly from them in the absence of a recorded pedigree. In addition to these beasts of pure-bred type a very large number are deliberately cross-bred, for some particular need of the farmer or for economy.

PARK CATTLE.

No truly wild Cattle survive in this country, but there are three herds of white Cattle (supposed to be of Roman (?) origin) which have lived a wild life in certain parks from very early times. The herd at Chillingham in Northumberland, 39 in number, is the purest in blood, without any recorded cross. They are white except for a faint line of red hair above a black muzzle, red ears, and black eyelashes and tips to the horns. They have short legs, straight backs, and thin skin, keen scent, a strange, wild cry and, while timid, are ferocious if alarmed or at bay. If approached by Man, they lower their heads, paw the ground, and stare. If he moves, they gallop off and return, forming a circle round him, and repeat this, narrowing the circle, until he escapes—if he can. Cows hide their calves in thick cover, returning to suckle them twice or thrice a day. The young couch and tremble if approached. The biggest Bull is master of the herd until defeated by a successor. They are said to kill wounded beasts. This herd has recently been saved from dispersal (for a time at least) by public subscription and the Zoological Society. The other two herds at Cadzow, Lanarkshire (27) and Vaynol, N. Wales (23) are known to have some 'foreign' blood. The former, polled until recently, is now horned.

---

[1] The main breeds thus: *Beef:* Some Shorthorns, Aberdeen-Angus, Devon, Galloway, Hereford, Sussex, and Highland. *Dual:* Some Shorthorns, Lincolnshire Reds, Longhorns, Red Polls, South Devons, Welsh Blacks, and Dexters. *Milk:* Some Shorthorns, Ayrshires, British Friesians, Jerseys, Guernseys, and Kerries.

SHORTHORN COW (Beef type)

SHORTHORN BULL (Beef type)
Scale ¹/₃₆

Tame herds of the same type exist in several other places.

The white of all these Cattle differs from that of others, being purer (less yellow) and a Mendelian dominant over all other colours.

A herd-book of Park Cattle was formed in 1918, and in 1935 recorded 18 herds, with 493 beasts, of which 257 were polled.

SHORTHORNS.

Of these some strains, if they stood alone, would be classed as butcher's Cattle and others as dairy Cattle. In fact, the shows exhibit them in separate classes as Shorthorns and Dairy Shorthorns. But there is only one herd-book, there are many intermediate strains, and as a whole it is essentially a dual purposes breed, ranking very high in both classes, though not supreme in either.

Its origin is obscure. There were large red and white Cattle with short horns, called Teeswaters, near Darlington in the 18th century. They probably had much Dutch blood in them.

The brothers Charles (1750–1836) and Robert (1749–1820) Colling applied Bakewell's principles of 'in and in breeding' to these Cattle and are regarded as the creators of Shorthorns. Their work was taken up by others, particularly by Thomas Bates (1776–1849) and the Booth family, father, sons, and grandsons (working from 1790 to 1878). The degree to which in-breeding was carried may be seen from one example: The Bull Belvedere (Bates) was so bred that a single Bull (Favourite 252) provided $\frac{53}{64}$ths of his blood, while one more 64th was that of Favourite's mother.

The breed soon became the most numerous in this country. In the middle of last century the breeders, under the influence of a beef demand from abroad, neglected milk. But in Scotland, Amos Cruikshank of Sittyton (1808–95) reverted to the older practice, laying stress upon the milking powers of beasts primarily bred for the butcher. Later, George Taylor of Cranford and Lord Rothschild at Tring built up dairy herds of which the carcass value was also improved.

The ideal still placed before its members by the Shorthorn Society is a quickly maturing, hardy, and adaptable breed, of which the cows should be generous milkers, having a large

DAIRY SHORTHORN BULL

LINCOLN RED SHORTHORN COW
Scale $^1/_{36}$

and well-proportioned carcass when fattened at the end of a long milking career, and the bull-calves, even of the best milking strains, should be worth steering for the butcher.

There are about 40,000 pedigree Shorthorns in England and Wales alone. Of all the Dairy Cattle whose milk yield is registered in those countries about 60 per cent. are Shorthorns. It has been estimated that 70 per cent. of all the Cattle of Britain (75 per cent. in Ireland) are of the Shorthorn type. They are exported to all parts of the world.

They are red, white, red and white, or roan in colour, neither the red nor the white dominating, so that the hybrids between the two are, in the first generation, all roans or red and whites, while the second generation segregate out in the usual Mendelian way. The flesh of the nose, palate, lips, and eyelids is pink and unmarked, and the hair of the eyelashes and inside the ears is cream. There is no black anywhere. They mature more quickly than any other Cattle, and for 2 years can add nearly 2 lb. a day to their weight. Average weight of adult Bulls about $17\frac{1}{2}$ cwt., of Cows and 2-year-old Steers $12\frac{1}{2}$ cwt., while fat Steers and Cows often scale a ton, and have scaled nearly a ton and a half. A Cow stands some 4 ft. 6 in. in height, a Bull 5 ft. They have a very good proportion (about 65 per cent.) of meat to live weight. The quality, while not equal to the best, is very good.

In the milking strains, the general reputation is of a large quantity of milk of a quality moderately rich in fat. Quantity usually ranks next after the Friesians and the butter-fat content is usually superior. One Cow is known to have given 2,917 gallons of milk in a year, in 1934 ten gave over 2,000 gallons each, and every year several thousand Cows give over 1,000. The 3-year average required of Shorthorns for a certificate of merit is 900 gallons. The great claim on behalf of the breed as milkers is that the high milking records are maintained over long periods without loss of flesh or injury to the breeding qualities of the Cow.

Lincoln Red Shorthorns had until the end of 1935 a separate herd-book and are now registered in a separate section of the Shorthorn (Coates's) Herd-book. They are of a whole-coloured rich red shade, but do not otherwise differ from other Shorthorns. About 10,000 in number, mostly dairy cattle, but good for both purposes, and some of beef type.

Shorthorn Bulls crossed with Galloway Cows give a popular blue-grey cross, and with Highland Cows give a large-horned Highland type.

AYRSHIRE BULL

AYRSHIRE COW
Scale ¹/₃₆

Ayrshire. This is the only native British dairy breed. Probably made up in the 18th century of Dutch and Tees-water Cattle with some Channel Island and local blood. They dominate the Scottish dairy market and are increasing in England. Of the *Bos longifrons* type, they (and Kerries) give the greatest dairy returns off poor land. Small, Cows weighing 7 to 9 cwt. and standing about 4 ft. 2 in. in height, Bulls 9 to 10½ cwt. and standing 4 ft. 10 in. A 2-year-old Steer weighs about 10 cwt. They are excellent cheese cows, the milk being rather white in colour, but abundant in quantity (usually, say, 800 gallons, but up to 2,047 gallons) and rich in curd, though not in fats (3·7-4 per cent.). They are almost all white, with more or less red marking, chiefly on head or neck. They carry the head high, having wide-set horns curving up and forwards. Black or brindled markings still occur, but are not approved. 7,186 females were registered in 1934.

BRITISH FRIESIAN BULL

BRITISH FRIESIAN COW
Scale $1/36$

British Friesians. Many Dutch Cattle were imported all along the east coast from the 17th century until 1872, when the trade was stopped by law. The breed was kept up and a herd-book was started in 1909. In 1914, and in 1935, some pure-bred Friesians were imported, and in 1934 a census showed 23,797 females in Great Britain, of which 5,612 were registered in that year. They do not differ from the native Dutch Friesians. They are large, Bulls averaging 14–16 cwt. (attaining over a ton) and standing 4 ft. 9 in., Cows often weighing over 12 cwt. (attaining 18½ cwt.) and standing 4 ft. 5 in.

Though the meat is good enough for the males to be worth steering, they are bred and valued as dairy cattle. The milk yield exceeds that of any known breed. So much so, that the standard required of them for certificates of merit is 1,000 gallons a year (for 3 years) as against 900 for any other Cattle. Several Cows have given over 3,000 gallons in a year. The lactation period is long, and although the fat content is lower than that of any of our other breeds there are better records in recent years. The calves are large and grow quickly, and are of value for veal. Now all piebald, black and white. Red and white seems to have been the original colour of Dutch Cattle and such sometimes crop up, but cannot be registered.

HEREFORD BULL

HEREFORD COW
Scale $^1/_{36}$

Herefords. Originally plough oxen and, seemingly, black and white in colour, having the characteristic pattern which is now red and white. They were improved by Benjamin Tomkins (1748–1815). They are now the leading English beef breed, admirable in form, giving first rate 'marbled' beef and rich, but scanty, milk. The average weight of Bulls is 16 cwt., of Cows 12 cwt., but they attain to 25½ cwt. and a ton respectively. A 2-year-old Steer weighs 11¾ cwt. The thick hide and long curly coat make them very hardy, and great numbers have been exported to all parts of the world. They are usually kept out in the open all the year and are almost free from tuberculosis. When crossed with other breeds the pattern is dominant, though the red will yield to black. Black marks on the muzzles and tips to the horns appear, but are not approved. There are some 10,000 registered pedigree Herefords in this country, chiefly in Hereford and the surrounding counties.

Crossed with a Shorthorn Cow they give a white-faced cross, and with a Galloway Cow, a polled white face.

ABERDEEN-ANGUS BULL

ABERDEEN-ANGUS COW
Scale ¹/₃₆

Aberdeen-Angus. A very mixed breed: local cattle crossed with Ayrshire, Guernsey, Fife, Galloway, and Shorthorns. Improved by Hugh Watson (1789–1865) and bred for symmetry and quality of flesh, which is marbled and of excellent flavour. Milk poor and scanty. Proportion of beef to offal unrivalled. Dressed carcasses have weighed $\frac{3}{4}$ of the live weight. They mature early, yet are hardy and adaptable. Two-year-old Steers average $12\frac{1}{2}$ cwt. (up to a ton on record). Black, with occasional small white belly patches, short legs, heavy, cylindrical bodies, thin skins, short silky hair, and a pointed crown on polled head. Apart from their other merits, the fact that both the black colour and the absence of horns are dominant qualities, makes them in great demand for crossing purposes as, whatever the other party to the cross, the first generation mostly look like the sire and have his qualities of quick maturity and good beef. The breed has greatly increased lately, 6,955 beasts being registered in the herdbook in 1934–5, of which 3,245 were females.

Jersey. This race, probably of French origin and protected by law from all crosses in their native island since 1763, has been imported in large numbers. In quantity the milk is fairly abundant, the minimum annual average over 3 years required for a certificate of merit being 800 gallons. The pride of the breed lies in the high, yellow, butter-fat content, usually between $4\frac{1}{2}$ and $5\frac{1}{2}$ per cent. The Cows are deer-like in appearance, fine in bone, and small in size, standing about 3 ft. 11 in., and weighing about 6 cwt., Bulls $8\frac{3}{4}$ cwt. Variable in colour, though usually self-coloured, fawn, grey, dun, cream, or white, rarely black. They have crumpled, small, yellow horns with black tips, dark muzzles surrounded with pink, yellow teats and skins. They are delicate and, out of Jersey (where it is almost unknown), in special danger of tuberculosis. The Cows are very docile, the Bulls very wild. In Jersey, Bulls are usually killed when 2 years old. The meat is almost unsaleable, with yellow fat, and Bull-calves are usually killed at birth. There were 3,500 females registered in England in 1935.

Guernsey. These are larger beasts of similar type, coming from all the other Channel Islands. Cows stand about 4 ft. 2 in., and weigh from 8 to $8\frac{3}{4}$ cwt. The quality of the milk is very similar and the quantity rather larger. They need more food (as 4 to 3) and give more beef, but it has yellow fat and is second-rate. They are slightly less numerous in England, 3,109 females being registered in 1934, chiefly in the south and west. They are thicker skinned, coarser, and more often marked with white patches. Here they are hardier.

JERSEY COW

GUERNSEY COW
Scale $^1/_{36}$

Galloway. The earliest polled breed known, though a few prehistoric polled skulls have been found. It has existed from the 17th century and is responsible for all our polled breeds, though horns still sometimes crop out. They have thick hide, long wavy (not curly) brownish-black hair and woolly undercoat. Some show white patches and a separate herd-book exists for those of dun colour and those which are known as **Belted Galloways.** Galloways have wide, short heads with low, flat foreheads, ears set far back and pointed forwards. Two-year-old Steers average 10½ cwt. They are very hardy, not closely in-bred, and often left out in winter with a ration of hay or straw. Though slow to mature, they give the finest quality beef. Milk excellent and rich, but usually scanty, though a herd of Belties has averaged 900 gallons a year. They are much used for crossing, and all first crosses are polled. When crossed with dark roans or reds, the young are mostly black; if with white or pale roan Shorthorns, blue-grey. 747 pedigree females were registered in 1935.

Red Polls. This breed was created early in the 19th century by blending the old red Norfolk Horned breed (good beef beasts suggestive of Herefords) and the Polled Suffolk Dun Cattle (good dairy beasts). The hornlessness of the latter, and of the blend, is said to be due to Galloway blood, and the breed was first recognized in 1862. They are small-headed and of deep red colour, the tail-tip and udder alone being allowed to show white. The nose must not be dark. In size they are medium (Cows standing about 4 ft. 3 in.) and rank high as a dual-purposes breed, the Steers fattening quickly and of good form. A 2-year-old Steer weighs 10½ cwt. Prize-winning Steers have been bred from 1,000-gallon dams. In quality the milk is about equal to that of Shorthorns, while in quantity the minimum 3 years average demanded is the same (900 gal.). Cows give milk for an unusually long time. They have been greatly improved in uniformity of late and increased in numbers and are widely exported. 2,185 females were registered in 1934.

BELTED GALLOWAY BULL

RED POLL COW
Scale $^1/_{36}$

Devons. These are among the oldest of our breeds. Originally bred for plough oxen, now for beef. Improved, by selection, by Francis Quartly of Champson and by Coke of Norfolk at Holkham between 1791 and 1823. Small, Cows usually standing about 4 ft. 1 in. in height and weighing 9–11 cwt., Bulls 10–14 cwt., and a 2-year-old Steer about 10 cwt. They are of perfect symmetry, give excellent beef, and have lately been bred larger. Skin is orange yellow. They are a deep blood-red ('Red Rubies'), usually with small white belly patches. Horns black-tipped and upcurved in the Cows and longer than those of the Bulls. Milk rich in fats but poor in quantity, usually 500 gallons, though some have given 1,000 gallons. Hardy, thriving on poor pasture, and well suited to the tropics. 882 females were registered in 1935.

South Devons. In S. Devon and Cornwall a breed has been evolved which, though known for 200 years, has only had a stud-book since 1891. Channel Island or French Cattle are supposed to have contributed to it. They are much larger than Devons (the largest of all our Cattle, though lately efforts have been made to reduce their size), coarser, paler, and yellower in colour. Recent records show their milk to be as rich as that of the Devons (4½–5 per cent. fats) and the quantity is much greater. Half the recorded Cows in 1922 gave over 700 gallons and in 1933 one certificate was gained with a 3-yearly average of 1,315 gallons. Steers between 2 and 3 years old averaged over 18 cwt. at Smithfield. 516 females were registered in 1935.

DEVON BULL

SOUTH DEVON COW

Scale ¹/₃₆

Sussex. An old breed from Sussex, Kent, and Surrey, closely akin to Devons. Larger and less compact, with longer and stronger horns, and a browner red in colour. They also were once bred for the plough, but now for early maturity of good quality beef. They are hardy, and have done particularly well in S. Africa. Fat Heifers weigh about 12½ cwt. and 3rd-year fat Steers 16 cwt. The average 2-year-old Steer weighs 12¾ cwt. An Ox is on record standing 5 ft. 6 in. and weighing only 10 lb. under 35 cwt. 364 females were registered in 1934.

Welsh Black. The North (small beef) and South (larger dairy) Welsh Breeds were amalgamated in 1914. They are perhaps the nearest to the Celtic Oxen of pre-Roman days. Still far from uniform. Usually a self-coloured brown-black, with sometimes some white on the belly and tail-tip; horns yellow and black-tipped (shorter and decurved in the Bulls), hair long and straight. Of slow maturity, but sometimes becoming very heavy. A 2-year-old Steer weighs about 11¾ cwt. Beef first-rate; milk good and abundant. Steers are bought for fattening on midland pastures. 367 females were registered in 1934. This breed has shown great improvement of late.

SUSSEX BULL

WELSH BLACK BULL

Scale $^1/_{36}$

Highlanders. A very old breed, doubtless consisting of survivors of the Celtic Oxen with such admixture only as cattle raids could provide. They are small beasts, of excellent form, with long, elegant, upturned horns and thick, shaggy coats. Originally black, they are now of all shades, white, dun, brown, brindled, and red-brown, usually self-coloured. The hardiest of all breeds, able to live in the open all the year on rough hill country, with a little hay or straw in the hardest weather. Of slow maturity, 2-year-old Steers average 9 cwt. Cows usually calve in their 4th year and, if in the open, hide their calf and become wild. Bulls are unusually docile. Beef unsurpassed, milk of good quality, but scanty and of short duration, serving only for the nurture of the calves, which are usually left to run with the Cows. Many Steers are bought to be fattened on lowland pastures. 149 pedigree females were registered in 1934.

Blue Albion. A dual-purpose breed (stud-book since 1921) centred in the Peak district of Derby. About 80 females are registered annually. They are dairy Shorthorns in which the red is replaced by 'blue', dark or pale. They are of Short-horn origin (the second entry in the Shorthorn herd-book was a blue), with, perhaps, some Friesian blood. The milk is of much the same average quality and quantity as that of other Shorthorns, though no such high yields have been attained. They are blue, blue and white, or blue-roan; the nose and horn-tips must be dark. They yield well on poor land and are hardy, often wintering out in that coldest of all our climates.

HIGHLAND OX

BLUE ALBION COW
Scale $^1/_{36}$

Longhorns. These are the beasts first improved by Robert Bakewell, but to-day, even after an effort to revive the breed, they survive only in very small numbers, about 30 a year being registered. Once good (cheese) milkers, giving large coarse beef, the improvement bettered the carcasses at the cost of their milking powers and their slow maturing has resulted in their being ousted by Shorthorns and other breeds. They have huge, decurved horns and, while coloured either as Shorthorns or brindled, have usually a white spinal ridge.

Old Gloucesters. This old breed was only rescued from extinction by the starting of a herd-book in 1919. In 1935 there existed 130 registered beasts. The milk was specially suited for cheese-making.

LONGHORN BULL

OLD GLOUCESTER COW
Scale $^1/_{36}$

Kerry. The only Cattle in Ireland from the earliest times to the 9th century. Survivals of the Celtic Ox.[1] They are very small, Cows standing 3 ft. 3 in. to 4 ft. 1 in. and weighing about 7½ cwt., while the Bulls weigh about 11 cwt. In shape, typical milking cattle, black, with orange skins and sometimes white patches, and with occasional reversions to brown. The carcass is poor, but the milk abundant and good in quality, though rather white in colour. There are Cows giving over 1,000 gallons a year; 800 a year for 3 years gains a certificate of merit. Chosen Cows give over 4·5 per cent. of butter-fat. There is a separate British herd-book in which 401 females were registered in 1935.

Dexters. This breed, also Irish in origin, is derived from chosen specimens of Kerries, probably with some mixture of Devon blood. It is doubtful whether the name comes from a Mr. Dexter, who was Lord Hawarden's agent in the 18th century and founded the breed, or from an Irish word meaning excellent. They are the smallest of all domestic cattle, short-legged, big-headed, toeing in, and black or red in colour. While thriving on poor land, they respond quickly to better. Cows should stand about 3 ft. 6 in. and, when breeding, not exceed 7 cwt., or the Bulls 8 cwt. Dual-purpose Cattle, they give excellent small joints and much milk. 600 gallons a year is quite usual, 700 for a triennial average earns a certificate of merit.

In Ireland they are almost extinct and have no longer a herd-book: in England 202 females were registered in 1935.

---

[1] Now replaced, mainly by Shorthorns, except in S. and W. Kerry, where their breeding is encouraged by the Free State Government.

KERRY COW

DEXTER COW
Scale $\frac{1}{36}$

SHEEP

Ovis aries

Origin. Probably descended from a number of Asiatic species of the genus *Ovis*,[1] and the European Moufflon (*O. musimon*) which still, barely, survives in Corsica and Sardinia. Only domesticated Sheep exist in this country, but those of Soay (St. Kilda) give a fair idea of the original, unimproved races. There are about 30 million Sheep in the U.K., 18 in England and Wales, 4 in Ireland, and about 8 in Scotland.

Uses. Meat, wool, and manure.[2] They serve many other purposes. Their milk is rich in fats and solids (for analysis see p. 16) and is used abroad for many famous cheeses (e.g. Roquefort). The skin and most parts of their bodies are used in some way, but, since the 18th century, they have been bred in this country mainly for meat, somewhat to the detriment of the quality of the wool, which is now a mere by-product. The finest qualities of wool come from Australia and Saxony. Great as is the value of manure to the land, it does not affect the type of Sheep aimed at by breeders, but only the method of management, the use of added food, the movement of flocks from hill pastures to night quarters on arable land, and the like.

Description. Sexes differ slightly. The males ('Rams' or 'Tups') are larger and, usually, more Roman nosed than the females ('Ewes'). As castrated males ('Wethers') fatten more quickly than Rams, and as one Ram can serve a flock of from 50 to 100 Ewes, castration is almost universal. In size and weight[3] Sheep vary greatly according to breed and condition. One adult Sheep may weigh as much as 7 others. The following are the measures and weights of good average Sheep of a large breed (Leicesters), all newly shorn and 16 months old: Ram stood 2 ft. 7½ in.; length of head 10½ in., from crown to root of tail 3 ft. 8 in.; weight 259 lb. The same figures for a Wether were 2 ft. 3 in., 9½ in., 3 ft.,

---

[1] *Ovis orientalis, O. vignei, O. ammon,* and *O. argali.*

[2] 'Sheep is gran' things. They ligs (= lay or spread) their awn moock an' troddles (= tread) it i' t'ground.' Yorkshire Keeper.

[3] The weights of Sheep as stated in the books are confusing, owing to the use of three distinct measures: (1) the Imperial stone of 14 lb. is used in stating live weights; (2) an 8 lb. stone (Smithfield stone) is used for carcasses, and (3) a Sheep is said to give so much per quarter in pounds. The reason of the Smithfield stone is that Cattle give roughly a dressed carcass weighing $\frac{7}{8}$ths of their live weight. Although in Sheep it is nearer $\frac{1}{2}$, the Smithfield stone is used for mutton as well as beef. To find live weight from dead, and vice versa, the following rough formula may be used: 2 lb. per quarter = 1 stone (of 8 lb.) dead weight = 1 stone (of 14 lb.) live weight.

and 170 lb., and for a Ewe, 2 ft. 3½ in., 9½ in., 3 ft. 3½ in., and 210 lb. Contrasted with these figures, a Soay Ram measured 1 ft. 10 in., 8 in., and 2 ft. 2 in., while an adult Welsh Mountain Sheep may weigh only 56 lb.

Oddly enough there is no scientifically accurate distinction between the Sheep and the Goats (q.v.). There is in some (but not all) Sheep, a smelly gland between the toes, giving scent on the trail, and a rudiment of the face gland below the eye found in the Deer. The long tail is believed to be a result of domestication.

Horns are present in both sexes in all wild races and in many domestic Sheep. They are permanent, hollow, bone-cored, rough, and angular in section, and more or less spirally twisted. Those of the Rams are larger and heavier. Normally 1 pair, symmetrically placed. There are one or two breeds in the world (one in St. Kilda) which have 2, or even 3, pairs. Most improved breeds are hornless.

Wool. All Sheep have both 'hair', thick and hard, and 'wool', thin, curly, and covered with minute, sharp scales, and therefore having the property of 'felting' when wetted and crushed. This coat is more or less mixed in the wild races. The cultivated breeds have the wool all over the body and the hair only on the face and legs. The muzzles are narrow and hairy. The fibre (or 'staple') of which wool is composed varies in length from about 3 to 20 in. It varies in fineness and other qualities according to the race, climate, and soil. Speaking generally, low rich land gives long, coarse wool, and fine hill herbage gives short, fine staple. The wool grows in summer and autumn, to be shed (in a state of nature) in the spring or summer, leaving a short coat of wool to grow for next winter. By Man it is shorn in one single coherent fleece, which varies in weight from about 3 lb. to as much as 30 lb., according to breed. Roughly speaking, the Ram's fleece weighs twice that of the Ewe of the same breed, while that of the Wether is only slightly heavier than the Ewe's. Any check to the healthy regularity of the Sheep's life is often marked by a thinning of the staple, which is liable to break at that point and spoil the fleece. Amid the wool is found a yellow, soapy exudation ('yolk') which is usually washed out before the wool is shorn. This reduces the weight of the fleece by about a third. Unless otherwise stated, fleece weights are those of washed wool. The finest (=most slender) wool in this country (Southdown) is about $\frac{1}{780}$th of an inch thick, the coarsest (Leicester) about $\frac{1}{500}$th. The finest Saxon Merino wool is $\frac{1}{2500}$th.

To become a woven material, wool must first be made into thread. This is done in two distinct ways: (1) by being 'combed' into 'worsted' thread. In this the separate filaments are left at full length, straightened out, and twisted together lengthwise, roughly as a pig-tail, thus:

Such threads make 'stuff' when woven (and 'hosiery' when knitted) and for this the longer, coarser wools are used. The felting power of the wool is immaterial.

(2) By being broken up, by 'scribbling' and 'carding', into minute

lengths (like chopped straw) and then held together by virtue of the felting power of the wool into thread. In such 'woollen' thread the ends of the pieces stick out in all directions, thus:

Such threads make 'cloth' when woven, and for this the shorter, finer wools are used, good felting being essential.

Teeth. Formula as Cattle. The upper molars are much narrower. The age of Sheep can be roughly told by the dates at which the larger adult incisors replace the milk teeth, as follows: i_1 at a year old, i_2 at a year and 9 months, i_3 at 2 years and 3 months, and c_1 at 3 years old. These dates are variable and are hastened in the early maturing breeds.

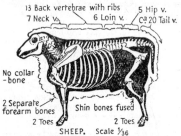

13 Back vertebrae with ribs
7 Neck v.
6 Loin v.
5 Hip v.
Ca 20 Tail v.
No collar-bone
2 Separate forearm bones
2 Toes
Shin bones fused
2 Toes

SHEEP. Scale ⅟₃₆

Structure. Differ from Cattle as follows: tail vertebrae variable in number up to 21. Ewe has 2 teats (some have 4 and even 6). Two of the toe bones of each outside toe (2 and 5) survive, with their hoofs. Skull is relatively larger and bones of the forehead thicker.

Life history. Usually 1 or 2 lambs at a birth, but up to 5 recorded. Fecundity depends greatly on breed and condition. 25–30 lambs from 20 Ewes is a good crop, but 40 is possible. Gestation about 152 days (146 to 161). Lambs are born open-eyed, woolly, and able to stand, but rather tottery. Can follow the Ewe in a few hours. Begin to eat at a month old and are weaned in about 3 months. Castrated at 2 to 3 weeks. The term 'rig' is used for an unsuccessfully de-sexed Ram, who may do much injury to a flock by upsetting the time-table. Young Ewes ('Gimmers') are usually mated when about 18 months old, so as to lamb at 2 years old.

Gimmers and Wethers, from weaning to their first shearing, are known indiscriminately as 'hogs' or 'tegs'. Lambs are sometimes, not usually, shorn during their first year. Sheep will die of old age at about 17 years.

Yearly life. Ewes are in season for 24 hours every 16 days. The time of pairing is dependent upon Man and varies according to breed. It is usually from 1st week in Sept. in the south, on low land, to 3rd week of Nov. in the hills. Exceptionally, it may be as early as April–May in Hampshire, and as late as the end of the year for some of the hill Sheep. These dates give from early Feb. to April (exceptionally from end Sept. to May) for the lambing. Before the Ram is admitted to the Ewes, the 4-year-old and unfit Ewes are removed, and good feed or extra oats given to the flock for 10 days or so. During the lambing time and for 2 or 3 weeks thereafter some protection (housing or hurdles) is given as shelter from the weather—the amount depending on the climate and the hardihood of the breed. About the time the lambs are weaned (say, May in the south, July in the north) the Wethers and Ewes without lambs ('eild' Sheep) are shorn, the Ewes with lambs, 3 weeks or a month later.

Daily life. While able to endure great cold, Sheep cannot stand damp ground. Most are found in the mountain and northern districts, fewest in the low grasslands of the midlands and E. Anglia.

The system of Sheep rearing in this country used to be much the same as that adopted for Cattle. Sheep reared in the hill districts were sold in spring to the grass farms of the lower lands to be fattened for summer consumption, and in autumn to arable farms to be penned and fattened for winter killing. The high cost of arable farming which required them to have added food (such as cake, oats, and barley), the competition of New Zealand chilled lamb, and the increasing demand for small joints, have almost put an end to this latter system, so that modern British Sheep-farming consists mainly of grass feeding and fattening. The daily life of Sheep, like that of Cattle, is one continuous meal occupying the daylight hours, feeding being continued until the paunch is full, when the beast lies down to chew (ruminate), feeding again as soon as the paunch is empty. Sheep lie down more than Cattle, only standing to chew in a bad storm, or on wet puddly ground. The night is spent in sleep. The fleece makes protection from weather unnecessary except when lambing. Such moves as they make, under the direction of the shepherd or his Dog, are caused by the need for fresh pasture, or because their manure is wanted upon arable land. Sheep are either penned in one part of a field and moved daily, or allowed to roam freely. This depends on the nature of the pasture and local custom. Lowland Sheep are proverbially unresisting and incapable of looking after themselves, and would soon be exterminated if not protected by Man. It must be remembered that they are deprived of their natural protectors, the Rams, who would make it no easy task to attack a flock. The mountain Sheep are fairly well able to look after themselves. In a snowstorm they huddle together and mark time swiftly with their feet to tread down the snow, and if buried they will nibble each other's fleeces. They will dig to get down to grass. They avoid Man and defend themselves against Dogs by massing together with horns outwards. The blow from a Ram's charge is terrific.

On downland it is usual after the Ewe has had 3, or at most 4, lambs, to take her out of the flock, either for the butcher or to breed on lower land. When the teeth get bad for close cropping, or scooping turnips, they can still crop better grass. The life of the Wethers, if not ended (as 'lamb') at the age of 4–6 months, usually lasts until after the first shearing in their 2nd year. The slower-growing mountain Sheep have longer lives.

Food. Purely herbivorous. The natural food is pasture with its aromatic herbs, and, preferably, hill pasture. Sheep feed close, taking what is too short for Cattle. On arable land a succession of crops is usually grown which gives green food throughout the year. In addition, cake, corn, maize, rice, bran, and hay are supplied for a period to breeding Ewes and to those fattening for the table. Where Sheep are on roots, no water is needed. Otherwise water is needed through the summer.

Gait. Though they usually walk, they can gallop and, if mountain bred, are agile climbers and hard to enclose. They follow a leader in file, jumping where he has jumped. When troubled by flies, they have a characteristic scampering trot with a worried wriggling of the tail. Kneeling to feed is a sign of foot-rot.

Voice. Except during the lambing time, when the 'baaing' and 'bleating' calls of mothers and lambs are persistent, sheep are very silent. Most sheep call when going into another field. Mountain Sheep give a warning signal between a hiss and a whistle.

The *Nomenclature* of Sheep is confusing owing to local variation, but the following gives some idea of it. Males are called *Rams* or *Tups*; de-sexed males, *Wethers* or *Wedders*; and adult females, *Ewes*. The young of all Sheep are called *Lambs* until weaned (say, for 3 months) and sometimes till the end of their first calendar year (say, for 9 months). From weaning to first shearing (at about 15 months old) all Sheep are called *Tegs* or *Hogs*. (The word 'teg' is derived from 'tag' and refers to the pointed tips of the unshorn wool.) Lambs and Tegs or Hogs may be distinguished by some prefix indicating their sex. (A He-Teg means not a Ram-, but a Wether-Teg.) From first to second shearing Rams are called *Shearling Rams* or *Two-tooth Rams*; Wethers, *Wether-Hogs* or *Shear-Hogs*; and Ewes, *Gimmers, Theaves, Chilvers,* or *Two-tooth Ewes*. After the second shearing the age of Rams, Wethers, and Ewes (Wethers rarely survive) is denoted either by the number of shearings (*3-shear, 4-shear,* &c.) or by the number of adult front teeth (*4-tooth, 6-tooth,* or *full mouthed*). A *Yeld* or *Eild* Ewe is one that has no lamb, and a *Rig* is an unsuccessfully de-sexed Ram. The terms *Hoggett* or *Hoggerel* are locally used for Hog.

Varieties. There are here three main types of Sheep: the Longwools, the Down or Shortwools, and the Mountain Sheep. Some breeds are intermediate between them. The Longwools, mainly raised on rich grass land, have large frames, coarse wool and flesh, and are of slow growth. Except the Wensleydales, they have white faces and legs. The Leicester is the typical breed. The Down Sheep, of which the Southdown is the type, are native to the short, sweet pasture of the chalk hills, and have small bodies, short, fine wool, great activity and hardiness, and delicate flesh. The Mountain breeds, typified by the Scotch Blackface, are small, still more hardy and active, with coarse, hairy wool, and the sweetest of flesh. The latter generally retain the horns.

The process of conscious improvement, begun, as in the case of Cattle, by Robert Bakewell (1725–95), has been almost entirely directed to the

SOAY RAM   LEICESTER RAM

BORDER LEICESTER RAM   LINCOLN RAM

Scale $^1/_{36}$

production of mutton, to the neglect of wool. This is partly because our best wool has been outclassed by that of the Merino of Spanish origin. For some reason the Merino has not done well in this country, but it is the basis of very successful flocks in Australia and elsewhere.

The points sought in all Sheep are: head small; neck short, thick, taper-ing, and slightly arched: jaws wide, ears thin, and hair on face short. The body, generally rectangular, well over the forelegs, broad at the shoulders (save in some Mountain breeds, which have sharp shoulders) and full behind the shoulders. The back flat (not drooping to the tail), broad, with ribs well rounded and deep, and underline level and straight. Haunch and hips wide. Legs straight (hocks not turning out), thick and fleshy to the wrist (knee) and heel (hock), and then light. Skin soft to the touch. Walk springy. The following are our chief breeds:

First the Longwools:

Leicesters. These are the original Longwool race im-proved by Robert Bakewell. Before improvement, they were big boned, coarse-grained, slow fattening, and with a heavy fleece of bad wool. To-day they are medium sized (see p. 208). An old Ram has weighed 472 lb. They are long-headed, with white face, and a faint bluish tinge, and soft hair on face and legs. Shoulders wide, thick through the heart, and bones very fine. They fatten early and are best under a year old, as the fat is put on externally, and the older mutton is poor and greasy. Not prolific: the Ewes poor milkers and the lambs delicate from in-breeding. Often weak in the hind quarters. 'Partridge-shaped.' Fleece, fair, curly, and lustrous; wool 7-8 in. in length, weighing 5-8 lb. and ending in a short, twisted curl. Their chief value lies in giving early maturity to other races.

Border Leicesters. Separated from the above about 1850 either from Cheviot cross or mere segregation. The head is still longer and held high. No tuft on head, wide-eyed, large, open black muzzle. Ears large and erect. Face-hair white and soft. Belly small. Wool long, close, lustrous, and soft, in little locks, giving a fleece of 8-10 lb. They are hardier than Leicesters, their step graceful and elastic, and they mature early, but the meat is too fat and coarse. Essen-tially a crossing race, the Rams are kept as Rams.

Lincolns. A cross of old Lincolns and Leicesters estab-lished about 1862. Largest and heaviest sheep. Small tuft of wool on forehead. Flabby dewlap. Wool, strong and

ROMNEY MARSH RAM

SOUTH DEVON RAM

DEVON LONGWOOL RAM

DEVON CLOSEWOOL RAM

Scale $^1/_{36}$

lustrous, and the longest known. Grows 12–18 in. a year, first clip may be 20 in. Locks about 2 in. wide. Average fleece 10–12 lb. (that of Rams up to 30 lb.), while as much as 26½ lb. has been recorded for a 14 months' shearling fleece. Very prolific, fatten well, average weight about 200 lb.

Romney Marsh or Kent. A hardy local breed, mainly locally improved. Rarely fed or sheltered in winter. Usually lamb in March–April. Fairly prolific. 25–30 per cent. twins. Forelock not always present. Mutton best of the Long-wools. Wethers are usually kept till 3 years old, when they weigh about 160 to 240 lb. Ewes weigh 126–54 lb. The wool is good, semi-lustrous, and fine. One of the closest long wools. Average fleece about 9 lb.

Cotswold. Once the largest Sheep of any breed, they have been so crossed with Leicesters as no longer to exist in a pure state.

South Devons. An old local breed. Large, symmetrical, with much lean mutton. Ears often black spotted. Head large. Hardy and thrifty, doing well on arable or pasture. Wool long, lustrous, close and heavy, many flocks averaging 15 lb. a fleece.

Devon Longwools. Very similar to Lincolns, but smaller, coarser boned, and wooled on crown and cheeks. Hardier than Leicesters, larger, and even quicker in maturing. Out all the year. Ewes give about 8–9 lb. of wool, long and of good quality. Wethers are fattened as Hogs in their first winter, weigh from 154–75 lb., and give 9–11 lb. of wool, although usually shorn of about 3 lb. as lambs.

Devon Closewools. Believed to be a cross of the last-named and Exmoor Horns, and occupying the Devon and Somerset Downs. Smaller than Longwools, the wool very close and of medium length. Hardy in cold or wet.

WENSLEYDALE RAM

SOUTHDOWN RAM

HAMPSHIRE DOWN RAM

DORSET DOWN RAM

Scale $^1/_{36}$

Wensleydale. Large, high-standing Sheep, resulting from a cross of old Teesdale Sheep and Leicesters. They have blue skin on face and ears, sometimes all over. Head carried high on long neck, nose wide and arched in the Ram. Hardy, with meat of good quality, but slow maturity. The wool long, open and uniform, in little knots (= 'pirls') covering nearly the whole body. Average fleece about 12 lb.

The next group is that of the Down or hill Sheep:

Southdowns. This breed, originally improved by John Ellman (1752–1832), has become the most valuable breed for improving all our short-wooled Sheep and has spread throughout the world. Short-legged, compact, symmetrical, wide-chested, and specially good in hind quarters, active and restless. Head, short and wide, small, neat, wooled to and on the ears and forehead. Naked ears are a blemish. Face and legs grey-brown and uniform. Essentially a Sheep of good land and sweet pasture. Wool, short (growing 3–4 in. a year), close and fine, ranking the highest of British wools. Fleece weighs 3–4 lb. Mutton is marbled and excellent if not too fat. Owing to the good shape there is very little 'offal'. They are small Sheep, and somewhat liable to foot-rot. Fit for the table at a year old, Wethers weigh from 112–54 lb., but if fattened 252–80 lb., with about 4½ lb. of wool.

Hampshire Downs. A cross of old Wiltshire Horned Sheep, old Berkshire Knots, and Southdowns, now occupying the Downs of Berks., Hants, Dorset, and Wilts. They are large, low, and strong-boned. Large head, strong Roman nose, faces and legs almost black, skin pink, wool free from black and growing round the ears and over the cheeks. The wool is close and fine, average Ewe's fleece 5 lb. They are very wide in front, but inclined to fall away behind the shoulder. The mutton is fine, firm, and lean. They are very early breeders, lambing in Jan., weigh about 84 lb. by March–April, and, with extra feeding, 150 lb. by Aug.

Dorset Downs. Separately enrolled since 1904. Differ from the Hampshires in being finer in bone and paler in face colour. They contain a larger strain of Southdown blood.

SHROPSHIRE RAM

OXFORD DOWN RAM

SUFFOLK RAM

DORSET HORN RAM

Scale $^1/_{36}$

Shropshires. These were evolved by crossing the old (horned) sheep of Salop and Staffordshire with Southdowns and Leicesters. First at R.A. Show in 1860. Largely exported. More fully wool-covered than any other breed, showing only the (black) tip of the nose, ears, and feet. Medium in size, body square, on straight, stout legs. Wool, very dense, fine, and of medium length, growing 4–6 in. a year. Ewe's fleece at 12 months 7–8 lb. Mutton of good second quality.

Oxford Down. The largest of the Down Sheep. An attempt (1830), by crossing Cotswold Rams and Hampshire Ewes, to get the size and weight of wool of the longwools with the quality of the shortwools. The mutton is firm, lean, and of good quality. Wethers average about 170 lb. at 12–13 months. The faces are dark and shoulders broad, but less so than Hampshires. They are very good mothers, strong and prolific. Wool, longer and less close than that of other Down Sheep, but of good length and fine quality. Average Ewe's fleece about $7\frac{1}{2}$ lb., Ram's sometimes 20 lb. Many have been taken to the Scottish borders.

Suffolks. A cross (1860–86) between the horned Norfolk and Suffolk Sheep and Southdowns and Hampshires. Tall, active, prolific, and early maturing. Face, ears, and legs long and covered with black hair. Neck long and carried high. Hardy, and good travellers. Wool, rather short, close and fine. Average Ewe's first shearing 8–12 lb. a fleece, yearly 5–7, Ram's up to 14 lb. yearly.

Dorset Horns. Old-established in Dorset, Somerset, and the Isle of Wight. Chiefly noted for their early mating. Pair in April, lamb in Sept., thus giving 'house lamb' for Christmas. They can be paired again within a fortnight and so give 2 lambs in a year. This is, however, rarely done. White all over, rather larger than Southdowns, with small bone and fair quality mutton. Wool, fine and close. Ewe's about 4–5 lb., Ram's, as usual, about double.

Western or **Wiltshire Horned** Sheep, of which very few survive, are a rather similar race, giving little or no wool, as what they have falls off in April or May.

RYELAND RAM

KERRY HILL RAM

RADNOR RAM

WELSH MOUNTAIN RAM

Scale $^1/_{36}$

Ryelands. An ancient breed found in S. Hereford. White all over, but the face dull. The old small size has been enlarged by Leicester crosses. Compact and hardy, almost free from foot-rot. Form good and mutton good. Wool (yearly, some 5–6 lb.) short and almost equal to Southdown, close and deep. Year-old Wethers average about 150 lb. and, if not shorn as lambs, give 7–8 lb. of wool.

The **Kerry Hill (Wales)** breed, found in many counties westwards of their native district of Montgomery, were the only Welsh Sheep to grow wool wholly free from hair ('kemp'). They have been kept pure and improved for the past 50 years. Faces and legs speckled, black and white. Hardy and very prolific. In character, as in origin, something between hill and mountain Sheep. Fleeces from 5–8 lb. Rams are valuable for crossing to give fat lambs.

Clun Forest, in SW. Shropshire, gives its name to another Welsh Border breed made up at the end of the 19th century from Radnor mountain Sheep and Shropshire Downs. Their faces are tawny, brown, or speckled, and they have not yet completely settled down to a definite type. The Ewes are excellent mothers. Fat Wethers and Ewes weigh about 160 lb., and the mutton and wool is of the best quality.

Lastly, the Mountain Sheep:

Radnor. Are short-legged, hardy little tan-faced Sheep of which few remain in a pure state, being usually crossed with Kerry Hills or Shropshires.

Welsh Mountain Sheep extend all over the higher hills of Wales. They are either with or without horns, which, if present, are usually smooth and cylindrical compared with those of the other horned races. The face is white, or else tinged with brown. This colour and the presence of hair (kemp) among the wool are both deemed to show hardihood. They are very active and difficult to fence. Will jump a 6 ft. wall. Mutton excellent and very small. Adult Sheep weigh from as little as 56 lb. to about 90 lb. The Ewes are usually brought down to the lowlands for their last lamb at 5 years old. The wool is coarse and loose, fleeces 2–3 (Ram's 3–5) lb.

Black Welsh Mountain. These, doubtless originating in collections of the black Sheep which appear in the white flocks, differ only in the colour, which is a uniform rich dark brown, making, undyed, a warm hard-wearing cloth.

Exmoor Horns, or Porlocks, are similar to Dorset Horns, but smaller and hardier, the horns sloping more backwards. They winter on the poorest enclosed land, with a few turnips and oats, and, after lambing, return to the moor till November. Mutton very good. 18-month Wethers weigh about 160 lb. The wool, close and fine (5 lb.). Loins very good, but inclined to be narrow behind the shoulder.

Dartmoors. Hornless, though Rams often show small (2 in.) horns. The largest of mountain Sheep, probably crossed with South Devons. Hardy and very free from liver-rot. They get roots and a little hay in winter and fatten quickly on richer land. Wool long (up to 10 in.) and of fine, wavy, strong texture. Ewe's fleeces up to 18 lb., Ram's 26–30 lb.

Derbyshire Gritstones. An old breed from the north of its county, prominent since 1907. Give good, lean, mutton of medium weight and prime quality. Weigh about 120–60 lb. They are very hardy, the lambs being born in the snow. Wool of medium length (Ewe's fleece 4 lb., yearling's 7 lb., and Ram's 10 lb.) fine and suited for hosiery.

Cheviots. Probably natives of the Border hills, despite a legend that they swam ashore from the Armada. Have replaced the Blackfaces in the extreme north of Scotland. Originally small, hardy, and with worthless, hair-mixed wool, shed before it could be shorn, they have been vastly improved by crossing with Leicesters. Now medium-sized. Cast Ewes, turnip fed, weigh 125–50 lb., Wethers weigh 200 lb., live weight and the mutton is good and excellent if heather

BLACK WELSH RAM

EXMOOR HORN RAM

DARTMOOR RAM

DERBYSHIRE GRITSTONE RAM

Scale $^1/_{36}$

fed, though they thrive best on grass. They are high at the shoulders and sharp at the withers. Very well developed behind. Rams still sometimes have thin horns, but these are disliked. Pure white, with short, fine, wiry hair on nose, erect ears, and legs. The fleece dense, straight, even and hairless, is fairly fine with a marked ruff at the neck and weighs $4\frac{1}{2}$ lb. (the Ram's 10–12 lb.). They are still very hardy, thriving on the poorest feed and fattening on lower ground. Scatter to feed. The tail is long and rough, usually cut.

There are several varieties of the **Blackfaced** Sheep of the Pennines and Scottish mountains and Isles, found, roughly, wherever there is heather north of the Midlands. They retain many of the characters of wild Sheep, being small, hardy, and agile, eminently able to look after themselves in the hardest weather, of slow growth and maturity, and very pugnacious and wild. If sharing pasture with other breeds, will drive twice their own numbers from choice feeding.

The **Scotch Blackface**, so-called, although they probably spread originally from the Pennines, are the best known and have had the most attention. Face and legs black or mottled, black and white (not brown); noses arched, nostrils black and wide. Rams have heavy twisted horns, Ewes, thin curving and flattened. The ears are completely hidden by the horn. There should be no wool on legs. Their bodies are rounded and compact, and the mutton, at all ages, excellent. Three-year old Wethers weigh 112–26 lb. The wool is long (yearly growth of 10–18 in.), loose, coarse, and hairy. The fleece, unwashed, weighs $3\frac{1}{2}$–5 lb. and is used for carpets. Their tails should be strong and not too long.

The **Lonk** breed, from the contiguous corners of Lancashire, Yorkshire, and Derby, differ from the Scotch Blackfaces as follows: they are larger, longer-legged, bigger-headed, longer-tailed, and with stronger horns in the Ewes. The fleece is shorter, closer, and heavier ($4\frac{1}{2}$–5 lb.). They are not quite so hardy, usually lambing on enclosed ground.

The **Rough Fell** Sheep of NW. Yorks. and Westmorland, black-faced with grey muzzle, is squarer in shape, stronger in bone, and with wool even coarser than the Scotch.

CHEVIOT RAM

SCOTCH BLACKFACE RAM

LONK RAM

ROUGH FELL RAM

Scale $^1/_{36}$

The **Swaledale** breed, extending from that valley into Westmorland, has the nose mealy and the legs mottled. They are larger and longer than the Scotch. Their wool is closer and finer (except on the breeches) than the Scotch, coarser than that of the Lonk.

Herdwick Sheep, found in N. Lancashire, Cumberland, and Westmorland, of which it is reported that they were found in a stranded ship of foreign (Spanish or Norwegian?) origin. Differ much from our other mountain sheep. The Rams are often polled, the Ewes, now, always. They show much grey in the wool, particularly underneath. The old Sheep have kemp in the wool, which is strong, and with a long hairy mane on shoulders and breast. Ewes clip about 5 lb. of wool, Wethers 5–8, and Rams 7–12 lb. They are very hardy, stand poor feeding, and are agile and wild. The Rams fight much in the spring. The Ewes are often not sold off until after 10 or 12 years' breeding. They do not lamb till end of April or May. When the lambs are born they have black faces and legs, the black gradually fading out to disappear in the 4th year.

SWALEDALE RAM

HERDWICK RAM

Scale $^1/_{36}$

GOAT

Capra hircus

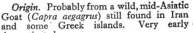

Origin. Probably from a wild, mid-Asiatic Goat (*Capra aegagrus*) still found in Iran and some Greek islands. Very early domesticated.

Uses. Milk, leather, meat. Some foreign breeds grow wool, which is known in trade as mohair. The meat is little used here. That of the young ('Kids') is good, that of adult females ('Nannies') poor, that of adult males ('Billies') uneatable. Morocco leather is made from goatskin and gloves from that of Kids. Goats are trained to harness for the amusement of children. In Scotland sometimes pastured with Sheep because they lead to higher ground and kill vipers. Here kept almost solely for milk. The quantity given in proportion to bulk is even greater than that of the Cow. A yearly yield of over 500 gallons is on record, and many Goats give a gallon a day for 9 months in the year.

The milk is highly digestible, of excellent flavour when fresh, and has the merit of being free from tubercle bacillus, to which nearly half our Cows are subject. It has two defects—it can convey Malta fever in countries where this disease exists and sometimes acquires a rank 'goaty' taste. This is completely absent in fresh milk and, it is said, can be prevented by perfect dairy cleanliness. For its analysis see p. 16. The butter is white and poor, some of the cheeses good.

Description. No clear line can be drawn between Sheep and Goats. The following points are usually found in Goats and not in Sheep. Horns, when present, as they are in all wild races, are flattened and scimitar-shaped; they do not twist down and round as is usual in Sheep. (As in Sheep, horns are much smaller in females.) Goats usually have hair, not wool, and a bare spot between the nostrils. Tails short and straight. No glands in front of the eyes, in the groin, or at the feet. Often a marked beard, and the Billies, particularly during the breeding season, emit a rank smell from the skin. Often 2 appendages ('tassels') hanging below the neck.

Teeth, limbs, and structure. As sheep.

Life history. Usually 2 Kids at a birth, once a year, often 3 or 1, sometimes 4, rarely 5. Gestation 21–3 weeks. Kids are born fully coated, open-eyed, and are agile within a few hours of birth. They may be weaned at between 3 and 6 months. So precocious as to pair at 3 or 4 months old, but should not be allowed to breed until their second year if good stock is wanted. Life 10 up to 14 years.

BRITISH ('WILD') GOAT

ENGLISH NANNY GOAT

ENGLISH BILLY GOAT

Scale ¹/₃₆

231

Yearly life. Nannies come into season in September, for 3 days every 3 weeks till December, then more rarely and for a shorter time till March. When at large they breed in the autumn, but by mating some in Sept., and others in Feb. and March, a continuous supply of milk can be had through the year.

Daily life. Extremely sociable, though in the breeding season the Billies fight fiercely, not as Rams do by a direct charge, but by rising on the hind feet to crash downwards with the horns. Enjoy displaying feats of rock-climbing and will go as high as they can to feed, the Billies feeding above the Nannies. Most intelligent (remarkable gate-openers) and highly affectionate. Vivacious, very wary, with very keen senses of smell, sight, and hearing. Here usually tethered because of the difficulty of enclosing them. Not so hardy in severe cold as Sheep. Where a high yield of milk is wanted they must be housed at night and should be stall fed. There is an unconfirmed and unexplained, but firmly established, belief that the presence of a Goat in stable or byre saves Horses from staggers, and Cows from abortion.

Food. Vegetarian. 'Capricious', preferring coarse feeding to rich pasture; bark, leaves, and savoury and aromatic herbs to grass. Eat a greater variety of plants than any other Ruminant and thrive on a varied diet. When stall fed, cake and grains are given as well as green foods.

Gait. Walk, trot, and canter. Wonderful climbers, using the smallest projections as footholds.

Voice. A warning whistle; bleat to summon the young; slight grunt if pleased; sometimes a groan if making an effort, and a loud cry when in pain. For 3 days after the removal of their Kids, Nannies bleat continuously.

Varieties. There are no truly wild Goats in this country, although a number of escaped Goats live in the wild life on the remoter hills of Scotland, Wales, and Ireland. These are usually white or brown, large, and of the types known as English or Irish. Horns of 44¾ in. are on record. Our native races are now rare in a pure state as breeders have preferred to cross them with foreign Goats rather than to improve them by selective breeding. The Eastern strain improves the quality, and the Swiss strain the quantity, of milk.

BRITISH ALPINE GOAT

BRITISH TOGGENBURG GOAT

BRITISH SAANEN GOAT

ANGLO-NUBIAN GOAT

Scale $^1/_{36}$

GOAT (cont.)

English Goats. These have short, medium, or long hair, sometimes with a woolly undercoat. The horns start wide apart and branch outwards. The Nannies are rather small and short-legged, standing about 22-4 in. and weighing 80-100 lb. Billies are 2-3 in. taller and 20 lb. heavier. No 'tassels'. They are hardy and have a long milking period. Good outdoor goats.

Irish. Longer haired, coarser, and uglier in the head. Horns usually run straighter backwards and are closer together. Mostly inferior milkers.

Welsh. Traditionally large and white. To-day like the Irish.

Anglo-Nubians. During last century various kinds of Goats were brought from Egypt, India, and Abyssinia to this country in ships to give fresh milk on the voyage. They were all Roman-nosed, lop-eared, and short-haired. Those bred here from them are called Anglo-Nubians. They are large, an average Billy standing 36 in., and without tassels. Their milk, though small in quantity, is far richer in quality than that of any of our other breeds.

The Swiss began scientific breeding about 1830 to improve the milk supply. They have at least 7 recognized breeds. For the last 50 years Swiss Goats have been brought here from time to time. In 1922 the first Saanens and a batch of Toggenburgs were imported for crossing with English Goats, and these form the basis of our present 'British' breeds. There are still some herds of these pure bred Swiss Goats. Three main types have resulted from crossing.

British Saanen. Similar to the Swiss *Saanens* from Canton Berne, but rather more robust. Our 1922 stock came from Holland. Pure white and large. Billies stand 32-8 in. and weigh 132-76 lb.; Nannies 28-32 in. and 110-32 lb. Both sexes have beards, larger in the male. Almost always tassels. Chest is long, deep, and round. Hindquarters inclined to be weak and sloping. An indoor winter-milking breed. Milk abundant, but poor in quality. 130-75 gallons a year is a usual yield and far more is on record.

British Toggenburgs. Similar to the Swiss *Toggenburgs* from Canton St. Gall, but superior as milkers. Brown and white. Hair medium short, beards and tassels. Smaller than Saanens (Nannies 28-32 in., weighing 100-10 lb.), finer boned and sturdy. Milk abundant, but even poorer in quality.

British Alpine. Black and white in colour: otherwise much as British Toggenburgs.

Until recently the above varieties, resulting from crosses of our own Goats with Eastern or Swiss stock, were mere types, any Goat being exhibited in the class it most resembled. Since Jan. 1936 an attempt has been made to turn these varieties into true breeds, and a Goat can now only be exhibited in the class in which its pedigree is registered in the herd-book. It will clearly be some time before they breed true to type.

RED DEER

Cervus Elaphus

Sub-spe. *C. e. scoticus*

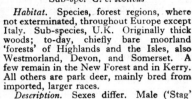

Habitat. Species, forest regions, where not exterminated, throughout Europe except Italy. Sub-species, U.K. Originally thick woods; to-day, chiefly bare moorland 'forests' of Highlands and the Isles, also Westmorland, Devon, and Somerset. A few remain in the New Forest and in Kerry. All others are park deer, mainly bred from imported, larger races.

Description. Sexes differ. Male ('Stag' or 'Hart'), height at withers 4 ft., varying from 42 to 50 in., weight about 280 lb., grows branching, cylindrical antlers, has a canine tooth ('tush') on each side of the upper jaw, and long hair on the neck in the winter coat. Female ('Hind') smaller, height 3 ft. 6 in., more lightly built, without horns, tushes, or long neck hair. Four teats. Both sexes have large face gland and scent glands on hind feet.

Teeth $\frac{0-\delta 1(\varphi 0)-3-3}{3-1 \quad - \quad 3-3} = \delta 34, \varphi 32$. The incisors and canines of lower jaw diminish from centre to sides, but only so that i_1 is as broad as i_2 and c_1 together.

Limbs. The weight rests on the two hoofs of the 3rd and 4th toes, the other two bones of which form the pasterns, and above these the foot bones of these two toes are fused into a 'cannon bone'. Two small toes (2nd and 5th) project downwards from the pastern behind and their foot bones are reduced to two splints at the upper part of the cannon bone. The two forearm bones are separate but closely connected. Those of the shin fused into one.

Structure. Vertebrae 7–13–6–4 and 11. No collar bone.

Antlers, on the Stag only, grow yearly from knobs in the skull (pedicles). They are of bone and are covered with a substance called 'velvet', made of skin, hair, and blood-vessels. This is sensitive until the bone hardens and the antlers are fully grown, when the blood-vessels close, the velvet dries, and the Stag rubs it off on heather or trees, leaving the horn clean. From the shedding of the old antlers the whole process takes the surprisingly short time of between 4 and 5 months. The larger the Stag the heavier the antlers in proportion to his weight. The antlers are divided into the 'coronet' or 'burr' at their root, the 'beam' or main shaft, and the 'tines' or points, which, from the 'burr' up, are named the 'brow', 'bez', and 'trez'. Points branching from the beam above the trez are usually known as 'points on top'. Native Stags rarely bear more than 12 points (when the Stag is a 'Royal'), though 14 (the bearer of which has

235

been termed a 'Wilson') are known. Park Deer often show 18 or more, and some continental forest races have as many as 30 to 47. No two heads are identical though close relatives show their kinship by marked similarity. The Stag uses his antlers in controlling his Hinds or in fighting Dogs, but in fights between Stags their absence is no handicap.

Life history. The young ('Calves') are born about the end of May or June (gestation 7–8 months) with hair dappled with white spots, which disappear in 2 or 3 months with the growth of the first winter coat. For about a week they are unable to stand and lie motionless if approached. The Hind hides them in thick heather or bracken and leaves them, returning only to suckle them. Then they follow the mother for 2 years, being able to gallop freely after about 2 months. Hinds breed in their 3rd year. The males grow the frontal knobs during their 2nd year ('Knobbers') and a pair of single-spiked horns during the 3rd. In the 4th the horns have 2 points each and, normally, 1 point is added to each antler yearly until the maximum is reached. The calves are born singly (twins are of doubtful occurrence) and mortality is very high during the 1st year (estimated at 50 per cent.). The Stag reaches full size in 6 or 7 years, and full power in 12. At about 18 he is believed to begin to deteriorate and the limit of age is probably between 20 and 30.

Yearly life. Red Deer are gregarious, but the sexes live apart, except during the autumn mating season ('rut'). January finds the Stags lonely and concealed, harbouring in the thickest cover available. The Hinds in numbers of from 10 to 40 are in herds (with their calves of the past year and year before) in their usual territories. If these are on high ground, they seek lower levels in hard weather. Every spring the Stags drop their horns in March or April. The new horns begin growing at once and most Stags are soon driven from thick cover to the heights by the flies, as the tender velvet is very sensitive. There they collect in stag-herds numbering from 3 to 20 or more. Some stay in the woods until the rut. Towards May the Hinds separate from their herds to drop their calves in bracken or long heather, assembling again as soon as the calves can follow. The stag-herds keep together until mid-Sept., when the neck hairs grow long and wiry and, their horns being clean, they separate to seek the Hinds. Each Stag who is strong enough to do so takes possession of a herd of Hinds, to which he adds any others which he can collect, and defends it against all rivals. Such a 'master stag' drives out all other males (except the year's calves and the knobbers) and jealously rounds up all straggling Hinds. The power of a master-stag may be gauged by the size of his herd, which may exceed a hundred head. During the rut constant challenges and occasional fights occur between the master-stag and rivals. Fights rarely involve death, as the weaker beast usually flees. A death is usually the result of accident due to the locking of horns, or a fall on dangerous ground. Fights or pursuits often lead to the capture of some outlying Hinds by a watchful third Stag. Owing to the fatigues of this period the first master-stag becomes emaciated and exhausted and, sooner or later, succumbs to, or retires before, a second-rate rival, who inherits his place and herd. Then he withdraws for the winter to recuperate. The second Stag may in turn give way to a third. The defeat of a Stag often leads to the dispersal of his Hinds among a number of rivals. The Hinds seem to show no partiality for any particular Stag, submitting to the command and discipline of any conqueror. The rut lasts about 5 weeks, ending about the end of Oct. The long-haired coat of both sexes is grown in Sept. and shed, in felted patches, in late spring.

Daily life. Herds (male, female, or mixed) feed in the evening and early morning, returning to their territories shortly after dawn and remaining quiescent almost all day to chew the cud and sleep until evening, when they resume feeding. The male herds in summer are very peaceful and orderly under the guidance of the strongest (or oldest?) Stag; whereas Hinds are more quarrelsome, fighting by 'boxing' with the forefeet. Hinds are the more vigilant, especially when with a Stag, whom they protect with intense watchfulness. Herds usually choose for the day's rest a sheltered, sunny place in their territory where there is a clear view down wind, and also where two winds meet, as, while their hearing and sight are about equal to those of a Man, their sense of smell is infinitely keener and can never be deceived. Man they can detect, up wind, at over a mile's distance under favourable circumstances, and they are most reluctant to cross a human trail. They are very suspicious and cautious and always ready to be off and away on any unexpected sight, smell, or sound. They are particularly shy of hidden or unseen danger, e.g. a man once seen and then lost to view. They are weather-wise, leaving the summits before a storm, and never caught by snow-drifts, facing out the snow on bare, wind-swept ground. One set of Deer moving will move all others within sight or smell. Disturbed Deer travel up wind and, usually, in single file, an old Hind leading and the Stag going last. Stags which have lost all fear of Man through tameness are very dangerous during the rut. Deer soon learn the limits of areas in which they are not in danger—sanctuaries—and make for them if alarmed. When hunted with hounds, take to water.

Food. Vegetarian; grass, young heather shoots, moss, seaweed, young leaves and shoots of trees. They chew the cud. They will also chew cast horns, or bones, found on the ground.

Gait. They walk, trot, canter, and gallop. The cloven hoof makes them very sure-footed and able to travel on soft ground. They swim strongly. A Deer fence has to be over 6 ft. in height and they show great nimbleness in slipping through between any loose strands of wire.

Voice. Both sexes are usually silent except the Stag during the rut. He then has a deep-toned, leonine, challenging 'roar', often repeated. He has also been heard to bark like a Hind. The Hind has a guiding bleat for her calf and a short, sharp bark used as a warning signal. Calves will scream, like Hares, if handled during the first week, or if alarmed by thunder, and give a high-pitched bleat in reply to a warning from the mother.

Varieties. Practically all our wild Red Deer are in Scotland. These,

Stag

Hind

Calf

RED DEER
Scale $^1/_{36}$

and the various foreign races, have been separated as sub-species, but as they merge into one another, it might be better to regard them as mere nationalities, varying greatly, as indeed do our own hill, island, forest, and park Deer. Many variations are known to occur: thus, hornless Stags ('Hummels', called in Devon 'Notts'), white Stags, and (more commonly) white Hinds, and deer showing varying unusual shades of grey and brown colouring and many abnormal varieties of antler formation.

Park Deer, owing partly to better feeding and partly to more infusion of foreign blood, vary in many respects. The Stags are often larger and heavier and grow antlers with more points. The Hinds will bear young in their second year and all the dates, given above for the Scottish Deer's yearly life, are earlier by a month or more.

JAPANESE or SIKA DEER

Cervus nippon

Habitat. The species is found in Japan and Manchuria. Imported first into Ireland, by Lord Powerscourt in Wicklow, later into Scotland at Loch Rosque (Ross) and, in England, into various parks in the midlands and elsewhere. They have strayed widely and become locally numerous. Sufficiently so to become a nuisance to farmers in some districts.

Description. Sexes differ, males alone having horns, and being larger. They are smaller than Fallow Deer, Bucks standing about 2 ft. 9 in. high and weighing 140 lb., Does smaller. Colour of both sexes in summer red-brown, spotted with yellowish white; in winter a uniform dark grey-brown. Pure white tail and white rump patch edged with black. Tail long as Fallow Deer's. Bucks grow a mane, as Red Deer. 4 teats.

Antlers. Of the Red Deer type, but thin and without bez tines. Maximum 10 points, but rarely more than 6 or 8.

Teeth, limbs, and structure. Generally as those of Red Deer. Tear gland of moderate size.

Life history. The rut begins earlier than that of the Red Deer but overlaps it, and interbreeding has been reported with that species. Very doubtful. The young are spotted with white.

Yearly and daily life. They are mainly woodland Deer. When living in deer forests, rarely stray far from the woods,

TYPICAL JAPANESE DEER. Buck. Winter

JAPANESE DEER, Manchurian var. Buck. Summer

Scale $^1/_{36}$

but come out to feed early and late. They are, like Red Deer, polygamous, the Bucks fighting very fiercely to collect and retain a small group of wives, usually 5 or 6. They are hardy, requiring no artificial feeding in our hardest climates, and afford good sport to the stalker, sharing the timidity and wariness of the Red Deer. There is a pack of hounds hunting these Deer.

Food. Vegetarian, mainly grass and mosses, probably also leaves and shoots, though they are deemed less destructive to woods than the Roe.

Gait. As Red Deer.

Voice. During the rut, the Bucks give an odd whistle changing into a scream. The alarm signal of the Does is a fluty whistle.

Varieties. We have imported two different sub-species:

Japanese Deer. *Cervus nippon.*[2] The typical race, as above described.

Manchurian Deer. *C. n. mantchuricus.* Somewhat larger. Bucks standing 3 ft. 3 in., antlers not larger. Colour similar, Does retain some spots on rump in winter.

FALLOW DEER

Dama[2]

Habitat. Mediterranean Europe, and Asia Minor. In U.K., park and woodlands. Probably introduced (by the Romans ?). Now living in a half-domesticated state in many parks and forests throughout the U.K.

Description. Sexes differ. Male, 'Buck', height at withers 3 ft. 2 in., weight about 196 lb., grows flattened antlers on a cylindrical stem, usually with no bez point, and palmated above the trez. Hind, or 'Doe', smaller, hornless. Winter coat of both sexes dark grey, without white spots. 4 teats.

Teeth. $\dfrac{0-0-3-3}{3-1-3-3} = 32$. Neither sex has upper canine. Incisors and canines diminish greatly from centre to sides, so that i_1 is almost twice as broad as i_2, i_3, and c_1 together.

Buck

Doe   Fawn

FALLOW DEER (Summer)

Scale $^1/_{36}$

243

FALLOW DEER (cont.)

Limbs and structure. Generally as Red Deer, but 14 tail vertebrae. See Fig. opposite.

Antlers. On Buck only. Of yearly growth. Above the trez tines they spread out into a broad, flattened plate, all other points forming projections backwards from this 'palm'.

Life history. Young ('Fawns') born in May or June, usually latter half of June, after about 8 months' gestation, with hair dappled like the adults. Can run within a few hours. One Fawn at a birth is usual, 2 not uncommon, and 3 on record. Male Fawns grow a pair of short (5-in.) prongs in summer of 2nd year (then called 'prickets') and, in the 3rd, a horn with two forward tines (brow and trez) and a flattened palm with indented edge. In the 4th year the palm is larger and more markedly toothed. In the 5th they are known as 'bucks of the first head', the palm being still larger. Successive years add to the number and prominence of the projections, known as 'spillers' or 'snags'. Head usually fully developed in the 6th year.

Yearly life. Less gregarious than Red Deer when wild, rarely in large herds, but the two sexes remain together in mixed parties from beginning of the rut until end of winter. In early spring Does frolic and race with last year's Fawns. Horns are dropped in May (by the prickets not till June) and are re-grown from May to Aug., being, in the English parks, clean in that month, about three weeks later than Red Deer. Rut takes place in Oct. and only lasts a short time. The first 'calls' about 25 Oct.

Daily life. Roam about feeding. Lie mainly in thickest cover available and come out into open glades at morning and dusk to feed. Are more restless than Red Deer, rising and lying down more often. Harder to stalk as they do not pause to look back when disturbed, and are quicker sighted. In winter move continuously. In summer rest most of the day. Fights during rut are usually bloodless. When changing coat, bite off old coat. Do not wallow. Though safer to men than our other Deer, Bucks have caused deaths.

Food. Purely vegetarian: grass, young shoots, leaves, bark of trees, chestnuts, acorns, &c.

Gait. As Red Deer, but gallop much more frequently. Great jumpers. Have cleared a 7-ft. fence.

Voice. Call of Buck (head down and jerked up) between a grunt and a bark. Doe has a whining cry of warning to her Fawn, similar to that of Red Deer Hind.

Varieties. Two races, light (as here portrayed and described) and dark, which keep separate. Are supposed to be of different origin, but little is known of this. Summer coat of dark race looks like winter coat of light race, while in winter they are slightly paler. Both may be seen on same ground, e.g. in Richmond Park. Also many other varieties of colour; white, cinnamon with black and brown head and neck and grey underparts, and a brown type with spots and light underparts. New Forest Fallow Deer have very poor, thin antlers and are chestnut with whitish spots in summer, dark brown with dun legs and underparts in winter.

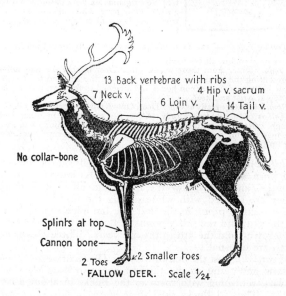

13 Back vertebrae with ribs
7 Neck v.   6 Loin v.   4 Hip v. sacrum   14 Tail v.

No collar-bone

Splints at top
Cannon bone →
2 Toes   2 Smaller toes
FALLOW DEER.   Scale 1/24

ROE DEER

Capreolus[2] Sub-spe. *C*[2] *thotti*

Habitat. Species: Europe, from Scotland and central Sweden south to Mediterranean, and east into Asia. Sub-spe.: Great Britain, originally everywhere, now common only in Scotland, a few (introduced) in Dorset, the New Forest, and a few southern parks. Not in Ireland.

Description. Sexes differ. Male ('Buck'), height 2 ft. 1 in. to 2 ft. 5 in., weight 35–63 lb., grows antlers. Female ('Hind' or 'Doe') hornless. Smaller, weight 25–45 lb. In both sexes tail barely visible. Coat foxy-red and short in summer; long, brittle, and warm grey in winter. Scent glands on hind pasterns, no face glands. Four teats. Our sub-species differs from the (Swedish) type in colour only, the face being darker than the body.

Teeth $\frac{0-0-3-3}{3-1-3-3}$ = 32. Generally as Red Deer. Incisors graduated in the same way, but all relatively longer.

Limbs. Differ from those of our other Deer in that the two splints, representing the hand bones and foot bones of the 2nd and 5th toes, are at the bottom of the cannon bones and attached to the toes, instead of at the top at wrist and heel.

Structure. Generally as other Deer. Only 6 tail vertebrae: 7–13–6–4–6.

Antlers. On the Bucks only. Of yearly growth as in other Deer. Rough, cylindrical, with one upright shaft, rarely exceeding 9½ in., with one forward tine and, above it, one backward. 3 points rarely exceeded, but up to 12 recorded.

Life history. The young ('Fawns'), usually one of each sex, are born about the 1st week in June (gestation about 10 months) and can follow the mother in about a fortnight. They are spotted with white during the first year. Males grow a single prong in the 2nd year, an added forward tine in the 3rd, and the full 3 points in the 4th. The best heads are grown from the 5th to the 9th years. Three Fawns at a birth are unusual.

Yearly life. At the end of May the Hinds drive away their Fawns and retire to the thickest cover to drop their new Fawns, returning with them to the Bucks in about a fortnight. The old Bucks shed their horns in Nov. Irregular

246

Summer

Winter

ROE DEER

Scale $^1/_{36}$

sheddings between Sept. and Jan. are on record. New horns are usually half grown by Jan. and clean by mid-April. The rutting season is during June and July, the first barking being noted on 20 June and pairing from 25 July to 8 Aug. After the rut, the Bucks often retire in loneliness to high ground for the months of Aug. and Sept., and during Oct. there is a second (infertile) pairing season. After this they stay together in family parties until the following May.

Daily life. Roe are forest Deer and mainly nocturnal. Not gregarious, living in family parties of 2–5, although at night several parties may congregate to feed in favourite fields. Seek thick cover during the day and are very timid and secretive. Rarely seen except when driven by beaters. In mid-summer they are more seen, coming more to open glades, and, on Deer ground, may take to the open 'forest'. In June and July much troubled by flies. May be seen rushing about to get rid of them, sweeping them off by galloping round bushes. They feed in the morning and at sunset, ruminating or sleeping during the day in thick cover. In winter they resort to pine forest or the thickest undergrowth. Scrape beds for sleep. Do not wallow. If scared in cover, will gallop forwards and then make several high leaps, looking back. During the rut the Bucks fight, and chase the Does in circular tracks which they wear into 'rings' in the grass. These are also used at other times. Sight and hearing keener than Red Deers', scent perhaps not so keen. As pets they are very dangerous when grown up, and during the rut. Cases of human deaths from Roe are on record.

Food. Grass, shrubs, leaves, corn, turnips, clover, hips and haws, moss, berries, bracken, and fungi.

Gait. As other Deer, but the trot is rarer, the usual gait being a walk or a series of bounds. Can clear a 6-ft. wall and slip through a very small space. Swim well, head only showing.

Voice. Both sexes a sharp, dog-like bark during the rut and if frightened.

Varieties. Hinds with small horns not very rare. Malformed heads ('peruke') result from sexual injuries. White Roe not uncommon.

ODD-TOED HOOFED BEASTS

Sub-order *PERISSODACTYLA*

This type of beast (to which the Rhinoceros, with 3 toes a foot, and other foreigners belong) is here represented only by two domestic species, the Horse and the Ass. They are walkers on dry ground.

In them, the whole weight of the body is borne on the sole surviving (3rd) toe of each foot. All the bones of the other toes have disappeared except 2 small splints. These are survivals of the hand and foot bones of the 2nd and 4th toes. They lie behind the upper parts of the strong hand and foot bones of the centre (3rd) toe, below the wrists ('knees') and heels ('hocks').

The real difference between these and the Even-Toed lies in the fact that the 3rd toe, which has gradually ousted all the others, is central and in itself symmetrical.

The gradual disappearance of the other toes has been traced in a complete series of fossil ancestors of the modern Horse from a wolf-sized animal of the Eocene, in which the 3rd toes were the largest. In this series the 1st, then the 5th, and lastly the 2nd and 4th together, disappeared. The hind legs were the first to begin this process, and ever since the Pliocene epoch the surviving splints of the 2nd and 4th toes have been growing smaller.

The teeth are of all 4 kinds, though the canines are small and obsolescent. The skull is long. There is a wide gap between the canines and the cheek teeth. The brains, though convoluted and highly developed, are very small. These beasts are wholly herbivorous and the cheek teeth (see p. 27) are the most perfect examples of vegetable grinders known—comparable only to those of the Voles.

They have a larger number of vertebrae in the back and loins (24) than the Even-Toed beasts and, like them, they have no collar bones. They have an additional projection (the 3rd *trochanter*) at the top of the thigh bone, for the attachment of running muscles.

They have no horns or antlers.

HORSE

Equus caballus

Origin. Domesticated ever since very early times, but later than Dog, Ox, or Ass. The exact race, or races, from which the Horse springs are unknown. Probably the first tamed Horses were dun coloured, striped with a few zebra-like marks, and living in some very cold central Asian climate. A large wild Horse from central Europe, and a wild mountain pony, were perhaps separately tamed. There are about 1½ million Horses in the U.K., of which ½ million are in Ireland and 150,000 in Scotland.

Uses. The Horse has served Man as food, to give milk, to carry himself and his goods, and to draw vehicles. Here it is no longer eaten and the milk is not drunk, while the pack-horse survives only in the remoter Highlands. The saddle-horse still serves both in war and peace. The following list gives some idea of its uses: cavalry, mounted infantry, officers' chargers, police, hacking, riding exercise for the old, tuition for the young, hunting, polo, flat racing, and steeplechasing. A similar list for draught-horses gives: artillery, transport wagons, railway shunting, canal towage, wains and farm carts, farm implements, mine trolleys, heavy drays and wagons, light carts, carriages and pony traps. The motor is rapidly supplanting the Horse, even on the farm. The Sparrow has flown from the petrol fumes of the mews to become a guest on the chicken farm. Soon the Horse may only be found working the land, in the hunting-field, on the race-course and polo ground, in the circus, and in the darkness of the mine.

Description. Sexes much alike. Males (Stallions) are slightly larger, thicker, more arched in the neck and narrower in the hips than females (Mares). The greater docility of unsexed Males (Geldings), and the fact that one Stallion can serve from 80–100 Mares has led to the practice of castrating almost all yearling males (Colts) except race-horses. The Gelding loses neither strength nor speed, but does to some degree lose endurance, and does not have the arched neck of the Stallion.

Though Horses vary greatly, some of their proportions are fairly constant. The length of the body from breast to rump is between 2½ and 2¾ times the length of the head, which is about equal to the depth of the body at the lowest part of the back. The main differences are in the bulk of bone and muscle, the width of the body, and the length of the legs. They vary in height at the withers (top of the back above the shoulder-blades) from 6 ft. (or 18 'hands', the accepted measure for Horses) to less than 3 ft. (9 hands), and in weight from over a ton to 168 lb. Horses have smooth skins, big chests and lungs, large nostrils, long legs, and powerful muscles of loin and rump. The winter coats grow in the autumn, beginning about Sept., and are shed in spring, being replaced by shorter summer coats. Old Horses keep their coats longer, not being clean until the end of June. There are tufts of longer hair at the 'fetlocks' (under the first knuckle of hand and foot) and long 'horse-hair' on the mane, forelock, and on the whole of the tail. 2 teats. The Stallion, rarely, has rudimentary tubercles in their place.

Colour. The coat is made up of black, white, or brown hairs. The brown may be dark or light and more or less tinged with yellow or red. Where the hairs are all of one colour, Horses are variously described as cream, dun, chestnut, bay, brown, and black. The terms sorrel, grey, red and blue roan are used for mixtures of white with other coloured hair. White Horses are rare, but Horses whiten as they age. White patches on face and 'socks' are common, and large areas of white on the body of black or brown horses give 'piebalds' and 'skewbalds' respectively. The 'horse-hair' is often differently coloured from the shorter hair. A bay always has black 'horse-hair', while that of a chestnut is of the colour of the body or paler. 'Dappling', and other similar markings, are common and some Horses (chiefly duns) show dark bands along the spine, down the shoulder and across the foreleg.

Teeth $\frac{3-1-3-3}{3-1-3-3} = 40$. The Canines ('tushes') are usually lacking in Mares, total 36. Except the tushes, all teeth are complex. Incisors have a depression in the centre of the biting surface. As they wear, this shows as a black 'mark' in the middle of the tooth until the wear has got below the depth of the depression. The age of a Horse may be roughly judged as follows. At 3 years old the middle pair of milk incisors in the lower jaw are replaced by the (larger) adult teeth (i_1 on each side). At 4 years, these are followed by the pair on each side of them (i_2), and at 5 by the 3rd and last pair (i_3). (The males have also grown their tushes (c_1) at 5 years.) As the incisors lose their 'marks' after about 3 years of use, 1 pair (i_1) lose their 'marks' at 6 years old, the 2nd pair (i_2) at 7 years old, and at 8 years all 'marks' have disappeared. After this the Horse is said to be 'aged'. The upper jaw behaves in the same way. The cheek teeth (all much alike) are of great length (*hypselodont*) and grow as they wear. They do not remain rootless, but, in the 6th year, close up at the roots and stop growing. They are of a highly complex, folded pattern, with crescent-shaped depressions (*selenodont*) filled with cement. Once wear has begun, this gives grinding surfaces of three different materials, which retain their efficacy until, in great age, they are worn down below the folds to a smooth surface of ivory and lose their value. See p. 27.

Limbs. The upper parts only of the smaller shin bones and forearm bones survive separately. All other bones beneath the wrist ('knee') and heel ('hock') have disappeared (except those of the 3rd toe) and are represented only by 2 small bones called 'splints', which are the upper parts of the hand and foot bones of the 2nd and 4th toes. The central hand and foot bones of the 3rd toes are called 'cannon bones' (though not double-barrelled as in Cattle) and the first 2 bones of the single toes are called the 'pasterns', the 3rd being enclosed in the hoofs. Thus the Horse stands and moves on the tip of one toe only of each foot. There are 2 callosities on each leg. One set (called 'ergots') are under the fetlocks, the other (called 'chestnuts') are on the insides of the legs, above the wrists ('knees') and below the heels ('hocks'). Some Horses have no chestnuts on the hind legs.

Structure. Vertebrae 7–18–6 (or 19–5)–5, and from 13 to 20 in the tail. There is no collar bone, and a single (non-ruminant) and small stomach. The skin on the rump is strongly reinforced with a thick hide called the 'shell'.

Life history. One single 'Foal' is born at a birth; twins are rare (perhaps 1 in 50) and undesirable, as both are weaklings. Gestation about 11 months. The foal is born fully covered with fine, short, woolly hairs, which differ in colour from the later coat. Those of greys are almost black, those of chestnuts or bays lighter than the adults. It can see and stand, and within 4 or 5 hours can follow the mother about. It is weaned at 5 or 6 months and, about the same time, grows its first adult coat. The young mares ('Fillies') can breed in their 2nd year, but it is better not to have them served until their 3rd. Mares may breed until a great age. 'Plaisanterie' bred at Sledmere in her 25th year, and breeding at 32 has been recorded. As to the limit of age in Horses, it must be remembered that few are allowed to die of old age. A Horse has lived to 50.

Yearly life. Mares are in season for about 3 days to a week, beginning early in the spring or on the 9th day after foaling, and again every 3 weeks during summer. The date of pairing is dependent upon Man, but is usually timed for the foal to be born about May, when warmth for the foal and grass for the mother are at their best. Many Horses can, and do, live in the open all the year in climates much hotter and colder than ours. They will dig through snow for food. Here it is, however, usual to afford shelter to most Horses throughout the year. A farm Horse usually has to work hard from Feb. to June, and again for 3 months from mid-Aug.; but this, naturally, varies greatly.

Daily life. This depends wholly upon the Horse's employment. Horses, unlike Cattle and Sheep, do not usually sleep all through the night. They are restless, alternately lying down to sleep and rising to feed throughout the night. Some Horses sleep afoot, but this is a vice, as they often fall and hurt themselves. When working, Horses should be fed thrice a day, as, owing to the small stomach, they need frequent and regular feeding and water. Should be watered before feeding and after work. Suffer from colic if watered after feeding. If not working, should have water always within reach. If spared all cruelty a Horse is rarely, if ever, vicious. They have an instinctive dread of unaccustomed movements above them —perhaps suggestive of the Leopard? In fighting, use fore and hind hoofs and teeth, and, if about to kick, lay back the ears and look back, showing the white of the eyes. In fear, sweat and shiver. Intelligent and loyal, the Horse gives unstinted obedience to Man: 'he mocketh at fear neither turneth he back from the sword': he will make repeated efforts at an impossible task, even unto death. On soft ground he travels ill and is easily bogged. Shares his rider's excitement in game or chase and 'smelleth the battle afar off'.

Food. Purely herbivorous. When at large, takes for preference the shorter and tenderer herbage. When stable fed, as he must be if working, hay and seeds of almost any kind— oats, beans, peas, lentils, barley, maize, or bran, but not wheat, which is unwholesome. Very fond of apples and sugar.

Gait. Naturally, Horses walk, trot, canter, and gallop. They can be trained to the 'running walk' and the 'amble'. The 'paces' of Horses have been more studied than those of any other animal. They vary much in different Horses and at different times in the same Horse, but the following are their normal forms. The letters H, F, R, and L are used for hind, fore, right, and left. In the track diagrams the prints of the forefeet are the larger. To avoid confusion, and yet keep to the proper horizontal distances, the successive sketches have been moved downwards. At all its paces (= gaits) a Horse uses the same method of progress, that is to say, walks, runs or skips, with both pairs of legs (F and H). He only jumps to clear an obstacle. When skipping (in canter or

gallop) the pace is always transverse (not rotatory)—the same
leg leads in both pairs.

A horse's walk may vary from $2\frac{1}{2}$ to 4 m.p.h. His trot can
be sustained at about 12 to 16 m.p.h. The gallop of the racer,
over short distances, attains about 34 m.p.h.

The *Walk* is that described on p. 34 as that of all walking
Mammals. The length of the step is about $\frac{2}{3}$rds of the length
of the Horse from hip to shoulder. When either pair of legs
is straddling from one footprint to the next, the other pair
is upright with one leg bearing the weight and the other in
the air swinging past it. When the stride is long (a 'good'
walk) the footsteps of the hind feet should be well in front
of those of the fore: when short, they will be behind.

The following sketches give the positions at the fall of
each foot and the track left.

    I. Fall of LF.
        RF is rising, LH is down, and
        RH swinging past it.

    II. Fall of RH.
        LH is rising, LF is down, and
        RF swinging past it.

    III. Fall of RF.
        LF is rising, RH is down, and
        LH swinging past it.

    IV. Fall of LH.
        RH is rising, RF is down, and
        LF swinging past it.

The next position repeats No. 1. The track is thus:

254

The *Trot* is as described on p. 35. Each hind foot falls in the vacated footprint of the forefoot on the same side, and at the same time as the forefoot on the other side. Thus the feet fall in couples in the following order: RH and LF together, LH and RF together, and so on, and with a distance of one step between them. The length of the step is the same as that of the Horse from hip to shoulder, and the length of each stride is two steps.

The following sketches give the positions at the fall of each couple of feet. The trot may be varied by taking shorter or longer steps; this shows in the track by the prints of the hind feet being behind or in front of those of the fore respectively, instead of coinciding with them.

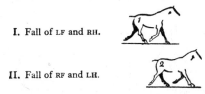

I. Fall of LF and RH.

II. Fall of RF and LH.

The next position repeats No. I. The track is thus:

The *Canter* (the pace of the Canterbury pilgrims) is as described on p. 35. Either foreleg may lead: here the right is assumed to be leading. There is usually an interval of time after the leading foreleg (RF) has been lifted and before the opposite hind leg (LH) comes down to begin the stride anew. Thus the legs fall in three time with an interval in which all 4 legs are off the ground, thus: LH, RH and LF together, RF, interval; LH, RH and LF together, RF, interval; and so on. The length of the steps is unequal as this is a skipping gait, those from L to R feet of each pair being less than those from R to L. The length of a moderate stride is about 12 ft.

The following sketches give the positions of a slow Canter at the three leg-falls and at the time of suspension.

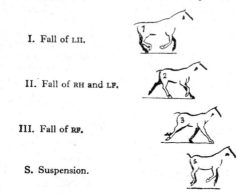

I. Fall of LH.

II. Fall of RH and LF.

III. Fall of RF.

S. Suspension.

The next position repeats No. I. The track is thus: depending in appearance on the variable length of the stride, between the footprints of the LH marked 1.

The simultaneous footprints are joined by dotted lines.

The *Gallop* is the transverse gallop described on p. 36. Like the Canter, it is composed of skips of both pairs of legs. It differs in the timing and in the skips being longer. The first foreleg to fall (LF) does not do so until after the fall of the second hind leg (RH), so that the gallop is in four time, followed by a suspension with all 4 legs gathered under the body, thus: LH, RH, LF, RF; LH, RH, LF, RF, and so on. The length of a stride may be up to 24 feet.

The following sketches are comparable with those above.

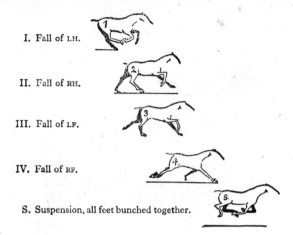

I. Fall of LH.

II. Fall of RH.

III. Fall of LF.

IV. Fall of RF.

S. Suspension, all feet bunched together.

The next position repeats No. I. The track is thus: depending in appearance on the variable length of the stride, between the footprints marked LH.

LH.   LH.   Next LH,
as in No. I.

There are variations in the gallop[1] and to the foregoing normal paces of the Horse must be added two others, which can be acquired by training, namely, the 'Running Walk' and the Amble. Of these enough has been said at pp. 34–35.

[1] Very rarely, at full speed, some Horses actually defer the fall of the first foreleg (LF) until after the second hind leg (RH) has left the ground. In this case a second period of suspension occurs, in which the 4 legs are outstretched, fore and aft, as in all artists' pictures of galloping Horses before the days of photography. Artists so drew a gallop, not because of these rare cases, but because the eye registers only the moments when each leg is motionless for an instant at its full stretch and the resultant picture was truer to human vision than those of the modern artist who copies the camera.

SHIRE STALLION

Scale ¹/₃₆

Unless compelled by Man, a Horse rarely swims.

Horses sometimes lie flat, cheek to ground, but more usually they lie on the bent legs of one side, with head and neck upright and inclined to the other. To lie down, they gather the legs together under them, then kneel and sink down. To rise, they straighten and rise on to the forelegs first.

Voice. Usually very silent. Horses 'neigh' when excited or alarmed and, sometimes, shriek when in severe pain. A slight, low 'whinney' is used to call the foal or to attract attention.

Varieties. Horses vary greatly. Differences are due partly to natural segregation owing to life in separate communities, remote mountainous or island districts where conditions vary and, of recent years, still more, to intentional breeding by Man to achieve a definite object, such as strength or speed. The following are the chief breeds developed in this country:

Shire Horses. The heaviest known Horse. Descended from the 'great horse', the old 'English War horse', or 'black horse' of our early records. Height 5 ft. 6 in. (16½ hands) to 5 ft. 9 in. (17 hands 1 in.) and, in weight, sometimes exceeding a ton. With short, stout legs, broad chest, and deep, rounded, powerful body, with broad, heavy rump, whose muscles show the spine lying in a groove, with large belly, and short, arched neck, and big, somewhat Roman-nosed head, all their movements are powerful and slow. They are of all known colours, but the most approved are bay, brown, or black, all with white stockings and much long, silky hair ('feather') all over the front and back of the lower legs. Although they walk and, if required, trot freely, they are almost too heavy for agricultural use, and are mainly used for heavy draught on smooth surfaces.

CLYDESDALE GELDING

Scale $^1/_{36}$

Clydesdales. A similar breed to the Shire, developed in Scotland, and much crossed with Shire Horses. Originally, probably, influenced by Flemish blood. Height 5 ft. (15 hands) to 5 ft. 6 in. (16½ hands). They differ from the Shire in having a smaller belly, longer quarters, more sloping shoulders and pasterns, narrower hocks, which incline inwards, straighter, proportionally longer and smoother leg bones, longer and more slanting hoofs, more crested necks, more prominent and wider-set eyes. They are usually bay or dark brown, sometimes black or grey, rarely chestnut, and have 'feather' on the back of the legs only. They are faster, more agile and mettlesome, have a quicker, free, active walk and good trot, and are most valuable for farm work as well as heavy draught of all kinds.

SUFFOLK STALLION

Scale $^1/_{36}$

Suffolk Horses. A typical agricultural breed long indigenous to the county and particularly adapted to its heavy clays. Little affected by any 'foreign' blood. Height about 5 ft. 5 in. (16 hands 1 in.). They are long and roomy in the body, with wide hips, rounded flanks, showing no 'waist', massive quarters and short, arched necks. The legs are short and without any 'feather'. Of fine constitution, long lived, handy, and active, they show unequalled pluck at a dead pull, but are slower than Clydesdales. Colour, always chestnut or sorrel, with little or no white on face or legs. The larger Horses are used for town draught, the smaller only on the farm and usually only in their own county.

PERCHERON STALLION

Scale $^1/_{36}$

Percherons. This famous French breed (from *le Perche*, the country west of Chartres) has been largely imported and bred here since the War. Now increasingly popular. Used for draught. Noted for clean legs (i.e. without long hair), deep, wide bodies, activity, and docility. Stud-book in England since 1918.

Thoroughbreds. The racing breed was developed in its present form by the crossing of such racing Horses as existed in England at the end of the 17th century (which probably had already some Eastern blood) with Arab and Barb (N. African) Stallions. Since 1731 (when the Godolphin Arabian first served here) no other foreign blood has been introduced into the stud-book and the English racehorse has been, ever since, carefully bred to one single end, speed. While recently the object sought has too frequently been early maturity of high galloping speed over a short course (5 or 6 furlongs), carrying a light weight (average 8 stone 6 lb.), the ambition of a breeder is to breed a horse that can win a race of 2 miles or thereabouts. Owing to the rules governing racing, the mating of thoroughbreds is usually timed to produce the foals as early as possible in the year (Feb. or March).

THOROUGHBRED FILLY

Scale $^1/_{26}$

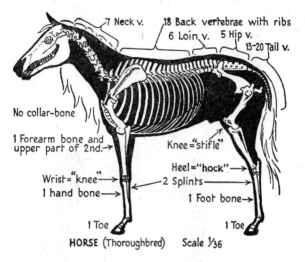

7 Neck v. 18 Back vertebrae with ribs 6 Loin v. 5 Hip v. 13-20 Tail v.

No collar-bone

1 Forearm bone and upper part of 2nd.→

Knee="stifle"

Heel="hock"→

Wrist="knee"→ 2 Splints

1 hand bone→ 1 Foot bone→

1 Toe 1 Toe

HORSE (Thoroughbred) Scale 1/36

Thoroughbreds should have bodies shorter than their height, with lean, small heads, and straight, or even slightly concave, profiles. Their chests should be comparatively narrow (so that the forelegs are not wide apart) and deep, their ribs long, well sprung, and extending far back to within a hand's breadth of the hip bone, their lungs and air-passages large, their necks long and strong, their loins flat and powerful, and the muscles generally long rather than bulky. Seen from behind, the widest point will not be (as in heavy horses) at the hip bones, but about 18 in. lower. They show all known colours, but not more than 2 per cent. are other than brown, bay, chestnut, or grey.

HACKNEY STALLION

Scale $^1/_{36}$

Hackneys. Two breeds (the Norfolk Trotter and the Yorkshire Hackney) were developed in the 18th century by crossing Thoroughbreds with heavy horses for use as quick-trotting saddle horses of great endurance. As roads improved further thoroughbred blood was introduced to fit them for light draught, and the two breeds were amalgamated. Later, still more thoroughbred crossing made them showy, light-carriage horses. Height 4 ft. 10 in. (14½ hands) to 5 ft. 2½ in. (15 hands 2½ in.). The mixture of blood is not yet very complete and they tend to separate into those in which the thoroughbred and the heavy predominate respectively. They should have heads somewhat large in profile above and tapering to the muzzle, arched necks of medium length, long, level backs and short, powerful forelegs. Above all, their trot should be high-stepping, far-reaching, and with a marked 'snap'. In colour they are chestnut, bay, and brown. Useful only as 'hacks', or in light traps, they are rapidly becoming extinct.

Cleveland Bays. A breed of great age, originally said to be a cross of Yorkshire Cart Mare and Barb Stallion. Used for agriculture and coaching. Later, as roads improved, crossed with thoroughbreds to produce good hunters and a clean-legged coach or light van Horse with sloping, thick shoulders, short back, and long quarters—generally heavy in front and light behind. Height 5 ft. 4 in. (16 hands) to 5 ft. 6½ in. (16 hands 2½ in.). Always bay in colour. Trot well, without the 'snap' of the Hackney. Hardy, and noted for longevity.

WELSH PONY

SHETLAND PONY

Scale $^1/_{36}$

Ponies. This word has no exact meaning. Even if it only meant Horses below a certain height, there is no agreement as to what height—4 ft. 4 in. (13 hands), 4 ft. 8 in. (14 hands), 4 ft. 10 in. (14½ hands), as for polo? or 5 ft. (15 hands)? But, in fact, it usually means more, namely, membership of an open-air, inbred, hardy, or mountain-dwelling race. Ponies grow bigger if richly fed for a few generations. We have native-bred Ponies living on Exmoor, Dartmoor, the New Forest, the Welsh mountains, the Hebrides, the Scottish Highlands, Connemara, and the Shetlands.

Shetland Ponies. Are very small—height 3 ft. to 3 ft. 6 in. (9 to 10½ hands)—beautifully formed, of perfect docility, and astounding strength and endurance. They can carry a man and his wife 16 miles in a day. In colour, bay, brown, or black, sometimes skewbald or 'belted' with white. Out of their native islands used mainly in the mines and for children. A medium-sized adult mare weighed 280 lb., and a tiny (30 in.) full-grown pony only 168 lb.

The above breeds cover only a small percentage of our horses. The great majority are the result of the crossing of various races. The term 'Half-bred' is used for such as have more or less thoroughbred blood, and such names as 'charger', 'hack', 'cob', 'carriage horse', and even 'hunter', represent occupations, for which horses have been selected by reason of their suitability, rather than breeds.

Hunters are often thoroughbreds, usually half-bred and, sometimes, the result of almost any mixed breeding. They require good speed, great endurance, good jumping powers, with an ability to carry a given weight, the amount of which will probably determine the breeding needed. Though the carrying of a heavy rider will require some 'heavy' blood, a thoroughbred will carry a stone more than a half-bred of similar appearance. They will be chosen for strong hindquarters and loins, long, sloping shoulders, pasterns of medium length, and powerful muscles above the elbows and in front of the shoulder-blades.

Scale $^1/_{36}$

ASS

Equus asinus

Origin. The domestic Donkey, unlike most of our tame animals, seems to be sprung from a single species only, the Wild Ass of Abyssinia (*Equus asinus taeniopus*). Domesticated before the Horse, some time in the Neolithic Age, they were not brought into England until the 9th or 10th century.

Uses. We use Asses for draft and for riding. Their milk (for analysis see p. 16) has valuable medicinal qualities, and their flesh has been eaten and declared to be excellent. It is not eaten in this country.

Description. Generally similar to the Horse, they differ as follows: they are smaller, varying from a height, at the withers, of 2 ft. 7½ in. to 4 ft. 10 in. The mane is short and erect. The tail is longer and has long hair at the end only. The ears are longer and have thick hair inside. They have no long hair on the fetlocks, no chestnuts on the hind legs, and their hoofs are narrower and more 'stilted'. They are usually higher at the croup than at the withers.

Teeth. As the Horse. The incisors in old age become more vertical than a Horse's and are narrower.

Structure. Differs from Horse as follows: Only 5 loin vertebrae (this is sometimes the case with the Horse); the male ('Jack') has two rudimentary teats; the thickened 'shell' under the skin covers the flanks as well as the hip bones; the skull is relatively larger and its eye-holes are squarer in shape.

There are the following other differences between Asses and Horses. The period of gestation is from 270 to 280 days. Asses are, on the whole, longer lived, habitually living to 25 years or more, while an age of 47 years has been recorded. The Ass is hardier, surer footed, stronger for his size, more patient and enduring. The reputation for stupidity is utterly undeserved. In countries where he is better known and appreciated than here he is always put at the head of a long team for his intelligence in picking a safe route. He is certainly obstinate, but this is often the result of ill-treatment. They sleep much less than Horses and, unless very weary, do not lie down to do so. They require little food, and prefer the coarsest herbage, such as thistles and plantains; they are particular in requiring the purest water, although they need very little.

Voice. A loud cacophanous 'braying' produced by a tremendous muscular contraction of the abdomen and chest.

Varieties. While the Ass is not incapable of improvement by careful selective breeding, no such efforts have been made in this country, where he is the beast of the gipsy and the poor man, so that little or no care has been given to him. There are therefore no differentiated breeds of Ass such as there are of Horses, and the chief differences are merely in colour. In this matter they differ less than Horses and rarely have any irregular markings, such as stars or stockings. The shoulder stripe varies a good deal in breadth and length, and there are often horizontal leg stripes. The nose, legs, and belly are usually pale in colour, and the body shade may be pale or dark grey, brown, or even a reddish brown, but they are never bright bay, chestnut, red or blue roan, or iron-grey.

MULE

Scale ¹/₃₆

MULE

Equus asinus × Equus caballus

The Horse and Ass will breed together with either as the male. The product of Jack Ass and Mare is the Mule. That of Stallion and She-Ass, called a Hinny, is smaller and inferior in all respects and, therefore, rarely bred.

Origin. Naturally, the two species prefer to keep to themselves, but Mules have been bred by Man since prehistoric times. To-day chiefly bred in Spain, Italy, and America.

Uses. Here, mainly for military transport, particularly mountain warfare. In peace but few Mules are seen.

Description. Derive from the Ass, short, thick head; long ears; small, narrow, and hard hoofs; short upright mane; no chestnuts on the hind legs, and tail hairy only at the end. From the Mare, height (12 to $17\frac{1}{2}$ hands = 4 ft. to 5 ft. 10 in.); weight (from 600–1,600 lb.); shape of body, neck, and croup; uniformity of coat and type of teeth. The skin is hard and insensitive.

Colour. Usually self-brown or bay-brown, but sorrel, grey, cream, and white occur also. Rarely parti-coloured, and sometimes have the darker cross-mark of the Ass.

Life history. Both sexes are completely sterile. Alleged exceptions are discredited. In breeding, the selected Jack Ass should run solely with Mares.

Yearly and daily adult life. Can subsist on a smaller ration and less water and can endure greater heat than Horses. They have the sobriety, patience, sure-footedness, and endurance of the Ass, and are also satisfied with coarse and scanty food, and refuse all but the purest water. They have the vigour and courage of the Horse. Temperamental, and sometimes sorely obstinate, stubborn, and vicious, though this is often traceable to ill-treatment. Unlike Horses, Mules will test a strain once and, if they fail, will refuse to try again. Without pride of ancestry or hope of posterity.

Gait. Paces as the Horse, but usually a steady, unvarying, hard trot—untiring to the Mule but not to a rider. Rarely gallops.

Voice. A feeble, hoarse braying. Unlike voice of Horse or Ass.

THE BATS

Order *CHIROPTERA*

The Bats are flying Mammals, the arms changed into wings. A membrane stretches between each of the long fingers and bones of the hand. The short thumb alone is free (from the wrist) and has a claw. The 2nd finger is short and forms the front of the wing. The 3rd is the longest. The membrane continues from the 5th finger, stretching along the arm to the armpit and along the flank and leg to the ankle. The exact point at which it ends on the leg varies in different Bats. Another membrane[1] stretches between the legs and tail, supported by a spur of bone[2] from heel along, or near to, its edge. The legs, much smaller than the arms, have each 5 small clawed toes, and are twisted by the shape of the hip bones so that the knees point backwards.

The eyes are small and sight poor. The hearing of Bats is keen for high notes, but they seem deaf to low notes, however loud. They have an acute sense of feeling (probably through the wing membranes and 'earlets'[3] or 'nose-leaves') which warns them of the nearness of any object, and so, even if blindfolded, they avoid touching twigs or other obstacles in flight.

NOCTULE BAT
Scale ¼

The hair is long and silky, mixed with an undercoat of finer wool, and is carefully cleaned with the tongue. Females have 2 teats on the breasts.

They have 7 neck vertebrae, short and broad: strong ribs, connected with a strong breast bone, which has a prominent keel, and powerful rib-vertebrae with upright spines. The spines and keel give support to the big flying muscles. Behind the ribs the back bone thins out into a weak cord. The collar bones are well developed. Brain small, and of a low type.

The teeth are numerous, varying in number in the different species, but are distinctly insectivorous in type, adapted to holding and crushing hard-shelled insects. The molars are W-shaped in plan, having points and hollows corresponding with hollows

---

[1] Interfemoral membrane.   [2] Calcar.   [3] Tragus.

and points in the 2 opposing teeth. The milk teeth differ entirely from the adult teeth and are shed very young.

Once a year, in the spring, 1 young one is born, blind and naked. Sometimes 2 abroad. Before the birth the mother turns head up and drops the young Bat into a pouch made by bending the tail forward. Then she lifts and cleans it and places it at her breast, to which it clings with its teeth, while also holding on to the mother's fur with thumbs and hind claws. It stays there, without hampering her flight, for about a fortnight, after which she removes it and hangs it up by its feet to be left during her flights, replacing it at the breast on her return. Towards autumn (when three-quarters grown) it begins to fly, apparently without teaching.

All Bats are gregarious and hibernate, mostly leaving their summer retreats and resorting to caves or other winter shelters, where they hang by the feet, asleep, upside down, with the wings wrapped round the body, their temperature dropping to that of their surroundings, while the breathing becomes light and slow. Some species wake and, being hungry, come out to hunt on warm winter days. In a cold winter they sleep soundly. Having slept through the winter, many Bats sleep most of the day and night in summer, coming out only to hawk for food at evening and morning, though some fly all night. The duration of flight differs for various species.

They are wholly insectivorous and so of great value to Man. Colonies of Bats have been established in the Campagna Romana to help fight malaria by destroying mosquitoes. Bats have to be destroyed in some cases because of the parasites which infest them and the smell of their droppings. They do not fly into women's hair.

THE EARLET BATS
Family *VESPERTILIONIDAE*

These have a well-developed 'Earlet' representing the small prominence in front of the human ear. The bones round the body at the shoulder are not fused. Tails are carried bent forward, forming a pouch, used as a nose-bag when eating large insects.

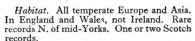

NOCTULE or GREAT BAT

Nyctalus noctula

Habitat. All temperate Europe and Asia. In England and Wales, not Ireland. Rare records N. of mid-Yorks. One or two Scotch records.

Description. Sexes alike. Golden brown. Span 13–15 in. Ears wide apart, broader than long; tail 2 mm. beyond membrane. Heel-spur ⅔rds of way to tail. Hair on wing under forearm. Strong musky rancid smell from glands in mouth. Feet big.

Teeth $\frac{2-1-2-3}{3-1-2-3} = 34$. i^1 much larger than i^2. Large gap in skull between front upper teeth.

Life history. One young a year born late June. Twins recorded abroad. Blind and naked. By Sept. half grown and covered with hair, darker than that of adults. Gestation 49 days (?).

Yearly life. Always gregarious. Hibernation begins Oct. (though squeaking, wriggling, and some flights occur in Nov.) and ends mid-March to May. Hibernates in old trees, eaves, and church roofs, not caves. Sometimes sexes separately. The daily sleep in summer is like hibernation, being very sound, with short breaths and fall of temperature.

Daily life. Frequent wooded districts. Time of evening flights varies with season, affected by weather and sunset. In early spring it is 20 or 30 minutes before sunset, in mid-Aug. 7 minutes after, returning to the relatively earlier time in Sept. Cold and wind keep them in, not rain. Come out of rest-place with much squeaking, sometimes in quick succession, sometimes at minute, or 2-minute, intervals. When alighting they land head up, holding by the thumbs, and then, at once, turn upside down and hang by a foot to perform an elaborate toilet, before hanging by both feet to rest. Flights are short, sometimes less than an hour.

Food. Mainly beetles, also some moths and gnats. Probably always taken on the wing, pouched in the tail-pouch if

NOCTULE

Scale ½

279

necessary, stripped of wing-cases and egs, by teeth and tongue, and chewed in flight. Will eat ¼th of their own weight at a meal. Drink, Swallow-like, on the wing.

Gait. Flight wavering at first, then straight, rapid, Swift-like, varied by zigzags, wheels, and swooping glides. High at first (with Swifts), later low.

Voice. Constant high squealing, inaudible to many people.

LEISLER'S BAT

Nyctalus leisleri

Habitat. Central Europe, West to Ireland and Madeira. In England, recorded from W. Riding, Cheshire, Avon valley (Stratford), and (once, long ago) Norfolk. Local and very rare. Commoner in E. Ireland.

Differs from the Noctule as follows:

Description. Much smaller. Span 10–10½ in. Lacks the smell. Colour either as Noctule or sometimes darker.

Teeth. i^1 and i^2 equal in size.

SEROTINE BAT

Eptesicus serotinus

Habitat. Central and S. Europe from England to Mediterranean, east into Asia. In England S. of the Thames only. In Kent common, less so in Sussex, Isle of Wight and Hants. Occasional records to Cornwall.

Description. Sexes alike. Span 12½ to 14½ in. Ears wide apart and long. Tail 10 mm. longer than the membrane. Wing springs from base of outer toe. Callous at base of thumb.

Teeth $\dfrac{2-1-1-3}{3-1-2-3} = 32$. All large and powerful. Upper front teeth double-pointed, lower triple. Can bite a Man severely.

SEROTINE BAT
Scale ½

Life history. One born yearly (June in France).

Yearly life. Hibernation begins end Oct. and ends early April to May.

Daily life. Sociable, living in small colonies in churches, hollow trees, or cottage roofs. Come out to feed rather late, at twilight, and retire early. Rarely out on cold or damp evenings. On waking, the members of a colony come out regularly and silently. Fly again in early morning.

Food. Insects, especially Cockchafers and, later, Brown Tailed Moths.

Gait. Flight rather fluttering and uncertain. At first very low, later gradually rising (on fine evenings) well above gun-shot. Noted for sudden 'headers' to lower levels.

Voice. A squeak: usually silent.

PIPISTRELLE or COMMON BAT

Pipistrellus[2]

Habitat. Europe and east into Asia. Common throughout U.K. and all islands. Save in a very few places, the commonest Bat everywhere, in country, farm-yard, village, and city.

Description. Sexes alike. Smallest of our Bats. Span 8–8½ in. Ears wide apart, longer than broad. Tail one (short) vertebra longer than membrane. Spur reaches more than half way to tail. Colour is variable.

Teeth $\frac{2-1-2-3}{3-1-2-3} = 34$. i^1 has 2 points.

Life history. One young a year, born July; 2 not uncommon abroad. 49 (?) days' gestation.

Yearly life. Hibernate for a brief time only, normally from mid-Oct. to mid-March: in warm winters much less. Large colonies in church roofs and towers and any cranny in house, tree, rock, or shutter, often in company with other kinds of Bat. Winter sleep light and disturbed by wrigglings

PIPISTRELLE

Scale ½

to get into warmth. More often out on warm winter days than other Bats.

Daily life. On the wing earlier than other Bats. Flight lasts long, perhaps all night. Usually follow a regular beat, round and round a tree or building. Will fly round a bright object.

Food. All taken on the wing, large insects pouched until mastered and then taken out with the mouth and eaten in flight. Will drink on the wing, hovering and dipping mouth, wings up.

Gait. Flight erratic and rarely above 20 ft. high. At first slow, moth-like and hesitating: later rapid and competent, dodging and twisting. Rise easily from flat surface. Crawl slowly, but steadily. Use tail to help in climbing and also to capture insects.

Voice. A high shrill squeak. Talkative in flight.

Varieties. Albinos recorded, also a white-winged variety.

DAUBENTON'S BAT

Myotis daubentonii

Habitat. Europe from central Norway to Mediterranean and from Ireland east into Asia, also N. Africa. 'Water Bat.' Over rivers and lakes in almost every county of England, Wales, and Scotland up to Elgin. The commonest bat in Aberdeenshire and the S. Highlands. Present in Ireland. Widespread and common.

Description. Sexes alike. Span about 10 in. Ears far apart and longer than wide. No hair on edge of tail membrane; tail projecting one vertebra beyond all but a thread of it. Spur goes ¾ way to tail. Wing rises from middle of foot. Whitish hairs on the toes.

$Teeth \dfrac{2-1-3-3}{3-1-3-3} = 38$. Slender and delicate.

Life history. One young a year, born June or July. First coat darker than adults'.

Yearly life. Hibernation (from end Sept. to mid-April) in

DAUBENTON'S BAT

Scale ½

caves, though church roofs (e.g. Christchurch, Hants) and other buildings are used. Winter resorts are sometimes deserted in summer, hollow trees, usually near water, being chosen for sleep.

Daily life. Usually gregarious, but sometimes seen singly among other Bats. Forest-loving and hawking mostly over water, they are dependent upon the existence of woods and sheltered streams or lakes. Fly about an hour before the sun sets and, probably, all night. Much squeaking before leaving sleeping-places.

Food and gait. Skim low over water, sometimes zigzagging Swallow-like, and sometimes hovering with quivering wing as a Sandpiper, often dipping to the surface to drink and take ephemerids. Frequently take a fisherman's fly.

Voice. A faint, soft chirp; lower in pitch than that of the Pipistrelle.

NATTERER'S BAT

Myotis nattereri

Habitat. Central and S. Europe, west to Ireland, north to S. Sweden. In England and Wales fairly general, but local, mainly in the W. 1 or 2 Scottish records. Probably all over Ireland. Over water.

Description. Sexes alike. Span about 11 in. Ears wide apart and much longer than wide. Earlet more than half the length of the ear. Tail membrane extends to end of tail in form of a reversed Tudor arch, and has a row of short hairs along its free edge. Spur is S-shaped and stretches half way to tail. Thumb small.

Teeth. Formula and type as Daubenton's.

Differs from Daubenton's as follows:

Yearly life. Sociable and gregarious, sharing summer resting-places with other Bats, near water. In autumn becomes more gregarious and hibernates in church roofs, other buildings, or caves. When hibernating very restless and quarrel-

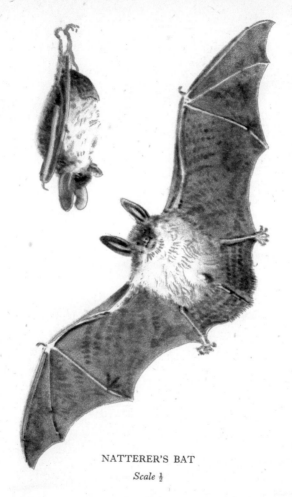

NATTERER'S BAT

Scale ½

287

some, owing to cold Bats trying to wriggle deeper into the mass. Recorded as coming out end Feb.

Daily life. Flies both high and low, usually at a higher level than Daubenton's, compared with which the wings look paler and redder.

Gait. Flight slow and steady, without twists or zigzags. Tail (unlike all our other Bats) straight out behind in flight, except when pouching insects. Feeds hovering over water. Can swoop at insects, but more usually picks them off trees or off water surface, without dipping the head. When alighting has been seen to do so as do all other Earlet Bats, holding with thumbs and then turning upside down, but slowly and clumsily; also as do the Horseshoe Bats (q.v.), but not so neatly.

Experiments on a blindfolded Bat of this species proved that it could fly about a room filled with criss-crossed wires without touching anything, and alight when tired on a chandelier.

Voice. Noisy and continuous chirping.

WHISKERED BAT

Myotis mystacinus

Habitat. All Europe and Asia to China and N. Africa to the limits of tree growth. In England general, except E. Anglia, and not uncommon. Few records from Wales, still fewer from Scotland, and few, but widespread, from Ireland.

Differs from Daubenton's Bat as follows:

Description. Smallest of the genus, span 8½ in. Earlet over half length of ear; spur goes more than half way to tail; wing membrane springs from base of outer toe; fur long; bristles on moustache, chin, and across forehead.

Life history. Young born June–July.

WHISKERED BAT

Scale ½

Yearly life. Said to awake 'early in spring'. Hibernate in sandstone tunnels in Cheshire. Also in caves, quarries, and house roofs. Usually solitary.

Daily life. Generally frequent trees, feeding among foliage, but also addicted to water. Rest for the day, usually alone, in trees, roofs, window-shutters, or stone dykes. Often seen in the day, even at midday. Sometimes (in captivity) sleep lying on a floor. Rise easily from flat surfaces.

Food. Insects and spiders, usually picked off trees.

Gait. Flight slow, steady, and silent—'quivering through the branches'.

Voice. Cry, low-pitched for a Bat. The silent flight distinguishes them from Pipistrelles in the field.

Varieties. Blacks are common.

BECHSTEIN'S BAT

Myotis bechsteinii

Habitat. Central and S. Europe, west to England, north to S. Sweden. Rarest of our Bats, very few records, all from S. England.

Differs from Daubenton's as follows: Ears much longer; earlet ⅓rd of ear's length; spur more than half way to tail; wing membrane springs from base of toes.

Little is known of its habits. Abroad it lives in holes, not caves or houses (?) and does not associate with other Bats (?). It comes out late, flies low over woods and houses, and stays in in windy weather.

Flight low and clumsy. Said to screech like young baby if handled.

BECHSTEIN'S BAT

Scale ½

Plecotus auritus

Habitat. Temperate Europe and Asia, Ireland to China, also N. Africa. All U.K., rarer in Highlands, recorded from Outer Hebrides. Among our commonest Bats, chiefly in trees and hedgerows.

Description. Sexes alike. Span about 10 in. Weight ⅛th oz. Huge ears (36 mm.) touching each other. These are sense organs: cannot fly correctly without them.

$$\text{Teeth } \frac{2-1-2-3}{3-1-3-3} = 36.$$

Life history. Single young born June–July. First coat darker.

Yearly life. Hibernate, usually alone, in hollow tree or old buildings, about mid-Oct. to mid-April. The lightest sleepers of all our Bats, they often delay hibernating till later and come out in winter, sometimes at midday to drink. Said to come out whenever temperature is over 46°. In summer they sleep out, hanging from tree trunks; on colder days take shelter in some warm retreat. Before sleep, fold ears under arms, leaving earlets erect. Sometimes gregarious and probably migrate. Swarms seen July and August.

Daily life. Mainly nocturnal and in trees. Come out late to feed—about ½ hour or more after sunset. Beat about the outer branches of trees. Probably stay out all night to within an hour of dawn. Do not come out on dull, thundery evenings. Quarrelsome, attacking other Bats. Cheerful in captivity. Make careful toilet.

Food. Mostly moths and flies taken from leaves. The Bats alight or hover, but also feed in flight. Tail pouch is used for larger insects.

Gait. Flight swift and direct when moving to another tree. When feeding, glide and hover as a humming-bird. Often cling to twigs. When travelling, drop to within a few inches of ground, and zigzag along. Alight head up and then turn

LONG-EARED BAT

Scale ½

over to hang by one or both feet. Run fairly fast in jerks.
Run best up a wall. Swim well.

Voice. Shrill chatter or chirping squeak in flight, conversation, or quarrel. Note inaudible to many. Querulous childlike note if handled.

Varieties. Albinos and black Bats recorded.

BARBASTELLE

Barbastella barbastellus

Habitat. Central and S. Europe, west to England, north to S. Scandinavia, east to Asia, and south to N. Africa. Here mainly in south east. Not in Scotland, Ireland, or Man. One Welsh record (1904). Commonest along the south from Cornwall to Kent, up to Lincoln on the east side and Warwick on the west. Recorded in Cumberland.

Description. Sexes alike. Span about 10 in. Ears touching each other, broad, not long. Almost black hair with yellowish tips.

$$\text{Teeth } \frac{2-1-2-3}{3-1-2-3} = 34.$$

Yearly life. Hibernate end Sept.

Daily life. Come out to feed early, usually in full daylight. Solitary. Rest during the day under thatch, behind shutters, in holes in walls or trees.

Gait. Flight low and uncertain, keeping near retreat. Higher in fine weather. Seen alighting as Horseshoe Bat.

Voice. Usually silent in flight. A buzz, or metallic squeak.

Varieties. Some are a rich brown in colour.

BARBASTELLE BAT

Scale ½

The HORSESHOE BATS

Family *RHINOLOPHIDAE*

These Bats differ from our others in not having any earlets. They have a remarkable growth on the face, the shape of which has earned it the name of Horseshoe, or Nose-Leaf. It is a sensitive organ for detecting the nearness of objects.

Structurally they have a solid ring of bone round the body at the shoulder, formed by a fusion of the first 2 ribs (which are flattened) with the back bone and breast bone. The latter has a keel to give added support to the flying muscles.

HORSESHOE BAT
Scale ¼

Except the thumb, the fingers have one fewer joint and the small shin bone is a mere thread.

Their skulls are differently shaped. Instead of there being a wide gap between the first incisors, these grow upon 2 small palate bones which project beyond and above the other upper jawbones and are partly cartilage and not joined to the rest of the skull. The milk teeth are shed before birth.

Their tails are much shorter than those of the Earlet Bats and are, in flight and when at rest, usually carried cocked up behind. They do not therefore pouch their prey in the tail membrane, but when mastering a large insect do so by pressing it with the mouth against a wing.

They have 2 'dummy' nipples on the groin, as well as the 2 breast teats common to all Bats. The mothers put the newborn young on to one of these, so that, when she hangs head down, it is head up. She transfers it to the true teats for feeding only.

Their flight is fluttering and lower than that of other Bats, among undergrowth.

GREATER HORSESHOE BAT

Rhinolophus ferrum-equinum

Sub-spe. *Rh. f.-e. insulans*

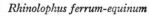

Habitat. Temperate Europe, Asia and N. Africa. Sub-spe.: England and Wales. Only in the south. Chiefly S.W.

Description. Males usually greyer, females browner. Span 13 in. Nose-leaf. No earlet. Pointed ear.

Teeth $\frac{1-1-2-3}{2-1-3-3}$ = 32. p^2 is minute and outside the row of teeth. Canines big.

Structure. The gap in the palate comes between the canines, and is filled by 2 narrow upper jaw bones carrying the incisors, close together. The last neck- and first rib-vertebrae, the first 2 ribs and breast bone are fused into a solid ring of bone round the body.

Life history. One young a year, born June or July, after 10-12 weeks' gestation. Born naked, with purple skin, and blind. Eyes open about 10th day. First coat pale grey.

Yearly life. Hibernate (the sexes separately) chiefly in caves, but also in large buildings (e.g. Wells Cathedral), moving for the summer to different parts of the caves. When hibernating they wholly wrap the body in the wings and hang, upside down, with feet together and ears folded.

Daily life. Very gregarious, clustering far in in caves. Do not associate with other species living in the same caves or buildings. Come out late and probably stay out all night till near dawn. There is much huddling and quarrelling during the day sleep. They feel the approach of Man even when hibernating.

Food. Moths and flying beetles, usually the larger ones. Food is taken in the mouth to the daytime resting-places to be eaten. Not pouched in the tail membrane. Captives will pick up dropped food, so that probably some food is gathered on the ground.

Gait. Flight, graceful sailing and fluttering, butterfly-like, and sometimes floating, gull-like. When alighting they turn

GREATER HORSESHOE BAT

Scale ½

298

a forward somersault, taking hold directly with the feet and hang upside down, wrapped in the wings. Can rest, spread out, on a table and easily rise from it. Clumsy on the ground, walking little and ill.

Voice. Very faint, chirping squeak. The young louder and more talkative.

LESSER HORSESHOE BAT

Rhinolophus hipposideros

Sub-spe. *Rh. h. minutus*

Habitat. Species, central Europe and Asia from Ireland to India, north to the Baltic. Sub-spe.: England, Wales, and Ireland. In England more widespread than *Rh. f.-e.*; not in E. Anglia; rare north of Ripon. In Ireland only in the west.

Differs from *Rh. f.-e.* as follows:

Description. Much smaller, span 8½ in.

Teeth. p_2 rather larger and almost in line; a gap opposite it between c^1 and p^1. c^1 relatively smaller.

Life history. Young born rather later—end June in S. Wales.

Yearly and daily life. Very shy of wind, staying in rather than face it. They must feed after beginning to hibernate, as dung has been found in Nov. which was not there in Aug.

Gait. Said to be more fluttering—wing-beats quicker; whirring and restless. Doubtful if the tail can be put forward at all. The leg can be brought up over the back to scratch the head.

Voice. Sharp 'Tchek-tchek', lower pitched than most Bats. Also a chattering talk.

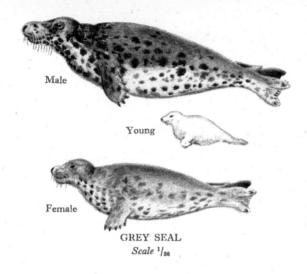

Male

Young

Female

GREY SEAL
Scale ¹/₃₆

The TRUE SEALS

Order *CARNIVORA*

Sub-Order *PINNIPEDIA*   Family *PHOCIDAE*

Marine, fish-eating Mammals, whose 4 limbs end in swim-ming flippers, webbed, furred on both sides, and with 5 nailed fingers or toes on each. The limbs are short, thick, and buried to the wrists and heels in the flesh. The fore flippers at the sides steer well in water, but are clumsy for progress on land. The legs stretch backwards beyond the short, thick tail, and cannot be turned forwards. The hind flippers are vertical, sole to sole, and act as a Fish's tail. They have thick, close fur (no under fur, 'sealskin', which comes from another family), and a large reserve of fat (blubber) under the skin. No external ear, but an entrance to the internal ear. Nostrils close with a valve to keep out water: sensitive whiskers and eyes large, with a flat surface for seeing in the dark under water. No collar bones; large, complex brains, and many resemblances in structure to the other carnivora.

They have powerful canines, but no specialized flesh teeth as, like all fish eaters, they swallow whole without chewing. The teeth are therefore mainly hooked and simple in structure. The mouth is a mere trap. Milk teeth are shed before, or just after, birth.

The adults come ashore only to produce the young and to bask on rocks. The young of our 2 species differ greatly in the degree to which they are marine.

THE GREY SEAL

Halichoerus grypus

Habitat. All North Atlantic, local. Abundant in S. and W. Ireland. Breed in Scilly Isles, about Fishguard, Farne Islands, Outer Hebrides (particularly on minor islets, as Hashkeir), Orkneys, and Shetlands. Migrating young move down the E. coast in winter to Golspie. Sometimes to Norfolk.

Description. Variable in colour, males sometimes black all over, except crown. Extent of black and grey varies greatly. Crown alone seems always grey. Length $7\frac{1}{2}$ to 9 ft., weight up to $6\frac{1}{2}$ cwt. Females paler, less variable, $5\frac{1}{2}$ to $6\frac{1}{2}$ ft., and about $2\frac{3}{4}$ cwt. Skin, particularly of males, has a strong, tarry smell. New coat in Oct., when males grow longer hair on neck.

Teeth $\frac{3-1-3-2}{2-1-3-2} = 34$. All uppers hooked and single pointed. Lower molars notched at base. Sometimes lack m^2 and m_2.

Limbs. First two fingers equal and largest, with large nails. All toes roughly equal.

Structure. Vertebrae 7–15–5–4 and 14. Male has longer jaw.

Life history. One young born, on land, after $11\frac{1}{2}$ months' gestation, early Sept. to mid-Oct. according to place. They are born in a white, woolly coat, and hidden by the mother in a cave, where they lie still for about 3 weeks. Drown if put into sea. The blubber is put on after birth, with the milk, and they soon become balls of fat. At 6 weeks old the puppy

COMMON SEAL
Dark and Light types and Young
Scale ¹/₃₆

coat is shed and a 2nd coat (yellow fur dappled with grey) is
grown. They stay ashore all winter, wandering sometimes
as much as ½ mile from the sea and up to heights of 200 ft.,
even (rarely) over snow. All this time the mothers feed them.
In April (aged 6½ months), after fading to odd colours, the 2nd
coat is shed, a 3rd (adult) coat is grown, and they take to the sea.
   Yearly life. Breeding season mid-Sept. to Oct., when the
breeding-grounds fill up and the males fight fiercely to collect
a harem of wives, severely wounding each other with their
teeth. They jealously exclude all rivals, even yearlings, and
the young males are not strong enough to fight their way into
the breeding-grounds until their 5th year. They swim about
together in daytime and lie up together on rocks at night, with
constant quarrelling. All winter keep to the open sea and, except
the mothers, who land to feed young, only come back to the
rocks in the late spring to bask and sleep.
   Daily life. Gregarious. More aquatic than the Common

Seal, with which they associate, except when breeding. Frequent the roughest exposed rocky points, only leaving them if the fish are storm-driven to deeper, or more sheltered, water. Pair and eat in the water. Sometimes fish at great depths. Sight, ashore, not remarkable; scent better, but not equal to that of Deer.

Food. Solely fish. Usually the slower kinds, but also Salmon and Sea Trout.

Gait. Swim perfectly, fish-like, propelled by lateral movements, steered by fore flippers. Take long dives, up to 15 minutes. In diving from the surface, roll forward, showing the whole back. Ashore, become sluggish with age, dragging forwards with fore flippers.

Voice. A gloomy 'Hoo', likened to a 'mooing dog's howl'. Angry, bear-like growls. Alarm by smacking water with flipper. The young hiss if scared.

Varieties. Jet-black variety recorded.

COMMON SEAL

Phoca vitulina

Habitat. North Pacific and Atlantic: on E. Atlantic coasts from Mediterranean (rare) to Iceland and Norway. In England, very few: Bristol Channel, S. Wales, the Wash, and Boston Deeps. In Scotland at all seasons, residents on all small islets of north and west. Also summer migrants, following Salmon, to the big eastern estuaries. On all Irish coasts (rare on E.) but rarer than the Grey Seal.

Description. Males 4½ to 6 ft. long, females 3½ to 6 ft. Old male weighs 1¾ cwt. Less variable than Grey Seals. The dark and light types, here depicted, are extremes. From July odd colour changes occur till the coats are renewed, male's in Sept., female's a fortnight earlier.

Teeth $\frac{3-1-4-1}{2-1-4-1} = 34$. All cheek teeth set obliquely and each with 3 (or more) points.

TOOTH

303

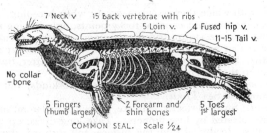

7 Neck v.   15 Back vertebrae with ribs
5 Loin v.   4 Fused hip v.
11-15 Tail v.

No collar
-bone

5 Fingers
(thumb largest)   2 Forearm and
shin bones   5 Toes
1st largest

COMMON SEAL. Scale ½₄

Limbs and structure. 1st finger (thumb) and 1st toe are the largest. Skull pointed. Vertebrae 7–15–5–4 and 11–15.

Life history. One young 'pup' (twins recorded) born, early June, on land after 9 months' gestation. It has already shed a prenatal white coat and generally resembles the adults. Takes to the water at once and swims with ease. Suckled for 2 months. 3 ft. long by September, adult in 4th year, adding weight after maturity.

Yearly life. Sexes together in winter. Females go away into separate herd before the birth of the young, remaining apart till Sept. (Aug. in Shetlands?) when, with the young, they rejoin the males and immatures. About Aug. the males begin to fight in the water with teeth and flippers. Promiscuous, pairing in water about Sept. All remain together till following summer.

Daily life. Gregarious, sometimes flocks of over 100. They choose small islands screened from gales by bigger ones, except in Shetlands, where the seals are larger and seem to like the gales. Remain in the same places, polishing the rocks smooth, except when obliged to follow fish. Spend much time ashore, coming to rocks or sandbanks, usually at half ebb, to bask, dry, and sleep. Choosing sites with a good view, they land, females and young first, old males last, after careful scouting. Seem to post a sentinel and all lie head to sea, diving on any alarm. Curious and, if un-hunted, tame, but soon become cunning and wary. Skilled at robbing fishermen's nets and evading capture. More amiable than Grey

Seals, and easily tamed. Sleep under water, remaining 15 minutes between breaths. If swimming, rise to breathe every 5 or 6 minutes.

Food. All fish; possibly sea-birds (?).

Gait. Swim as Grey Seal, but dive differently, sinking slowly and not turning over till under water. Speed about 10 m.p.h. On landing, clap hind flippers to dry them. On land, speed about 3 m.p.h.

Voice. Plaintive 'Hoo-i', long-drawn and repeated. Often at night.

Note. In addition to the species above described four other True Seals, all Polar residents in the Arctic, have been recorded as rare and occasional stragglers to our coasts. They are:

The **RINGED SEAL.** *Phoca hispida.* Blackish grey, with yellow or white spots in o's or 8's. Jaw smaller than Common Seal's and teeth in a straight line: bones of upper jaw longer: average length 4 ft. 7 in. Essentially an ice Seal, lying close to its breathing hole, kept open—how?

The **HARP SEAL.** *Phoca groenlandica.* Males, yellow-white with a black face and large black marks along the sides of the back, giving a piebald appearance. Length 5–7 ft. Females, blue-grey above and only marked with a few spots, length under 5 ft. Migratory and gregarious.

The **BEARDED SEAL.** *Erignathus barbatus.* Very variable in colour, mostly grey with blackish blotches on back and underparts: males 10–12 ft. in length, females 7 ft. Small, round head, teeth weak, whiskers flattened.

The **HOODED SEAL.** *Cystophora cristata.* Male has a large air-sac on the head, forming an inflated fur cap. Teeth $\frac{2-1-4-1}{1-1-4-1} = 30$.

One other member of the order Pinnipedia has once or twice strayed to our waters:

The **WALRUS.** *Odobaenus rosmarus,* differing greatly from the True Seals. 15 ft. in length: hind feet turned forwards and used in walking. Teeth $\frac{2-1-3-2}{2-1-3-1} = 30$, c^1 forming huge tusks. All teeth except $\frac{1-1-3-0}{0-1-3-0} = 18$ are usually shed early or remain concealed by gums. All except the tusks are small, simple cones.

WHALES and DOLPHINS

Order *CETACEA*

These are not fish, but hot-blooded marine Mammals. The forelegs have become fins, mere oars, moving freely only at the shoulder. The usual bones of the arms and hands are there, with several extra finger-joints and sometimes those of an extra finger, but the fingers are not separate. They have no hind legs (which are represented by bones floating loose in the body) and no collar bones, but they have wide, horizontal tail flukes and, usually, a back fin, both boneless. Their heads are large, eyes small, and brains small but convoluted. There is no neck. Mere holes in the skin lead to the ears, which are hidden. Hearing is acute, possibly more so when nostrils are open. The nostrils, single or double, are on the top of the head and so come first to the surface of the water. No sense of smell. The windpipe does not communicate with the mouth but goes from the nostrils, across the gullet, to the lungs. This, in many Whales, reduces the gullet to a narrow passage. The stomach is complex, divided into separate chambers and somewhat like that of the Ruminants. The skin is thick, smooth, and generally hairless, covering a thick underskin of fat (blubber)—a tough substance, requiring a sharp knife to cut it, which protects them from the cold and acts as a reserve of food. A few hairs grow on the very young and on the adults of some species, chiefly round the mouth. The young are like the adults and are suckled on the surface of the sea, sucking with the end of the mouth, while the mother lies on her side. 2 teats in the groin are covered by the lips of slits running lengthwise. Whales' milk has 5 times the fat of Cows' milk and will not mix with sea water.

All are strictly carnivorous. All live wholly in the water, never willingly coming to shore, though sometimes stranded when they are helpless and suffocated by their own weight. They breathe air and, owing to large lungs, can stay long under water, but rise to breathe ('blow') at the surface.

Blowing is the letting out of air and water vapour from the lungs. It is followed by a swift and silent inhalation. Some water is usually spouted as well, due to their beginning to blow before reaching the surface and to water having entered the nostril on inhalation. Such water is trapped in side pockets of the nostril passages and expelled at the next blowing.

Like all Mammals, they have 7 neck vertebrae, very short, and often more or less fused together; the others vary in number, but are all free and never fused. They are thought to live some 30 or 40 years, but little is known of this.

Except Man, the Killer Whale, and some parasites, the great Whales have no enemies, but whaling must be considered because it has almost exterminated them. The oceans being no man's land, it has been found impossible to make effective game laws. Stranded carcasses first proved their value to Man. Some primitive tribes had killed Whales, and the Basques began to do so in the 10th century. Dutch, English, Americans, and others followed. Until the 18th century the Right Whales (the right whales to hunt) were the prey sought. These gave far more whalebone and oil than any others, were slow swimmers, and so oily as to float when dead. By the middle of the 19th century these were almost exterminated, and the trade became unprofitable. After 1712 the Americans began killing Sperm Whales (which had no whalebone but more valuable oil) with the same result, until, about 1860, their chase became fruitless. Two final blows were the discovery of petroleum (1859) and the use of steel to replace whalebone, which became worthless—it is now actually thrown away. By about 1900 whaling was almost extinct. Oil, still used for soap and margarine, and the residues, used for manure, alone remain as inducements to slaughter.

Three things revived the trade: the use of steamships, the invention of deadlier weapons, and the practice of inflating the dead whale with air for towage. For the first time these solved the problems of how to hunt the giant Fin Whales, so swift, so huge, and so heavy as to sink when dead. This forced the only remaining family of large Whales to face extermination.

Scottish Right Whalers reported Fin Whales in the Antarctic in 1891 and the Norwegians developed whaling there

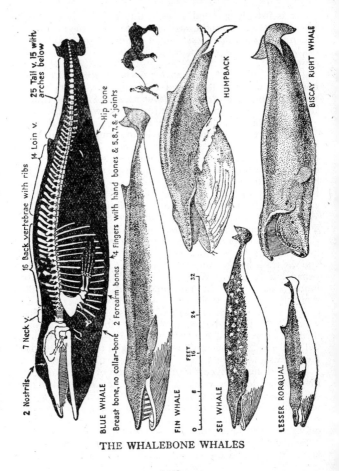

2 Nostrils

7 Neck v.

16 Back vertebrae with ribs

14 Loin v.

25 Tail v. 15 with arches below

Hip bone

4 Fingers with hand bones & 5, 8, 7, & 4 joints

2 Forearm bones

2 Breast bone, no collar-bone

BLUE WHALE

FIN WHALE

SEI WHALE

LESSER RORQUAL

HUMPBACK

BISCAY RIGHT WHALE

FEET

0   8   16   24   32

THE WHALEBONE WHALES

from 1904 onwards. These are to-day almost the only Whales killed, and it looks as if they could not long survive. The 'fishing' which in Job's day seemed remote, even to the Lord, has again become possible, and Man, with his 'sore and great and strong sword' punishes leviathan. The only chance for the Whales lies in the facts that pursuing them ceases to pay when very few remain, and that even now it does not pay to hunt those under 40 ft. in length. This has saved the Sperm Whale, whose females are small, from total extinction.

Whales are divided into two main groups, the Whalebone Whales and the Toothed Whales.

THE WHALEBONE WHALES
MYSTACOCETI

These are toothless. Lower jaw very wide. From the palate round the upper jaw hangs a thick curtain of many plates of whalebone. This is not bone, but a horny substance more like hair. The plates hang with their flat sides close together and their edges, one towards the outside of the mouth, and the other towards the tongue. The outer edges are smooth, the inner frayed into a fringe of stiff hairs. Water, with any small objects floating in it, flows freely into the mouth between the plates, the hairy fringe being pushed inwards by its flow; but when it flows outwards, on closing the mouth, the hairs catch any solid objects and filter the water, which alone escapes, leaving the solids inside the mouth to be swallowed. These Whales eat mainly minute fish and shrimp-like creatures which are singly almost invisible, but whose vast numbers give a pink tint to the water. At or near the surface, the Whale swims with open mouth through a shoal of these 'krill'. The nostrils are double.

KRILL. *Euphausia inermis*
Adult from N. Atlantic
Life size

All are purely oceanic and, except one, all are practically extinct in the N. Atlantic.

THE LESSER RORQUAL

Balaenoptera acuto-rostrata

Habitat. All oceans. Seem to approach U.K. from north of Scotland, not the Channel. 13 stranded 1927-32, mostly early in the year on the W. coasts, late on the E.

Description. Sexes alike. Length 30-3 ft., or less. Brown above, white below, and a large white patch on the outside of the flipper. Many narrow grooves or pleats under the throat. These increase the capacity of the mouth. Flipper about ½th or ⅛th of the total length. Whalebone about 14 in. long and all white or yellowish.

Structure. Lower jawbone straight in profile with 2 marked upward projections at the skull end. Neck vertebrae very short, but separate: some neck movement. 1st rib connects with a cross-shaped breast bone. Shoulder blade wider than long.

Life history. Single calves born after nearly a year's gestation (?), mostly in summer. Born about 10 ft. long. Cows probably calve in alternate years.

Yearly life. Migrations probably bring them north in summer to feed, and south in winter to breed.

Daily life. Gregarious. When feeding, circle round Krill to mass them and then go in to the mass with open mouth and flipper raised.

Food. Mainly Krill, but Dog-fish have been found in them.

Gait. Progress by tail strokes, up and down if in haste; flippers used only to balance and steer.

Voice. Silent except for blowing, a moaning sound of escaping steam. Spout is conical and upright.

The following other Whalebone Whales, which once frequented the NE. Atlantic, are here treated only so far as is necessary for identification.

SEI WHALE.   *Balaenoptera borealis.*

One stranded 1929. Larger, length up to 52 ft. Whalebone (20 in. long) is black with fine silky white hairs, some 330 plates. Tail flukes dark underneath. Flippers small, ₁₁th of length. Upper parts brown, usually white spotted. Back fin, large, has curved front edge. Blow only once or twice at a time. Spout 8-10 ft. high.

FIN WHALE.   *Balaenoptera physalus.*

Two stranded 1927-32. Much larger, length up to 70 ft. Whalebone (3 ft. long) outside in bands yellow and slate with a 4 ft. patch of white at the front on the right side, the hairs white or yellowish, up to 370 plates.

Tail flukes white below. Flippers $\frac{1}{9}$th of length. Upper parts brown, under white. Back fin, well astern, has straight upper edge. Blow 7–12 times in succession. Spout 10–15 ft. high.

BLUE WHALE. *Balaenoptera musculus.*

None stranded for many years. The largest of living creatures. Length up to 85 ft., maximum 102 ft. Whalebone and coarse hairs black, up to 400 plates. Back, and both sides of tail, colour of corrugated iron. Flippers $\frac{1}{9}$th of length. Spout 15–30 ft. high.

HUMPBACK. *Megaptera nodosa.*

None stranded for many years. Differently shaped from the above (Rorquals), thicker, bigger-headed; flippers almost $\frac{1}{3}$rd of total length, with scalloped lower edge. Length up to 52 ft. Usually black, with some white on flippers, belly, and under flukes, but vary much, the white often covering all underparts and all flippers. Whalebone 2 ft. long and all black. Belly grooves few (18–26). Some hairs on lower lip. Barnacles on lips and fins. Spout forms a round 'puff ball' about 12–15 ft. high.

BISCAY RIGHT WHALE. *Balaena glacialis.*

None stranded for many years. One killed off Faroes in 1903. Large, 45–50 ft.: black all over: no back fin or throat grooves: whalebone 6–9 ft. long.

THE TOOTHED WHALES

ODONTOCETI

These have no whalebone but, after birth, grow teeth. In some species there are only 2 teeth, hidden in the gum, in others they are very many and they vary in size only, being usually smaller towards either end of the jaw. They are all permanent teeth, only 1 set being grown during life. They are widely spaced and, where there are teeth in both jaws, those of each jaw are opposite the gaps in the other. The nostrils are joined before reaching the skin, where they issue as a single blow-hole. The windpipe does not obstruct the gullet as in the Whalebone Whales, so that they can swallow large objects. Thus their food does not consist of minute surface-feeding organisms, and many of them habitually swim deeper.

Structurally they are remarkable for the lop-sidedness of their skulls—the jaws being always twisted to some degree either to right or left.

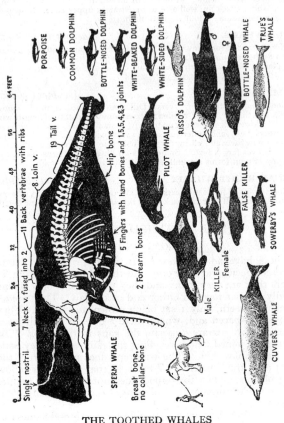

PORPOISE

COMMON DOLPHIN

BOTTLE-NOSED DOLPHIN

WHITE-BEAKED DOLPHIN

WHITE-SIDED DOLPHIN

RISSO'S DOLPHIN

BOTTLE-NOSED WHALE

TRUE'S WHALE

64 FEET

56

48

40

32

24

16

8

0

19 Tail v.

Hip bone

8 Loin v.

11 Back vertebrae with ribs

7 Neck v. fused into 2

5 Fingers with hand bones and 1,5,5,4,& 3 joints

2 Forearm bones

Single nostril

SPERM WHALE

Breast bone,
no collar-bone

PILOT WHALE

♂

♀

FALSE KILLER

SOWERBY'S WHALE

Male

Female

KILLER

CUVIER'S WHALE

THE TOOTHED WHALES

312

Some of them are coastal and entitled to rank here as British species. They approach our coasts voluntarily. The others are either coastal species, belonging elsewhere, or oceanic, and they appear here only when astray or when, as it were, shipwrecked. The Killer is intermediate between these two in habit, sometimes visiting coastal waters, though more often on the high seas.

COMMON PORPOISE

Strandings
1927–32 (76)

Phocaena[2]

Habitat. All N. Atlantic, rarely Mediterranean. Common in the Channel all the year. Herds which summer in the N. Sea seem to winter in the Baltic. Coastal, often stranded, 76 in 1927–32.

Description. Sexes alike. Smallest of our Whales. Length 4–6 ft. No 'beak'. Fins and flukes dark on both sides. Back fin sometimes has tubercles on the edge and is forward of the centre point.

Teeth $\dfrac{22 \text{ to } 26}{22 \text{ to } 26}$ = 88 to 104. Numerous, small, similar: shaped like spades on playing-cards. Used to kill and hold, not to chew or grind.

Structure. Neck vertebrae all fused. Ribs 12–15, total vertebrae 64–7.

COMMON PORPOISE. Scale ⅟₃₆

Life history. Single calf born, after 10 months' gestation, in the summer. Size of young at birth remarkable, often more than half the mother's length. They have 2 thick moustache bristles, soon shed.

Yearly and daily life. Very gregarious, feeding or playing in smooth water. Usually near shore and often up rivers.

Probably follow herring shoals. Tumble and roll in play. When rising to spout, do so successively, line ahead. Pairing season June–Oct.

Food. Fish: small salmon, trout, mackerel, herring, &c. They drive the fish together and help fishermen to locate shoals.

Gait. Swim with vertical tail strokes, fins used only to steer or stop.

Voice. Nil. 'Bellowing' fictitious. Breathe with a sighing noise, but without visible spout. When feeding, less than ½ minute under water.

COMMON DOLPHIN

Delphinus delphis

Strandings
1927–32 (17)

Habitat. Warmer parts of Atlantic and Mediterranean. Fairly common in the Channel. Probably not North Sea, except as an occasional visitor from the Atlantic. Absent from our coasts in June and, usually July, returning when the young are born. More oceanic than the Porpoise.

Strandings 17 in 1927–32, many fewer than in previous period.

Description. Sexes alike. Length 7–8 ft. Beak 6 in. long. Flippers dark and arising from the light parts. Flippers and back fin sickle-shaped. The white underparts grow greenish in winter. Eyes have eyelids and heart-shaped pupils.

Teeth $\frac{40 \text{ to } 50}{40 \text{ to } 50} = 160$ to 200. Conical, sharp-pointed, and about ⅛th in. in diameter.

Structure. Ear-hole will just admit a pin. Ribs 14–15.

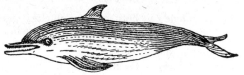

COMMON DOLPHIN. Scale ¹⁄₃₆

Life history. One calf born in early summer, having 5-7 moustache hairs on each side. The mothers carefully guard their young.

Yearly and daily life. Usually in 'schools' of moderate size, though schools are often close together. They often play round the bows of vessels.

Food. Small fish, mackerel, herrings, &c., as well as cephalopods and crustaceans.

Gait. As Porpoises, very swift: can do 18 knots. Leap clear of the water in progress.

Voice. None. The visible spout rises to about 5 ft.

BOTTLE-NOSED DOLPHIN

Tursiops truncatus

Strandings 1927-32 (26)

Habitat. Fairly common in the Irish Sea and Channel and through the Dover Straits to the North Sea as far as Suffolk. Spread eastwards as the year advances.

Differs from the Common Dolphin as follows:

Description. Length 8-11 ft. Beak 3 in. Lower jaw rather the longer. Flippers come from the dark parts. No grooves on palate. Eyelid mobile.

Teeth $\frac{20 \text{ to } 22}{20 \text{ to } 22}$ = 80 to 88. Larger (diameter ⅜ths in.) and vertical.

Structure. 12-13 ribs, of which 5 two-headed. Strandings, 26 in 1927-32. More than the Common Dolphin in these years, fewer before.

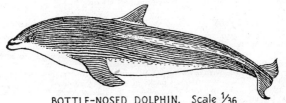

BOTTLE-NOSED DOLPHIN. Scale ⅟₃₆

The following species are here treated only so far as is necessary for identification. If coastal, they are not so commonly on our coasts as to be stranded every year. Others are purely oceanic. The numbers of the strandings given is for the 6 years 1927–32.

WHITE-BEAKED DOLPHIN. *Lagenorhynchus albirostris.*

North Sea: sometimes spreads to our W. coasts in autumn. Coastal. Strandings, 8. Fewer than before. Length 9–10 ft. Beak 50 mm. Upper lip white. Flippers almost straight, and arising from dark parts. Teeth, 22 to 25 pairs in each jaw = 88 to 100. 6 mm. across. 13–15 ribs, 6 two-headed.

WHITE-SIDED DOLPHIN. *Lagenorhynchus acutus.*

Arctic, coastal, sometimes straying to our coasts, usually to Orkneys or Shetlands. Strandings, 4. Length 9–10 ft. Beak 50 mm. Upper lip black. Flippers much curved, arising from the white, but joined to the black by a dark mark. White patches on each side behind the back fin. Teeth, 30 to 34 pairs in each jaw.

RISSO'S DOLPHIN. *Grampus griseus.*

More southerly, straying to our SW. coasts. Coastal. Strandings, 9. More than previously. Length 11 ft. Grey all over, marked with white scratches. 'Forehead' bulging, no beak. Teeth, 2–7 pairs in each jaw.

PILOT WHALE, Caa'ing Whale or Blackfish.
Globicephala melaena.

Arctic and Antarctic. Coastal, not unusual off Orkneys, Shetlands, and Hebrides. Strandings, 6. Sometimes whole herds at a time. Herds of up to 2,000 in number recorded. Length 11–28 ft. Black, with small white throat patch. 'Forehead' bulging, no beak. Flippers long ($\frac{1}{5}$th of length), narrow, and pointed. Teeth, 8 to 10 pairs in each jaw, less than 12 mm. across. 11 ribs (6 two-headed). As many as 11 finger-joints in 2nd fingers. They follow a leader in echelon formation and can thus be driven into shallow water and killed. 'Caa'ing' means driving or herding, not calling. Silent. Spout shows a round puff about 5 ft. high.

KILLER WHALE. *Orcinus orca.*

All oceans, also sometimes willingly coastal, and even visits our rivers. 3 came up the Thames to Teddington. Strandings, 5. Males much larger (up to 30 ft., back fin, upright, to 6 ft.) than females (15 to 20 ft., back fin, curved, about 2 ft.). Colour black above, white below, in a marked pattern, with a yellowish purple patch under the back fin on each side. They live in small packs of 5–36 and, alone of Whales, prey mainly on other marine Mammals, even killing great Whales. Also fish, including sharks.

FALSE KILLER.   *Pseudorca crassidens.*

One large school of over 150 stranded in Dornoch Firth in 1927. Oceanic. Differs from Killer in being all black. Flippers pointed and narrower.

WHITE WHALE.   *Delphinapterus leucas*

One stranded at Stirling in 1932. Arctic, coastal. Length 12–14 ft. All white, the young grey. No back fin. Teeth, 10 in upper, 8 in lower jaw. Up to 20 mm. across.

BOTTLE-NOSED WHALE.   *Hyperoodon rostratus.*

Oceanic, once common, now rare in N. Atlantic. Strandings, 5. Sexes differ in old age, males growing large bone and blubber formation above snout. Black all over, but old males are marked with white, especially on head, the oldest becoming white all over. Length, males 25–30 ft., females, 20–4 ft. Long beak, 6–7 in. Two grooves under throat. Teeth, 1 or 2 pairs, usually hidden in gum. Gives spermaceti and ambergris.

CUVIER'S WHALE.   *Ziphius cavirostris.*

Oceanic. Strandings, 5. Size up to 28 ft. 'Forehead' not prominent. Snout nearer blow-hole. White above a line from chin to back fin, gradually darkening into black below that line. Teeth, 1 pair of large teeth (up to 34 mm.) at tip of lower jaws in males, females rarely cut the teeth.

SOWERBY'S WHALE.   *Mesoplodon bidens.*

Oceanic. Twice stranded. Size 15 ft. Narrow beak, without prominent 'forehead'. Mostly black, but usually blotched and streaked white. Males have a large tooth on each side of the lower jaws, half-way along: concealed in females.

TRUE'S WHALE.   *Mesoplodon mirus.*

Oceanic. Once stranded. Slightly larger, 17 ft. Male's 2 teeth at the tip of the jaw, and flattened sidewise.

SPERM WHALE or CACHALOT.   *Physeter macrocephalus.*

Oceanic and almost extinct, but 1 stranded in 1936. Sexes differ much in size, males up to 64 ft. long, females under 40 ft. Black all over. Single S-shaped nostril to the left of centre line and near end of snout. Teeth, 20–7 pairs on very narrow lower jaw, rarely a few smaller teeth on upper. They are curved, without enamel, and up to 8 in. long. See page 312 for structure. The gullet is big enough to swallow a Man. The huge snout is filled with 'spermaceti' or 'sperm oil', and the bowels produce a valuable substance called 'ambergris', which has the property of making scents stronger and more enduring. Dives last for 20–80 minutes. Spout lasts for 3 seconds and is repeated 60–70 times, taking 10 minutes. It slopes forward and rises 15–20 ft. Flukes show when 'sounding' (= diving).

REPTILES

Class *REPTILIA*

Reptiles, once the lords of animal life, are to-day only a degenerate and puny remnant, and here are few, small, and unimportant.

The Tortoises, Lizards, and Snakes differ greatly from each other (far more so than do the Orders of Mammals), but they have the following attributes in common.

Like the Mammals they are vertebrates, with an internal skeleton of skull, back bone, ribs, and (except the Snakes) 4 limbs. They also have lungs.

Unlike the Mammals they are cold-blooded, the temperature of the body being at or near that of the surrounding air, and their vitality varies with the temperature. The skull has a smaller brain-pan and a single knob (*condyle*) to connect with the first vertebra. The lower jaw is made of 5 or 6 separate bones, and hinges on another bone (*quadrate*). This often hinges on the rest of the skull and is mobile.

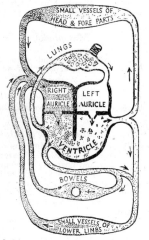

The part of the heart which pumps out the blood to the body (*ventricle*) is only partly divided into two, so that the blood cleaned by the lungs is mixed with blood soiled by passage through the body. There are two arteries (*aortas*), which leave the heart at different places, so that the degree of cleanliness of the blood in them varies. The circulation is so arranged that the cleaner blood goes to the head and fore limbs, the dirtier to the bowels, and an intermediate mixture of the two to the lower limbs and tail. A glance at the diagram will explain this. The red corpuscles of the blood are oval and convex in shape, having a dark central nucleus. There is no diaphragm.

REPTILES. Diagram of Heart & Circulation

They produce their young in

eggs, except some of the Snakes and Lizards, which hatch the eggs at or before birth. The eggs are relatively large and have much yolk to support the young until the time of hatching, after which they are capable of looking after themselves. Reptiles are without hair or feathers, but the outer skin hardens into an external horny coat of scales and, sometimes, in addition, a lower layer of the skin ossifies in a series of plates of bone, making an outer skeleton under the scales. There is only one single vent which serves for the bowels, kidneys, and for generation. There are no glands in the skin. With few (foreign) exceptions, they are completely promiscuous.

THE TORTOISES

Order *TESTUDINES*

We have no native Tortoise, though some Turtles have been stranded on our shores, but land Tortoises are largely imported and live contentedly in our gardens.

The COMMON (Spur-thighed Mediterranean) TORTOISE

Testudo graeca

Habitat. Mediterranean area to Iran. Imported here, but do not breed.

Description. Sexes alike, males remaining slightly smaller, with rather longer tails and concave under-shells. Those of females are flat. Shell length 6 to 10 in. One broad scale (sometimes 2 narrow ones) just above tail. A spur on the thigh. 7–10 scales down forearm. The head, 4 limbs, and tail can be withdrawn inside shell, the head by an 'S'-shaped bend in the neck.

Teeth. None. A horny, bird-like beak, or sheath, edges the jaws.

Limbs. Short and strong. Shin and forearm bones separate, the latter uncrossed. 5 nailed toes on forefeet, 4 on hind.

Structure. Vertebrae: 8 neck, 8 with ribs, 2 touching hip bones and about 20 in tail. No collar bone. Long projections from shoulder blade meet in front to form collar. There are 2 shells of bone, the upper made of the ribs and vertebrae flattened and its edges of bones formed in the skin, as is the lower shell. The 2 are joined only by the skin. Both have an outer covering of plates of horn ('tortoiseshell') formed in the outer skin and connected with a system of nerves. These plates are fewer than the inner bony plates, and placed so as to cover the cracks between them. As the Tortoise grows, each outer plate gets bigger by new growth round its edges, showing annual rings. Their skulls look more like their heads than those of any other beast. The mouth does not expand, as the bones (*quadrates*) on which the lower jaws hinge are rigidly fixed to the skull. Ear is covered by the skin. Eyes have 3 lids. Vent is a lengthwise slit. The rigidity of the ribs, fixed in the shell, and absence of diaphragm, oblige them to breathe with the throat muscles (see Toad, p. 347), so that, although the lungs are large, breathing is sluggish and all their life slow.

Life history. Do not breed here. Abroad pair from May onwards. 2–4 white, hard-shelled eggs (34 × 30 mm.) are left in a nest dug in the soil. Young hatch out soft and leathery, quite independent, and soon bury themselves for the winter. Their life is long, but how long? Gilbert White's Tortoise, 'Timothy', had been 54 years in captivity when he died, and Archbishop Laud's over 90.

Yearly life. Hibernate from Nov. to April, digging in to earth. Eat little for some time after waking and again before retiring. Voracious only in mid-summer.

Daily life. Live on dry land, soon drowning in water. Diurnal, waking late and sleeping early. Sit and graze in the sun—in shade if very hot—feeding twice a day. Keen of sight, hearing, and smell. Sensitive to noise or contact, withdrawing into the shell. Dread rain, which hammers on the shell, and so take cover. Know their territory well and go to a chosen spot to rest, remembering it after months of absence. Distinguish persons and will come to be fed. Said to listen eagerly to music. Courtship lasts many days, the male 'piping' and tapping on the female's shell. They are equally slow a-dying. The heart has been seen to beat 2 or 3 days after removal from the body, and a Tortoise is said to have moved 200 yards 24 hours after being decapitated.

Food. Vegetarian. Juicy plants, lettuce, cabbage, dandelions, and clover: also grass. Will eat bread and milk. No drink if food is moist. Probably no living thing.

Gait. Slow, laboured hoisting forward of the body.

Voice. A slight piping. Hiss if annoyed.

Note.—The other Tortoise sometimes imported, the **Spur-tailed Mediterranean Tortoise** (*T. hermanni*) differs in never having 2 scales over the tail, in having a spur at the end of it and none on the thighs, and only 4–6 scales down the forearm.

COMMON TORTOISE and EGG
Scale ½

SKELETON, with limbs, tail, and head under cover. Neck drawn back between shoulder blades.

Note. Drawn without flesh and with the near side of the shells sawn off. Sawn bone is shown dotted: sawn tortoiseshell black and the inside of the further part of the shell shaded.

SNAKES

Order *SQUAMATA*

Sub-order *SERPENTES*

Of all Reptiles Snakes are creepers in the strictest sense of the word. Our three Snakes have no vestige of any limb, though some Snakes have.

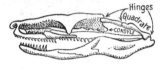 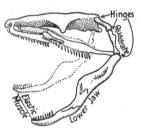

SKULL OF GRASS SNAKE
with mouth shut and open.

Their skeletons consist solely of skull, back bone, and ribs. The skulls are remarkable for their elasticity, the lower jaw bones being joined at the point of the chin by an elastic muscle (instead of being fused together) and also being hinged to a bone (*quadrate*) which is loosely connected with the skull (instead of being hinged to a fixed part of it), thus enabling them to swallow objects much larger than their heads. The teeth do not grow round the jaws, but on a number of bars of bone running lengthwise in the mouth. The number differs in different species. The teeth are recurved sharp hooks, all alike except the poison fangs of the Viper. The two outermost bars form the lower jaws. They can be moved independently and work backward and forward. The hooked teeth of one bar rake the victim down the gullet with their backward movement. When the bar moves forward its teeth disengage because the victim is held by other bars. Each in turn continues the process until the huge mouthful disappears. The teeth grow in a groove along the bones (not in sockets) and when grown are fused to the bone itself. If worn out or broken, they are replaced by an indefinite succession of others.

The back bone has 3 types of vertebrae: neck vertebra (1 only), ribless and bearing the skull; body vertebrae (roughly 150), each carrying 2 ribs and extending all the way to the vent; and tail vertebrae (about 50), without ribs, but the first few have widespreading projections which look like short ribs, until, farther back, they diminish to nothing and leave a back bone of mere beads. The vertebrae have a cup in front and ball behind. There is no breast bone.

The ribs are attached to the back bone by cup and ball joints so that they can be moved freely. They can open wide (especially at the forward end of the Snake) to allow bulky, undigested food to pass. They can also move backwards and forwards and, as each pair is connected with a scale across the belly overlapping the one behind it, when they do so, the Snake moves forward, 'rowing on the earth, with every scale an oar'.

The skin, strong and elastic, is covered with scales, small and lozenge-shaped, on the top and sides; on the belly in bands stretching right across. On the head are some larger scales, the number and position of which help to classify the species. The designs are not invariable. Extra scales are often developed and neighbouring ones are often fused. When the skin is stretched the scales become separated. Outside the skin and scales is a horny transparent layer of outer skin, covering the whole Snake, including the eyes, which are mobile and without lids. As this does not grow, it is moulted, or 'sloughed', periodically. It first loosens round the mouth, where the Snake, by rubbing against some obstacle, frees its head and then glides out, turning the slough as one does a stocking. There is no exit from this outer skin near the eyes, so that the tears escape at the nostrils. The ears are rudimentary and hidden under the skin. Snakes seem to be deaf to sounds (?) but feel the slightest ground vibration. The tongue, long and forked, is a sensitive organ of touch. The windpipe comes well forward into the mouth and can be thrust out so as not to be blocked during the act of swallowing.

The organs, which are in pairs (e.g. lungs and kidneys), are placed one behind the other, instead of side by side. The right lung is the larger and cellular in front only, the back part being a mere air sac. They breathe by moving the ribs. There is only 1 vent, which is a crosswise slit serving the use of bowels, kidneys, and sex. In this vent the males have 2 sex organs, but only 1 may be used at a time.

Most Snakes lay soft, membranous eggs, but in some cases the young leave the eggs at or before birth. No attention is paid by the parents to either eggs or young and the latter

VIPER
Scale ½

go off at once independently. Snakes grow throughout life, keeping the same number and disposition of bones and scales.

Man habitually kills all Snakes at sight, as they are not easily known apart and the Viper is poisonous. There is no doubt that the innocent and useful Snakes will continue to die for the crimes of the Viper, but perhaps some day Man may learn not to be proud until he has made sure which Snake he has killed!

VIPER or ADDER

Vipera berus

Sub-spe. *V. b.*[2]

Habitat. Species: all N. Europe and Asia from Wales to Saghalian, and from 67° N. in Scandinavia to the Alps and Pyrenees. Sub-species: as above except for Yugo-Slavia and the Peninsula. Not in Ireland or the Isles, except for the Lewis, Mull, Arran, Islay, and Skye.

Description. Sexes inclined to differ in colour and size, females being about an inch longer. Vary much in colour, from dark brown and brick-red to whitish or pale grey, while the darker marks differ much in depth. Usually the duller colours, darker and redder ground colours, are on females; the brighter, paler with blacker markings, on males.

Males are also slimmer and more active. The central zigzag line is usually present, but it may be broken up into spots or lost in a dark background. Length averages 1 ft. 10 in. and rarely exceeds 2 ft. Largest recorded (female) 2 ft. 11 in. General form wide and clumsy, narrowing rapidly at vent. Tail short—usually about ⅐th and ⅑th of total length in males and females respectively.

For scale pattern see coloured plate, noting: (1) that the eye has a ring of small beads below, behind, and in front of it, and there are also small beads separating the 3 forehead scales between the eyes, and (2) that there are in general many small, and few large, scales on the head. There is only one scale in front of the vent. Behind it they are in pairs.

The eyes are coppery red with a vertical, cat-like, pupil. Each scale of the upper part has a rib or 'keel' down its centre. Scales arranged in diagonal rows, usually 21 (19–23). The colour markings do not coincide with the scales.

Teeth. Two large hooked poison fangs on front of upper jaw, bored with a channel from near the top to near the tip. These fangs are worked by a device best seen in this sketch. The opening of the mouth pushes down that part of the upper jaw on which the fangs grow, thus cocking them for use, and the same movement squeezes the gland in which the poison is kept so that it runs down the fang. The poison is a saliva which

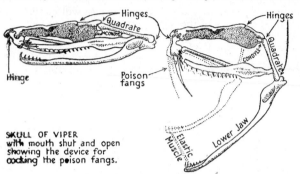

SKULL OF VIPER
with mouth shut and open showing the device for cocking the poison fangs.

digests the prey as well as paralysing it. When the jaws are shut the fangs lie horizontally, pointing backwards along the upper jaw. There are some small, reserve fangs, similar to the poison fangs, which grow behind them and replace them if broken. The other teeth are mere hooks, all of the same size, and serve only to rake the victim down the throat as described on p. 322.

Structure. As all our Snakes, see pp. 322–3. Vertebrae: male, 1 neck, 132 to 150 with ribs and 32–46 tail. Female, 1 neck, 132 to 158 with ribs and 24 to 38 tail.

Life history. The young are born alive in Aug. (rarely end July) or Sept., having hatched out of transparent, membranous eggs at or before birth. 5–12 (? 20) at a birth. The number seems to increase with the size of the mother. Gestation about 4 months. Like adults, and 4–8 in. in length. They go off at once on their own, separately. The poison is present in minute quantity at birth and increases with growth.

Yearly life. Hibernate from mid-Oct. to April, usually 2 or 3 together, though a dozen has been recorded, in hollows under stumps, heather, grass, sticks, or moss. They have been known to come out and pair in Dec. in very warm winters. On first emerging, spend much time basking in the sun. Pairing usually occurs April and May, though this date and that of awakening vary with the warmth of the season. Promiscuous. Entwined masses of Vipers have been seen at this time, though 1 male, with 1 or 2 females, is usual. Often hide in sheaves at harvest and in haystacks.

Daily life. Mainly nocturnal, beating a chosen district in search of food. Spend the day in holes, or under thick cover, or sun-basking on a favourite spot, particularly after rain. Take cover from rain and avoid water. Hide in moss in extreme heat or cold. Gather round fires at night. Chiefly on commons, heaths, waste lands, or hedge bottoms. Cross tarred roads freely at night. Our only poisonous reptile. Bite at once if surprised or cornered (unless lethargic from being gorged or cold) but will escape if they can. If captured will disgorge a meal. In captivity often refuse food and die of starvation. French figures show mortality of 8 per cent. among persons bitten by Vipers. Here there are very few deaths and no good explanation is known. Fingers or toes are the parts most often bitten because of the small size of the Viper's mouth. Dogs and cattle are frequently bitten.

[If bitten: instantly tie a ligature above the bite: cut between the fang marks to a depth of $\frac{1}{2}$ in.: squeeze out the blood (do not suck for fear of abrasion in the mouth): drench with ammonia and permanganate: and call a doctor. Effective remedies are by injections of Snake poisons.]

Their chief enemies are Man, Hedgehogs, Poultry and other Birds, Goats, and Cats.

Food. Mainly small Mammals, Mice, Voles, Shrews, &c., and small birds. In default, eggs, Lizards, Frogs, Toads, Slow-worms, Newts, and insect larvae. The prey, paralysed by the bite, is swallowed whole. Go to water to drink.

Voice: A low hissing. *Gait*: As all Snakes, a swift, forward gliding, in lateral curves, propelled by the overlapping belly scales. Usually lie with neck drawn back in short zigzags, to be ready to strike, and, if attacked, lie flat in a coil, with head in centre. Rarely climb trees, but have been reported as slipping off branches to ground.

GRASS SNAKE and EGGS
Scale ½

GRASS SNAKE

Natrix²

Sub-spe. *N.*³

Habitat. Species: Europe and Asia, north to England and SE. Scotland and S. Sweden. South to Algeria. Not in Ireland. Sub-spe.: Same, except Spain, Sardinia, and Sicily.

Description. Generally similar to Viper, but larger. Adult males average 3 ft. females 4 ft. Recorded up to 6 ft., and 8 ft. in Italy. Males are slimmer. Growth continues throughout life. In colour variable; usually olive-grey, brown, or dark green with darker markings, and grey or black and white belly. The yellow and black neck marks are usual, but the yellow is sometimes white and sometimes lacking. General form beautifully tapered both fore and aft: tail long ($\frac{1}{5}$th of length).

For scale patterns see colour plate, noting: (1) that the eye rests directly on the lip scales and the eyebrow scales touch the central (shield-shaped) scale on the top of the head. There are no small scales round the eye. (2) There are, in general, few small scales on the head. (3) Of the 4 scales under the chin the 2 hindmost are, if anything, the larger. There are 2 scales just in front of the vent, as well as pairs behind it: the nose scale, seen full face, is wider than it is tall.

The eye is yellow in colour, with a circular pupil. The scales, as in the Viper, are 'keeled' except towards the tail end. There are 19 diagonal rows.

Teeth. There are no fangs, all the teeth being simple hooks for raking down the food. The teeth on the outer edge of the upper jaw gradually increase in size towards the back.

Structure. The skull is widely expansible, but the forward part of the upper jaw is horizontal, with teeth on the lower surface, and remains in place when the mouth is open. There are glands near the vent which emit a nauseating stench. Vertebrae: 1 neck, 166 to 173 rib, and 62 to 74 tail.

Life history. From 12 to as many as 53 eggs (older mothers laying most) are laid, and left in July or Aug. (2 months after pairing) in rich mould, weed or manure heaps. Many females may lay together, 1,200 eggs have been found in one heap. They are soft, cream-coloured, membranous ovals, about an inch in length, and attached to each other by the ends in a string, soon swelling with absorbed moisture, and sticking together in a lump. In from 6 to 8 weeks, according to temperature and moisture, the young hatch out, helped by a sharp point on the nose (like a Bird's 'Egg-tooth'), which is shed in 2 days. They are from 6–8½ in. in length and resemble the adults, living at first on soft insects and worms. Unable to swim. Can eat tiny Frogs at a few weeks old. Males breed in the 3rd year, females in the 4th. Life is long: a female in captivity lived for 9 years, growing from 35 to 44 in.

Yearly life. Hibernate in large numbers together (up to 100 recorded) about Oct. till March or April, under tree roots, in brush pile or stack, or deep holes. Pairing occurs (infertile) in May or June and again end-Sept. In autumn considerable numbers have been seen massed together promiscuously in bright sunlight. Outer skin is sloughed several times a year.

Daily life. Diurnal. Largely aquatic, preferring long grass near water, but also found in dry places. Eat seldom, but gorge themselves, hiding to sleep off lethargy for a week or so after a meal. Wild when captured, hissing, striking with the head (but rarely biting) and voiding the stinking excrement, which is their only means of defence. Soon become tame, know people apart, and will stand handling. Are perfectly harmless, with teeth too small to hurt us. Immune to a Viper's poison. When captured will disgorge a recent meal. Enemies are those of Vipers. The young are eaten by Toads and Frogs.

Food. Almost entirely Frogs, raked down alive, though Toads are said to be preferred. Also tadpoles and eggs, Newts, insects, and fish, captured in water and brought to land to be eaten. Said not to touch Reptiles or Mammals. Do not constrict. Drink much water.

Voice. A whistling hiss if annoyed.

Gait. As all Snakes. Swim well and readily (head about 6 in. above water) and dive. Can climb trees. Rarely cross a smooth road.

Varieties. The question of dividing this species is at present unsettled. One writer has made up 20 sub-species (if he be right ours would be *N² britannicus*) but they are not yet accepted.

SMOOTH SNAKE

Coronella austriaca[2]

Sub-spe. *C. a.*[3]

Habitat. Species: Most of temperate Europe, from England and the Peninsula to Berlin and south-east to Asia Minor. Sub-spe.: As above, except Italy, Peninsula, S. France, and Mediterranean Islands. In England rare and local, found only in a few southern counties: Hants, Dorset, Surrey, and Berks.

Description. In size between the Viper and Grass Snake. $23\frac{1}{2}$ in. to $35\frac{1}{2}$ in. Here rarely exceed 2 ft. In shape, slim and gracefully tapering. The neck narrows little except when the head is widened by the opening of the mouth. In colour, usually a brownish-khaki, with darker khaki markings, the belly very variable. All colours very variable and easily mistaken for a viper. Tail long, $\frac{1}{4}$ of length in the male, $\frac{1}{5}$ in female. For scale patterns, see plate, noting: generally as Grass Snake, with the following differences, viz. (1) the nose scale, seen full face, is taller than it is wide, and (2) of the 4 scales under the chin the 2 foremost are the larger. Eye as Grass Snake. The body scales are more angular in shape and are not 'keeled' but smoothly rounded, giving a smooth surface to the touch. There are 19 diagonal rows.

Differs from the Grass Snake as follows:

Teeth. Those on the outer edge of the upper jaw are all of equal size.

Structure. Vertebrae: male, 1 neck, 168 to 174 rib, and 58 to 67 tail. Female, $1+171$ to $182+45$ to 51.

Life history. No eggs are left to hatch. 2–15 young (usually about 6) are born from an egg membrane (which is broken at the moment of birth) late in Aug. or Sept. They are from 7 to $7\frac{3}{5}$ in. in length. A second pairing occurs in more southern countries.

Daily life. Definitely terrestrial, frequenting heaths and dry places, hunting chiefly in the evening, loving sun and warmth. May, however, as they drink and bathe, be found near water. Lie up in deserted Mole, Vole, or Mouse holes, or in crannies. Perfectly harmless and can be tamed, but when captured, and for some time afterwards, hiss and bite deliberately and fiercely, but without hurting. Males fight.

Food. Sand Lizards, Slow Worms, and small Snakes, also Voles, Mice, and Shrews (which they constrict), and beetles and other insects. Not amphibians or Fish. Seen to drink rain drops from leaves.

LIZARDS

Sub-order *SAURIA*

There are far more species of Lizards in the world than of any other Reptiles. They are mostly found in warm climates and are comparatively recent, not being found before the chalk. We have only three species in this country, but they give a good idea of the diversity of the Lizards.

In many ways they are like the Snakes. So much so, that Snakes and Lizards are both classed as Sub-orders of Scaled Reptiles (Order *Squamata*).

Unlike the Snakes, the skulls are not elastic because the lower jaw bones are solidly fused at the point of the chin, and there is no such hinging of the bone (*quadrate*) to which the jaw bones are attached as there is in the Snakes. They cannot, therefore, swallow anything disproportionately large. When they open their mouths, there is some upward movement of the upper jaw bones, as well as the downward movement of the lower jaw. Like the Snakes, some Lizards have teeth on some of the bones of the palate as well as those on the edge of the jaws.

Unlike the Snakes, they close their eyes in sleep, having 3 eyelids, which shut from above, below, and from the front corner of the eyes. They have external eardrums.

Most Lizards have 4 fully developed limbs, furnished with claws, and even those which have not have distinct traces. They have collar bones and breast bones. Therefore they cannot creep as the Snakes do by movement of the ribs.

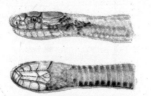

SMOOTH SNAKE

Scale ½

LIZARDS (*cont.*)

Those which have limbs walk or run, dragging the smooth belly over the ground, and those which have not (like the Slow Worm) advance by wriggling in curves.

The tongue is a sensitive organ of touch as in the Snakes. It is black, thin, and notched, but not forked.

The skin is dry, horn-coated, and generally Snake-like, and the arrangement of the scales helps in classification. The belly scales are many and small, instead of stretching from side to side as in Snakes. They are beautifully coloured.

The vertebrae of the tail are each composed of two parts loosely connected, so that the tail is brittle, always breaking in the middle of a vertebra. The Lizard can snap it off at will. Lost tails, and even limbs, can be grown again from the stumps, though they are usually somewhat ill formed.

Most Lizards lay eggs, but in the case of 2 of our 3 species the young hatch out at, or before, birth. No attention is paid by the parents to eggs or young.

SLOW WORM or BLIND WORM

Anguis fragilis

Habitat. All temperate Europe, Algeria, and into Asia. All over Britain, commoner in SW. Not in Ireland.

Description. Snake-like, **legless.** Large ones about a foot in length, of which more than half is tail. Males slightly smaller. Maximum 17 in. Whole surface, including belly, covered with small, rounded scales. Colour varies, usually metallic brown above and blackish below. The markings on skin are smaller than scales. Eyes small, bright, with movable lids and orange iris. In no way blind. Inconspicuous ear-hole. Tongue broad, flat, and notched: thrust out as organ of touch. Head smaller than neck. Females have sides of head, neck, and body a darker brown.

SLOW WORM
Scale ½

Teeth. Small, solid, and hooked, fang-like, placed in grooves along jaws; renewed, when needed, by others grown between them, not in the same place. Faintly grooved down the front.

Limbs. None, but represented internally by small traces of shoulder and hip bones.

Structure. Under every one of the scales all over the body is a small scale of bone. The brittle tail breaks off in the middle of a vertebra and is slowly replaced by a hard point some 20 mm. long. Jaws are not elastic, lower jaw bones being firmly united in front.

Life history. 7–19 young at a time, once a year, bursting out of soft, transparent eggs as, or just after, they are laid, in Aug. or Sept. Born silvery-white with three lines of black above and black belly, 3–4 in. in length, their heads larger than the neck. There is a rudimentary egg-tooth. From birth they fend for themselves, living first on minute spiders and insects, later on worms. Grow slowly. Males breed in 3rd year, females in 4th, such young females breeding a month later than older ones. Have been kept captive for 19 years.

Yearly life. Hibernate in early autumn, sometimes in Aug., digging themselves (with the head) into rotten wood or loose earth in dry, warm spots, often a dozen together. Sometimes use a small Rodent's hole. Earliest Reptile to wake and emerge (March). Sloughs some 4 times a year, sometimes losing skin in shreds, as Lizard, sometimes all in one piece, as Snakes. Pairing season May, when the males fight, biting the head and then writhing.

Daily life. Diurnal, but inclined to seek shade. Feed mainly in afternoon and evening. Avoid hot sun. Spend night under moss, leaves, or stones. Chief enemies, Man, Hedgehogs, Vipers, Birds, and Pigs. Only defence is trick of snapping off tail by a muscular contraction. After severance, tail wriggles and jumps about, attracting attention, while its owner slips away. Absolutely harmless and wholly beneficial to Man.

Food. Slugs and Snails, also insects and earthworms, which are sucked and then chewed.

Gait. Snake-like, but moving by lateral bends, without

help from the small belly scales. Not particularly slow, but rarely in a hurry.

Voice. Nil.

Varieties. Albino recorded.

THE COMMON LIZARD

Lacerta vivipara

Habitat. N. central Europe to 70° N. Lat. South to Pyrenees, Alps, N. Balkans, and Macedonia. Throughout U.K., but commonest in the south and scarce in the Lakes and Highlands. The only Reptile in Ireland.

Description. Sexes differ. Males have the tails enlarged at the base, are smaller (about 6 in., of which tail 3⅞), shorter in the body, and different in colour. Females 7 in., of which 4½ tail. Scales all over, small on back, throat, neck, and feet, and larger on head, collar, and body. Those of the tail are narrow, long, pointed, and ribbed.

The following statements about the scales are usually true, but there is much variation. There is a mark under the chin suggesting a fold, and sometimes an actual fold, but this less pronounced than in some other (foreign) species. The lower edge of the collar-scales is serrated. Central scale on the top of the head (*occipital*) is smaller than that in front of it (*interparietal*). The nostril is pierced between 2 scales, so that immediately behind it is only 1 scale (*postnasal*), and behind, and touching that, is only 1 scale (*anterior loreal*). Among those on the temple is 1 larger central scale (*tympanic*). Two semicircles of small scales round the large scale in front of the vent (*anal*).

They have eyes with round pupils and 3 eyelids, visible ear-drums, and a long tongue divided into 2 rounded tips.

Teeth. In a groove round the inside edge of the jaws. Small, sharp, and each with 2 or 3 points. When worn or lost, replaced by others growing between them. Rarely any teeth on the palate.

Limbs. 4 limbs, all 5-toed. Forearm and shin bones separate. Toes slender and smoothly covered with small scales. A claw to each toe. On the thighs are about a dozen pores, which exude a yellow, sticky substance, possibly useful to prevent slipping; more marked in males.

Structure. Skeleton generally like that of a Mammal, having the 5 kinds of vertebrae, ribs, breast bone, and 4 limbs. There are many ribs, of which 5 reach the breast bone. They have collar bones. The vertebrae of the loins and upper part of the tail have rib-like projections. 2 vertebrae are fixed to the hip bones. The tail is brittle, and it and the limbs can be regrown. Crosswise vent serves for all excretion and generation. Males have 2 sex organs, of which only one may serve at a time.

Under the large head-scales (not elsewhere) are bones formed in the skin, which roof over the holes in the skull at the temples.

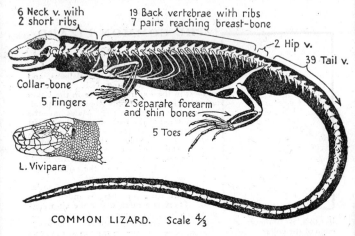

6 Neck v. with 2 short ribs

19 Back vertebrae with ribs 7 pairs reaching breast-bone

2 Hip v.

39 Tail v.

Collar-bone

5 Fingers

2 Separate forearm and shin bones

5 Toes

L. Vivipara

COMMON LIZARD. Scale 4/3

Life history. The young (6–12) emerge from soft, parchment-like eggs before, at, or very shortly after being laid, about July or Aug. They are ¾ in. (19 mm.) long, plus tail 1 in. (22–8 mm.), and almost black. They are dropped under a stone or in any hole, without preparation of any nest, and for the first few days lie still, growing by absorbing the remains of yolk into the body. They have a small, useless (?) egg-tooth on the nose, which is shed on the 1st or 2nd day. Then they feed on minute insects and are self-supporting. No attention is paid to them by either parent. Can breed in 3rd year.

Yearly life. Hibernate from Oct., often in numbers together, in deep holes in the ground, dug with head and hands,

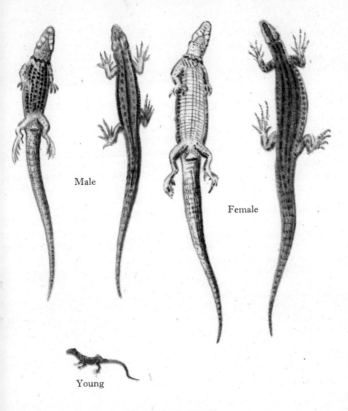

Male

Female

Young

COMMON LIZARD
Scale ½

COMMON LIZARD (*cont.*)

or under mould, where they are safe from frost. In spring, from mid-March to April, they come out and pair. Before hibernating, and for a time after waking, they feed little. The outer skin is changed from time to time as growth requires, peeling off in patches rather than as an entire slough. It splits down the neck and head.

Daily life. Live in holes or crevices of stone, heath, or thick herbage, preferably in moist places. Sluggish in cold or dull weather, but very active in heat and sunshine. Have a small range of ground where they know every stone and blade of grass, basking in certain spots, and running a regular course for food. If off their own ground, they seem lost and are easily caught, but not by the tail. After eating, they wipe the mouth with hands and on grass. The eyes move, wink, and are closed in sleep. All senses are acute and they are full of dangerous curiosity. Main dangers are Birds, Cats, Foxes, and the feet of Man.

Food. Insects, spiders, worms (sucked dry and then swallowed), and caterpillars (sucked, but not swallowed). All caught with the mouth. No vegetable food. Drink water.

Voice. Nil.

Gait. Usually rest on belly and thighs, with fore part only raised on hands. Run swiftly in the same position, straight on smooth surfaces and, in grass or heather, jump from tuft to tuft. Climb walls and tree-trunks.

Varieties. Colour very variable, sometimes black through life.

SAND LIZARD

Lacerta agilis

Sub-spe. *L. a.*²

Habitat. Species: Central Europe from England and S. Sweden to Pyrenees and Alps and from France to Asia. Sub-spe.: Same, save in Russia, Armenia, and Balkans. Here very local; recorded only from Dorset, Hants, Surrey, and near Southport, Lancs. Differs from Common Lizard as follows:

Description: Larger. Males 8 in., females 8¾ in. Stouter and, despite its name, less agile. Colour is different, but very variable. The 'Arabic writing' on the male's belly and the white dots are distinctive. The male's green is brightest in spring, sometimes of emerald brilliance. Rarely, the back is green too.

The scales usually differ thus:

Nostril pierced between 3 scales, 2 behind it and 2 behind them. No larger temple scale. Single semicircle of small scales round the large vent scale.

Teeth. Usually some additional small teeth on the bones at the back of palate.

Life history. Hatched from eggs (5–8 in a clutch) laid in the ground, or under leaves or weeds, in June or July (May in France, where a 2nd clutch is usual) some 4 weeks after pairing. Eggs are thin, but firm and parchment-like. They hatch out in from 41 to 90 days, according to weather. Young when hatched are about 64 mm. long, like the parents in colour, and with a sharp egg-tooth on the end of the nose, with which the egg is broken. It is shed on the 3rd day. Males breed in their 2nd year, females 3rd.

Daily life. The name Sand Lizard reflects the facts. Here, at least, they are found only on sandy soils. The breeding males fight much, with arched back and lowered head—'Cat-like attitudes'. In courtship the male arches his back, puts up the tail, and seizes the female with the jaws at the neck or flank. She quivers and opens her mouth. Can

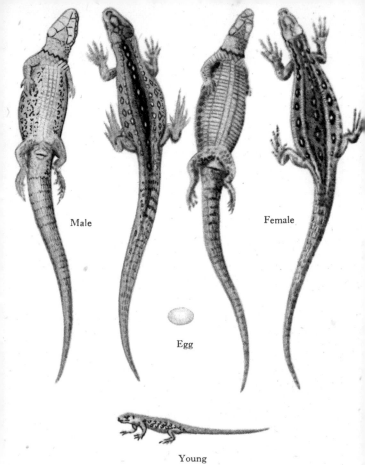

Male

Female

Egg

Young

SAND LIZARD
Scale ½

342

be easily made fearless of Man. Young hibernate before adults.

Gait. Recorded as swimming voluntarily.

The AMPHIBIANS

Class *AMPHIBIA*

These are back-boned creatures with gills when young and lungs when adult. All somewhat aquatic. They made an important step in the progress of the vertebrates. Before them all back-boned creatures lived wholly in the waters. Though perhaps not the first to have 4 legs, they were the first to use them ashore and to develop lungs, a 3-chambered heart, a passage between nostrils and mouth, vocal chords, and a muscular tongue. There are only 7 species in this country, though the Common Frog is very numerous. All frequent fresh water, a very small percentage of salt killing most of them at once.

They have skeletons which generally resemble those of the Mammals, having a skull, back bone, and 4 limbs, but little, or no, signs of ribs. Born in water from gelatinous eggs, they develop first into Larvae (which breathe the oxygen dissolved in the water through the skin and external feathery gills); then into Tadpoles (which breathe the water, as Fish do, through a mouth and internal gills); and at last they change into air-breathing adults.

Like the Reptiles, they are cold blooded, the temperature of the body being that of their surroundings. All our species keep throughout life the habit of returning to the water, at least to breed. Their skin has no scales, hair, claws, or feathers, but is smooth and moist, and has a great number of glands. There is a very thin, horny, outer layer which is cast (sloughed) periodically.

The skull has (Mammal-like) two knobs (*condyles*) to connect with the back bone. The lower jaw consists of three pieces on each side and, as in the Reptiles, hinges on the quadrate bone, which, however, is not itself hinged. So the mouth cannot expand. Some have teeth, some not.

The heart and circulation system of the adults is rather like that of the Reptiles, but the Amphibian's heart is in three simple parts, with no attempt to divide the ventricle. There is only one large exit from the heart, but it is so placed that when it divides into arteries leading to (1) the head and fore limbs, (2) the body and hind limbs, and (3) the lungs, the blood conveyed in these directions is progressively less clean. The cleanest goes to the head, less clean to the body and legs, and the dirtiest to the lungs, to be cleaned. The red blood corpuscles are oval, convex, and have a nucleus.

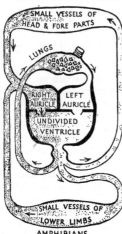

AMPHIBIANS.
Diagram of Adult Heart and circulation

The cleansing of the blood of Amphibians by the lungs occurs only in the adults, and even then is still supplemented by skin-breathing (*cutaneous respiration*). So important is this that the Frogs and Toads cannot live by the use of the lungs alone and the Newts can even survive the removal of the lungs. This skin-breathing is water-breathing, the small blood-vessels of the surface of the skin exchanging their carbonic acid gas for the oxygen dissolved in the water. It continues when the creature leaves the water because the surface of the skin, and of the inside of the mouth, is kept wet by moisture supplied by the blood-stream. The walls of the surface blood-vessels are porous, so that they exude water when the creature is in dry air and absorb it in moisture. There are numerous reservoirs, or lymph sacs, under the skin which, by the action of so-called lymph hearts, gather the water from the surface blood-vessels and pump it back, through a separate system of lymph vessels, into the veins. These sacs, replenished when the creature is in water and depleted by evaporation when in dry air, keep a constant supply of water in the blood to wet the skin when needed, and so enable it to breathe.

As in the Reptiles, one single vent (*cloaca*) serves for the bowels, kidneys, and generation. There is no physical union of the sexes. This, and the early Tadpole life, show their kinship with the Fishes.

Our Amphibians belong to two Orders, easily distinguished:

FROGS AND TOADS (*SALIENTIA*). Tail-less, jumpers.

NEWTS (*CAUDATA*). With tails and crawling.

FROGS AND TOADS

Order *SALIENTIA*

These, when adult, have no tails or open gill clefts. They have 4 limbs, of which the hind legs are the larger, 4 separate fingers on the hand (no thumb) and 5 toes, more or less webbed, on the foot. There are also tubercles on the inside of the 1st finger and big toe, which contain minute bones, and may be traces of the thumb and of an extra (pre-first) toe. Other tubercles are found under the palms and at the joints of all fingers and toes.

There are few (9) vertebrae and no ribs. The tail vertebrae (which are separate in the Tadpoles) become fused in the adults into a single long bone (*urostyle*) stretching backwards between the hip bones, which are shaped like the merry-thought of a fowl.

The eggs are laid in the water by the female and are there fertilized by the male, who grasps the female (retaining his hold throughout the period of laying, which may last for some days) and sprays the eggs with his seminal liquid as they are laid. To help his grip he develops a hook on the hands during the breeding season.

The eggs become Larvae and then Tadpoles, of which the hind legs appear first. The tails are gradually absorbed and the adult animal takes to the land. Tadpoles, but not adults, can re-grow a severed limb.

The lymph sacs under the skin in these creatures are far larger and fewer than in the Newts. So much so that the connexion between skin and muscle, which alone separates these sacs, is only along certain narrow lines (like the seams of overalls), and all the space between is occupied by the sacs.

In the skin are glands containing different pigments. These can be squeezed, so that the colour is driven to the surface, or relaxed, so that it sinks back into them and does not show. This gives the power of adapting their colour to their surroundings which some Amphibia (and some foreign Reptiles) possess.

TOAD

BUFO[2]

Sub-spe. *B.*[3]

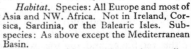

Habitat. Species: All Europe and most of Asia and NW. Africa. Not in Ireland, Corsica, Sardinia, or the Balearic Isles. Subspecies: As above except the Mediterranean Basin.

Description. Sexes alike, males smaller. Size varies much; males of 65 mm. and females of 90 mm. are unusually large in England, but a foreign female of 153 mm. (= 6 in.) is on record. The skin is rough, warty, and fairly dry, varying in shade according to environment from dark brown to sandy. The warts are skin glands, giving out, when the Toad is hurt, a defensive irritant poison, harmless to our skin, but painful to lips or eyes. No Dog will touch a Toad a second time. Largest warts behind the temples. The space between the eyes is equal to the size of the eyes. Iris deep red, black dotted. Pupil contracts horizontally. ◉ ⊖

Teeth. None.

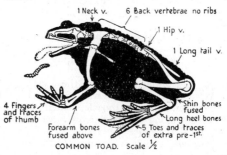

COMMON TOAD. Scale ½

Limbs. 4, with the 2 shin and forearm bones fused into 1. The hands have 4 fingers, each with hand bones and 2–2–3–3 joints respectively. No thumbs, but minute bones. The foot has 2 of the ankle bones lengthened so as to give an extra joint to the legs. It has 5 toes, partly webbed, with foot bones and 2–2–3–4 and 3 joints respectively. No claws.

Structure. The adult Toad's skeleton generally resembles that of a ribless Mammal. The skull has a very narrow and small brain-case, and

346

wide upper and lower jaws, the latter hinged to an immobile (*quadrate*) bone. No elasticity of jaw. Owing to the prominence of eyes and nostrils, Toads can see and breathe when almost wholly under water. The wide boneless space between brain-pan and upper jaw bone leaves the muscles behind the eyes free to help in swallowing. A Toad seems to be trying to swallow his own eyes when these muscles sink to press food down the gullet. There are 9 vertebrae, concave in front and convex behind, of which the 1st alone forms the neck. Then come 7 with mere lateral projections (there are no ribs) and the 9th (*sacral*) has 2 dilated projections, thrust up and outwards, to which the long tongs-shaped hip bones are attached. Behind the 9th vertebra the back bone is continued in a single long poker-like bone, lying between the hip bones, and made of the vertebrae which formed the tail of the Tadpole. There are collar bones which overlap in front of the chest and, with the shoulder-blades, form a girdle.

The absence of ribs and diaphragm throws the work of breathing upon the muscles of the throat. A Toad breathes thus: He opens his nostrils and expands his throat, thus filling the throat cavity with air. He then shuts the nostrils and compresses the throat, keeping the mouth tightly closed, which pumps the air down into the lungs. This can only be done with the mouth shut. If the mouth is held open he suffocates. The lungs are elastic, with a natural tendency to contract. He has, therefore, only to open nostrils or mouth to empty the lungs.

There are numerous pores all over the skin and in the mouth through which some respiration occurs. This suffices during hibernation. The tongue is large, flat, pink, sticky, elastic, and rounded, attached to the front of the mouth with the tip pointing backwards so that it can be flicked out to a distance of over 50 mm. (= 2 in.), curled round the prey and whipped back into the mouth. The act is instantaneous, and amazing to observer and victim. One vent serves all purposes of excretion and generation.

Life history. Toads go through the stages of Eggs, Larvae, and Tadpoles before changing into Toads. The process is as follows, but the time-table varies with the temperature and food.

Eggs, from 2,000 to 7,000 in two parallel strings, 10 to 15 ft. in length, are laid in the water of stagnant ponds and wound round the weeds by the moving female, who uses her hind legs to thrust the spawn rope backwards. They are black, about 1 mm. in diameter, and surrounded by gelatinous matter which swells in the water to a width of 6 mm. The embryo develops a body and tail, which it begins to move, and in about 10 days the Larvae, then about 4 mm. in length, come out of the jelly and, after hanging from it for a few days, swim

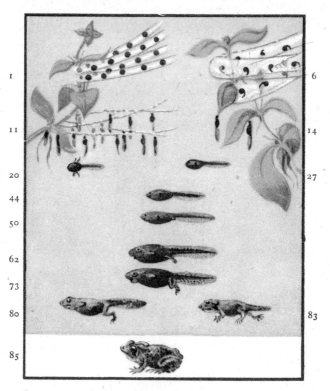

TOAD DEVELOPMENT. *Life Size*

The figures down the sides, which number the various stages, are those of the days given in the text (1 being the day of laying the eggs and 6 the 6th day, &c.) The green background ends when the Toad leaves the water.

off and attach themselves to the undersides of weeds. At this stage they have body and tail, a vent situated centrally under the tail, and a sticky gland on the body (wrongly called a 'sucker'). Soon a mouth and external, feathery gills develop, and the Larvae begin to feed on water-plants and to grow.

In about a month a change occurs. The external gills are absorbed and replaced by gills inside the cover of a gill-case, or fold, formed out of the sticky gland. This fold has only 1 exit (*spiracle*) pointing directly backwards on the left side, where the water taken in at the mouth comes out after passing over the gills. The mouth grows a horny beak with 5 rows of minute teeth. The Larva has become a Tadpole, breathing water, no longer through the skin, but (as a Fish does) by the mouth. At this time the Tadpole is about 13 mm. long, still feeding mainly on plants, though they also eat animal matter.

About 50 days after the eggs were laid, the hind legs begin to show in the form of a small tubercle, which soon grows. The Tadpole is now about 20 mm. in length. Actually the forelegs grow first, but they grow inside the gill-cases and do not show until fully formed. Lungs are developed, and the Tadpole begins to come to the surface to breathe.

At about 73 days it reaches its greatest length (24–40 mm.). Then begins a time of fast, life being sustained by absorption of the tail. The beak is discarded and at the same time, about 83 days, the circulation short-circuits the gills, which disappear; the forelegs, fully formed, burst out, the right leg through the skin and the left through the spiracle, which it closes.

In about 85 days, the tail has been absorbed and, on the first warm wet day, they leave the water in thousands to begin life as fully-formed carnivorous Toads, about 15 mm. long.

They develop slowly, taking 5 years to reach maturity, and are subject to a terrific mortality, as the 2,000 to 7,000 eggs are needed to produce one pair of breeding Toads. The death-rate decreases with age. The spawn is largely protected by its jelly, but Ducks, Newts, Fish, and Water-beetles devour the Tadpoles and, if short of other animal food, they eat each other. The young Toads are the victims of countless

TOAD
Scale ½

accidents, being trodden on, and falling into ruts and holes from which they cannot get out. From then on their enemies are birds and Grass Snakes, and the larger they grow the less they are attacked. Crows skin them. Of Mammals, Rats only will touch them, killing, but not eating them.

Yearly life. Toads hibernate, becoming sluggish but not asleep, from Oct. to March, in deep, dry holes, far from water. Soon after coming out, usually in the first warm April showers, they make for carefully chosen ponds (probably where they were born) to mate, sometimes travelling far. The males, the more numerous, struggle with each other, and the successful grasp a female firmly from behind, his fists under her armpits. They stay so embraced for a week or more, swimming and crawling in the water. The eggs are fertilized after leaving the female and, when all are laid, the Toads leave the water, separate, and remain, solitary, on land until next year. Toads live long: how long is not known, but more than 12 years is proved.

Daily life. Nocturnal. Hide alone all day in a cool, shady, and slightly damp spot: mousehole, under cabbage, stone, or in tree trunk, or the like. If skin gets dry they suffer. But, save when breeding, avoid wet places. The same resort is used every day for months. At night wander in search of food, returning before dawn. Will eat nothing until it moves.

Insatiably voracious. The outer skin is shed every few weeks, splitting down the back, and is removed with hands and feet, and eaten. Alarmed, they rise to full height on 4 limbs and turn rear flank to you.

Food. Purely carnivorous. Eat beetles, caterpillars, meal-worms, snails, slugs (?), and all small moving things. A large Toad will even eat a Mouse. Worms are gripped in the hand while eaten. Invaluable in gardens, only fools kill them.

Gait. Crawling walk, and short heavy hops. A clever climber. Swim slowly with the forelegs held close against the head, pointing forwards. If diving hastily, lay them backwards straight along the body.

Voice. When breeding, the male keeps up a continuous 'whining bleat'. Both sexes croak. Will grunt if squeezed. There is no vocal sac.

Scale ½

NATTERJACK

Bufo calamita

Habitat. Europe west of Russia. Not south-east of Alps and Carpathians or north of S. Sweden. Local but numerous in England and Wales. Common in SW. Ireland (Kerry). Rare in Scotland. Frequent sandy spots, especially swampy heaths.

Differs from Common Toad as follows:

Description. Smaller, sexes alike in size, not over 75 mm. Head narrower, more pointed, space between the eyes less than their width. Skin almost smooth and different in colour. 'Golden back.' Warts on temple smaller, with larger ones on forearms and thighs. Iris green. Males have a large vocal sac inside throat, and 'holding brushes' on the first 3 fingers.

Limbs. Hind legs relatively shorter; foot even less webbed; toes merely fringed.

Life history. Only 3,000–4,000 eggs, in strings 5–6 ft. long. Larvae very small. Tadpole, at longest, under 27 mm. Changes swift. Leave the water (10 mm. long) in under 42 days. Only 20 mm. at a year old. Males breed in 4th or 5th year (length about 45 mm.), females much sooner.

Yearly life. Breed later (end April to June), then looking big because the lungs are distended. Less nice in choice of breeding ponds, often go to mere temporary puddles. In the autumn males hibernate first, sometimes climbing to the holes of Sand Martins.

Daily life. Mainly nocturnal, but less afraid of light. Will bask in the sun. Climb and dig much, making holes for the

352

daytime. Live nearer water, to which they go, particularly at night, swimming and running about in the mud. If disturbed, lie 'doggo'. The skin-poison has an odd smell. Can stand salt, sometimes even breed in brackish water.

Gait. Do not hop, or crawl. 'Running Toad.' Run quickly a short way, pause, and then run on. Swim near surface with weak strokes and the forelegs forward, touching the face.

Voice. Male's love-song, a loud, rattling croak ('bra bra bra'), is audible a mile off. When one croaks others answer in chorus. Green Woodpecker's 'laugh' will set them off.

COMMON or GRASS FROG

Rana temporaria

Sub-spe. *R. t.*²

Habitat. Species: Central and N. Europe and mid-Asia from N. Scandinavia to Galicia and Alps. Sub-species: Same except NW. Spain. Throughout Britain. Introduced into Ireland in the 18th century and now common.

Differs from the Toad as follows:

Description. Longer and slimmer. Size 60–85 mm.; females heavier and yellower underneath than males. Males have two 'song sacs' in throat. They have some power of adapting their colour to their surroundings according to light, damp, and heat. Skin smooth, tight, and moist. No warts and no effective poison protection. The distance between the eyes equals their width. Iris yellow with black dots.

Teeth. None on lower jaw: many minute horny teeth on upper. Also two small groups (*vomerine* teeth) on palate behind the nostril hole. All slope backwards and serve to hold slippery food, not to bite or chew.

Limbs and structure. Compare this sketch with Toad on p. 346. Hind legs longer than Toad's, and twice as long as front. 4th and 5th

FROG. Scale ½

353

hind foot bones diverge. Hind foot fully webbed. The projections from the 9th (hip) vertebra are narrower and rise up backwards, giving the humpbacked look—the 'essential frogginess'. Collar bones do not overlap, but join in a breast bone. Tongue-tip has 2 rounded ends.

Life history. Goes through the same stages, but (1) fewer eggs, 1,000–2,000. Spawn laid in a large, conglomerate mass of individual spheres 2–3 mm. in size. The mass swells to the size of a man's head (each egg to about 10 mm.) and floats to the surface; (2) the time-table (like that of the Toad) is variable, but in one recorded case was as follows. On 6th day after being laid, the young left the eggs, 4 mm. long; 10th day, they were 13 mm., and 28th day, 26 mm.; on the 66th day they were 40 mm. with hind legs developed, and reached their full length (45 mm.) on the 78th day, when the forelegs came out. At 84 days they came to land, with tails still 20 mm. long, and a total length of 35 mm. The tail is absorbed in a few days. This was probably a quick change. (3) In the Tadpole the vent is on the right side, the water exit (*spiracle*) on the left but pointing upwards. The crest along the back begins at the level of the spiracle. There are 8 or 10 rows of teeth. They swim singly, not in shoals.

The small Frogs are about 20 mm. before hibernating.

Yearly life. Hibernate, in holes in the ground, under moss, straw ricks, or in rockeries, from October to early spring.

GRASS FROG
Scale ½

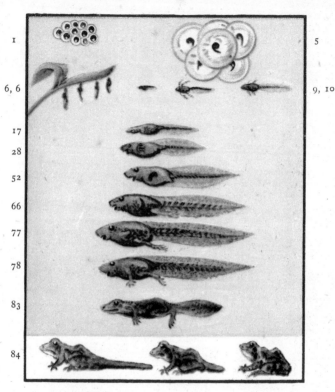

FROG DEVELOPMENT. *Life Size*

The figures down the sides, which number the various stages,
are those of the days given in the text (1 being the day of laying
the eggs and 5 the 5th day, &c.). The green background ends when
the Frog comes ashore.

Often out by February. Show carelessness in choosing breeding pools, often spawning in shallow puddles which dry and kill the spawn. Breed usually about March (2 to 4 weeks before Toads) and in Cornwall sometimes as early as Jan. The males then assume a bluish hue on the white parts.

Daily life. Less terrestrial than Toads, sometimes living on irrigated land, or even in water. Rarely take to water for safety, but hop fast for a few jumps, and then squat under cover. Do not climb into holes. When first caught, wild and addicted to suicidal jumps: soon become calm. More diurnal. Because of its diet of great value to Man. Have countless enemies; eaten by Foxes, Stoats, Rats, Moles, Shrews, Grass Snakes, fish, and by Man abroad. Also much used by Man for scientific experiment.

Food. Insects, snails, and worms, eaten when moving.

Gait. Hop in long, vigorous leaps. Do not crawl or climb. Swim well, with forearms laid back along the body, making feeble strokes with them when moving slowly.

Voice. Both sexes can croak, either above or under water. No 'community singing'.

Varieties. None. Colour varies from Frog to Frog, and time to time.

EDIBLE or WATER FROG

Rana esculenta

Habitat. Europe west of mid-Russia up to S. Sweden except Peninsula and Balkans. Here, in England only. Very local—Norfolk, Cambridge, Bedford, and Oxford. Possibly indigenous (?) but many imported to the Fens in the 18th century.

Differs from the Common Frog as follows:

Description. Head narrower, space between the eyes only half their width. Usually greener and less brown, but very variable, brown, green, grey, or black, with or without black spots. Lack the mark on temple. Slightly larger, males 64 mm., females 78 mm. Males have 2 'song sacs', the size of big peas, outside the throat, white when singing.

Teeth. Those on palate level with nostril.

TADPOLE. *Life size*

EDIBLE OR WATER FROG
Scale ½

357

Life history. More eggs—5,000–6,000—laid in several separate masses. Eggs smaller (1·5 mm.), their jelly swelling to 7 or 8 mm. Spawn sinks in water even when swelled. Timetable given as follows: 5th or 6th day, Larva leaves jelly with eyes, mouth, and beginning of external gills visible. 14th day, gills gone, spiracle formed and tail developed; colour olivebrown above, yellowish-white below; still holding by suckers to plants or the bottom. While hind legs grow they swim about in huge shoals. Much larger: at longest (about 69th day) 55–111 mm. Tail sharp pointed. Whole change takes 3–4 months but is usually so delayed that some young hibernate as Tadpoles. Barely 14 mm. when tail is gone. Mostly on land for first season only. Males do not breed for three years.

Yearly life. Breed later (May–June) without migrating, as they live where they are born, unless their pond dries up. Hibernate in the mud, emerging mid-April or May. Nuptial embrace rarely lasts more than a few days.

Daily life. Aquatic. Squatting on a water-lily leaf, or similar seat, to take insects. Dive instantly on any alarm and stay some minutes under water. Then cautiously reappear. Soon forget a motionless watcher. If caught, even wilder than Grass Frogs. Excellent eating if well cooked: novices mistake them for young chicken.

Voice. Small croaking 'Ooaar' used to signal 'all clear'. From May to July the males perform great feats of community singing, lasting all night, especially on hot, moonlight nights. 'Brekekekex coax coax!' Heard a mile off. 'Whaddon Organs' or 'Dutch Nightingales'.

Food. Insects, worms, snails, small Grass Frogs, and fish fry.

THE NEWTS

Order *CAUDATA*

Of these we have 3 species depicted opposite.

They have a long, Lizard-like body, with a tail which remains throughout life and with which they swim with fish-like sideways movements. The limbs are of minor importance in

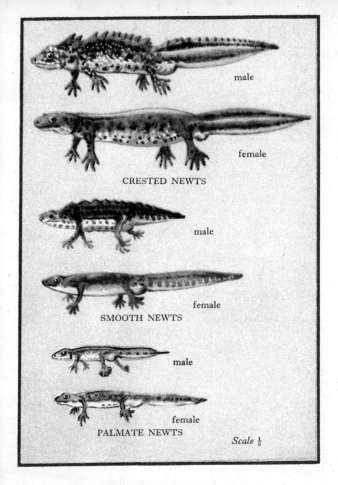

male

female

CRESTED NEWTS

male

female

SMOOTH NEWTS

male

female

PALMATE NEWTS

Scale ½

THE BRITISH NEWTS IN WATER

the water. They have 4 fingers (no 5th) on the hand and 5 toes on the foot. If lost, a limb can be re-grown from the stump.

There is only 1 neck vertebra, 14–17 with ribs, to the last of which the hip bones are attached, and some 26–36 more in the tail. Separate forearm and shin bones.

Though like Lizards in appearance, they differ in having no claws, a soft, moist skin, a white, fleshy tongue, and a tail flattened vertically. Also, they dislike great heat, and move sluggishly on land.

The male deposits in the water a transparent germ-case shaped like a small inverted cone. This is grasped by the female with the lips of her vent and emptied of its germs, so that the eggs are fertilized in her body before being laid. She lays them singly, against a leaf of weed, to which they adhere. From them emerge Larvae, generally resembling the adults, but having gills and, in the early stages, lacking hind legs. When both legs are grown and they are ready to leave the water, lungs appear to replace the external gills.

There seems to be only one record of the number of eggs laid by any of our Newts, attributing 287 eggs (laid in 64 days) to a foreign sub-species of the Common Newt, and a maximum of 720 to the same species.

CRESTED NEWT

Triturus palustris

Sub-spe. *T. p.*[2]

Habitat. Species: Britain and S. Sweden, through Europe to Iran. Not in S. France or the Peninsula. Sub-spe.: As above, north of Alps, Carpathians, and Caucasus. Here rarer in W. England. Not in Cornwall, the Highlands, W. Scotland, or Ireland.

Description. Sexes differ, males usually smaller (up to 144 mm.) than females (162 mm.) and alone assume the nuptial crests. Skin soft and warty, with distinct pores on the head and along flanks; marked fold under chin. The crests disappear when they go ashore and they lose all brilliance of colouring and the skin becomes

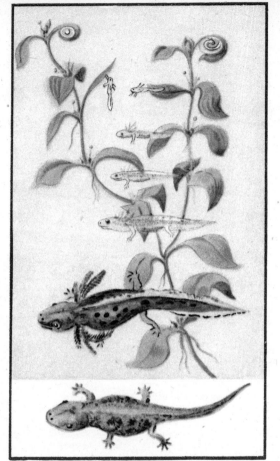

CRESTED NEWT DEVELOPMENT. *Life size*

Plate numbered as p. 348 and p. 355

dry and Toad-like, their general appearance being that of Lizards, with which they were long confused.

Teeth. Numerous, similar, recurved, holding teeth. Round both jaws and also on the palate, the latter arranged in a 'V' pointing forwards.

Limbs. Forearm and shin bones are separate. Hands 4-fingered (lacking thumbs), feet 5-toed. No nails. Finger bones 2–2–3–2, toe bones 2–2–3–3–2.

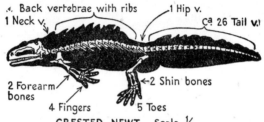

CRESTED NEWT. Scale ½

Structure. No. 1 vertebra alone forms the neck and No. 17 or 18 the sacrum, with rib-like projections for attachment to the hip bones. The body vertebrae have short, back-pointing ribs, and are convex in front and concave behind. The first few of the tail vertebrae (26–36 in all) have backward side projections and the rest spines above and below. The small size of the ribs makes them breathe as does a toad. The skin has many sense organs, especially along the flanks, at the base of the tail, and in the bridal crest of the male.

Life history. The eggs are laid, 1 by 1, in the rolled leaf of a water-plant (in default, stuck to stones). The young hatch out in about 13 days, in a more advanced state than the Toad Larvae, having already grown 3 external branched gills, which they retain until they leave the water, rudiments of forelegs, and a pair of thread-like filaments (one at each side of the upper jaw) by which they hang on to the weeds. They are opaque, yellowish-green, with 2 black bands on the back and a whitish edge to the tail fin. Within the next 10 or 12 days the eyes and final mouth are fully developed and the whole body becomes transparent. They are more slender, less big-headed, than Toad Tadpoles, and the forelegs appear long before the hind and are never much smaller. The fingers appear successively. In some three months they are 50 mm. long and cease to be transparent. General colour olive-brown. The black bands have broken up into dots. Flanks and belly, golden. About 10 days later, the gills and crests disappear, the lungs have formed and (after coming to the surface for breathing, with a 'popping' sound, for a time) they usually leave the water, not to return to it until ready to breed in their 3rd or 4th year. Although they usually, thus, leave the water before winter, they do not always, but may hibernate with remains of gills. Some females have produced eggs while still in the Larval stage in the following year. The egg laying is usually in May and June.

Yearly life. Live on land except during the breeding season, though sometimes stay in the water until autumn, or even all the year. Generally hibernate under ground, often in large numbers twisted together. Early in April they come out and travel to ponds for the breeding season, sometimes going a long way. The method of pairing is remarkable. The male frisks round the female in the water, rubbing her with his head and patting her with his tail. He then drops one or more minute gelatinous objects, shaped like hollow collar-studs, to the bottom of the water. The female swims down and picks these up with her vent, so that the eggs are fertilized before being laid. After breeding they leave the water and go to some damp, cool place.

Daily life. On land, mainly nocturnal, hiding by day in moss, crannies, or sand. The outer skin is shed all in one slough, and eaten. Food is caught with the mouth, not the tongue. When two Newts get hold of the same worm they pull and twist until it breaks, or until the stronger gets the whole.

Food. Ashore, insects, worms, centipedes, and snails. In the water, all small life—mainly Frog Tadpoles and smaller Newts. Do not drink. Absorb water through the skin. Young eat Frog Tadpoles.

Gait. Ashore, a slow walk. In water, swim by fish-like sideways movements of the tail.

Voice. Only sound recorded is the 'pop' when coming up to breathe in water.

Varieties. Colour varies much.

SMOOTH NEWT

Triturus vulgaris   Sub-spe. *T. v.*[1]

Habitat. Species: As the Crested Newt, but extends to Ireland and only to half of Asia Minor. Sub-species: Same, except Italy, W. Balkans, and Greece. Here scarcer towards north and west.

Differs from the Crested Newt as follows: *Description.* Smaller, about 70–80 mm. up to 104 mm. Breeding crest of male is of waving outline, without sharp points, and continuous from head to tail. Toes are fringed with membrane but not fully webbed. Female has shorter toes. Skin is smooth. Fewer rib vertebrae. Only 1 bone to 1st finger and 1st toe.

Life history. The Larvae are spotted along the sides with yellow, and their tails end in a thread like that of the adult Palmate Newt. Adults never stay in the water after the breeding season. Not so careful in folding a leaf round each egg. Sometimes lay several together and merely place them in the fork between leaf and stem.

PALMATE NEWT

Triturus helveticus   Sub-spe. *T. h.*[1]

Habitat. Species: W. Europe from Britain and the N. of the Peninsula to Switzerland and W. Germany. Sub-species: Same except N. Portugal. In Britain, local in the SE. but commoner than the Smooth Newt in the west. Not in Ireland.

Differs from the Crested Newt as follows: *Description.* Much smaller, 60–80 mm., rarely exceeds 77 mm. Tail ends in a thread, short in the female, up to 10 mm. in the male. Skin smooth. The breeding male develops black webbing between the toes, a fold in the skin along each side of the back and a low, unbroken, crest. Webbing much less marked in female. Ashore the webbing becomes a fringe to each toe. Fewer rib vertebrae. Only 1 bone to 5th toe. Can stand saltish water.

BIBLIOGRAPHY

THE works here named are suggested to the reader who wishes to study in greater detail the subjects dealt with in this book.

The manners and habits of our Beasts are described inimitably by Gilbert White in his *Natural History of Selborne* (1789), which should be the first text-book of all those who are interested in Beasts or Birds. It can be got in good modern reprints and will be read and re-read. The second book is Charles St. John's *Wild Sports of the Highlands* (1846). The above, with Thomas Bewick's *Quadrupeds* (1791), are the classics. There are many recent works on the habits of the wild animals, such as Miss Frances Pitt's books (*Wild Creatures of Garden and Hedgerow* and others) and A. R. Thompson's *Nature by Night*. Others, such as *Tarka the Otter*, by H. Williamson, and most of E. Thompson Seton's work, take the form of fiction.

Much is to be found in General Natural Histories covering the whole world (such as that edited by C. Tate Regan and published in 1936), and there are some books upon the wild species of Britain: primarily J. G. Millais's *Mammals of Gt. Brit. and Ireland* (1904-6), a great and beautifully illustrated 4-volume quarto. Others are: Thomas Bell's *Brit. Quadrupeds and Cetacea* (1837), and *Reptiles* (1849), W. Macgillivray's *Hist. of Brit. Quadrupeds* (1843), R. Lydekker's *Handbook to the Brit. Mammals* (1895), F. G. Aflalo's *Sketch of the Nat. Hist.* (*Vertebrates*) of *the Brit. Is.* (1898), and Edward Step's *Animal Life of the Brit. Is.* (1921). In some respects far the most satisfactory book on our small Mammals (Bats, Insectivora, and Rodents) is G. E. H. Barrett-Hamilton and M. A. C. Hinton's *Hist. of Brit. Mammals* (1910-21). This book gives a full account of the species and sub-species together with almost all that is known about them and has the great merit of citing the authority for nearly every statement. It has, alas, owing to the death of the first author, so far remained unfinished and, except for such parts as had already been issued to subscribers and are thus available in some libraries, it is unobtainable.

I know of no book dealing with just the same field as this book of mine, for, except in the world-wide Natural Histories, the rejection of the domestic animals seems to be universal.

On the domestic animals there are fewer general books. Darwin's *Animals and Plants under Domestication* (1868) should be read. Much is to be found in farmers', butchers', and veterinary manuals. The classic books are those by W. Youatt, written about 1840, on Cattle, Pigs, Sheep, and Goats. The Ministry of Agriculture's *Brit. Breeds of Livestock* keeps one up to date. James Ritchie's *Influence of Man on Animal Life in Scotland* (1920) gives a good account of the history of some domestic animals. Their lives and habits must be gleaned from various sources (such as the description of wintering Sheep in C. J. Cornish's *Wild England of To-day*, 1895). Even good descriptions of domestic animals are hard to find. I commend to any reader a search for the measurements of any breed of Sheep!

BIBLIOGRAPHY

Among foreign animal books I strongly recommend the elementary school-books, *Les Auxiliaires* and *Les Serviteurs*, by J. H. Fabre, who, although his original work was in the realm of Insects, in these books brought his acute powers of exposition and generalization into the animal field. E. Seton Thompson (later Thompson Seton) wrote in 1909 a book on the Mammals of Manitoba (*Life Hist. of Northern Mammals*) which, though only touching a few of our species, is of great interest, particularly on animal mentality and habits. The species found in France are sufficiently like our own to make Edmond Perrier's condensed *Faune de France, Vertébrés* (1924) useful and interesting.

There are studies of individual animals or groups to which a brief reference must be made. St. George Mivart's *The Cat* (1881) is more than this, branching out as it does into an introduction to Zoology of general interest. R. I. Pocock's recent papers on wild and tame Cats are buried in the pages of scientific periodicals, as is much other interesting animal observation. The Dog has a large literature of its own, giving, as I cannot here, a review of the countless breeds (e.g. *The 20th Century Dog*, by H. Compton, 1904). There is: *The Badger*, by J. F. Blakeborough and A. E. Pease (1914); *Ferrets*, by N. Everitt (1897); *The Grey Squirrel* (1931) by A. D. Middleton; M. A. C. Hinton's (unfinished) *Monograph of Voles and Lemmings*, vol. i (1925); *The Book of the Goat* (1910), by Holmes Pegler; A. G. Cameron's *Wild Red Deer of Scotland* (1923); W. M. Hayes's *Points of the Horse* (1903); *The Life of the Bat*, by C. Derennes; *Whales and Modern Whaling* (1932) by J. T. Jenkins; Sir S. F. Harmer's *Cetacea Stranded, 1913–26* (and its continuation *1927–32* by F. C. Fraser); G. A. Boulenger's numerous books on Snakes, Lizards, and Batrachians; R. Rolinat's posthumous *La Vie des reptiles*; and the old (1821) *Amours des salamandres*, by Mauro Rusconi.

The subject of Gait was studied by Eadweard Muybridge. About 1880, he had a large fund given him by the University of Pennsylvania and described in detail the method of animal motion. He was at the same time a forerunner of the makers of moving pictures. He wrote several books (*Animals in Motion*, 1899, *Zoopraxography*, 1893, &c.). Oddly enough, I know of no book treating of animal motion with film-strip illustrations, although what in 1880 cost much and had to be done by many cameras and trigger-wires, can be done to-day by merely turning a handle. On Gait see also E. J. Marey's *Le Mouvement* translated by E. Pritchard (1895) and J. B. Pettigrew's *Design in Nature*, 1908.

The modern lore of Heredity is treated in a way suited for beginners in the small *Animal Genetics*, by F. A. E. Crew (1925), and for a new aspect of the relations between groups of different animals and plants, see C. Elton's *Animal Ecology* (1927).

Nomenclature is here taken, as regards wild species, from the recently published (1935) *List of Brit. Vertebrates* issued by the British Museum. The B.M. *Catalogue of the Mammals of Western Europe* (1912) by G. S. Miller has been relied upon for much of the information about structure and teeth and for many of the measurements in this book.

GLOSSARY INDEX

In addition to being an Index, this is meant to explain the technical terms used in the book (mainly in the Notes), and some of those which will be met with in other books. Where the word is not in this book, the page reference (in italics) is to the page on which it might have appeared. Also all the scientific names which seem to need explanation are translated (in brackets) under the **ENGLISH NAMES** of the animals to which they belong.

GLOSSARY INDEX

GLOSSARY INDEX

GLOSSARY INDEX

GLOSSARY INDEX

GLOSSARY INDEX